Technician
Chemistry
2

This book covers the standard unit in Chemistry at level 2 (U76/019) of the TEC Programme C1: Science and Technology. Additional material recommended by the Royal Society of Chemistry has also been included. The book is written in a clear, easy to follow style and is illustrated with a number of line drawings and half-tones. The learning objective structure of the syllabus has been closely followed and there are many short-answer questions and progress tests. A knowledge of chemistry to GCE 'O' level/grade 1 CSE, or to the TEC standard level 1 unit (U76/018) is assumed, such as that covered in *Technician Chemistry 1* by the same author.

Dr M. D. Hawkins is Head of Physical Sciences at Bedford College of Higher Education. He is responsible for Chemistry, Physics, Laboratory Techniques, Safety and Laboratory Practice and the Biochemistry TEC teaching in the college. Dr Hawkins has had many years experience teaching technician students and is an experienced author and contributor to chemical and other scientific journals.

Technician
Chemistry
2

M. D. Hawkins
M.A., M.Sc., Ph.D., C.Chem., F.R.S.C.

Cassell · *London*

CASSELL PUBLISHERS LIMITED

Artillery House
Artillery Row
London SW1P 1RT

© M.D. Hawkins 1981

First published 1981
Reprinted 1987

I.S.B.N. 0 304 30549 9

Line drawings by Oxford Illustrators Ltd.

Set in Monophoto Times by
Northumberland Press Ltd., Gateshead, Tyne and Wear.

Printed and bound in Great Britain at
The Camelot Press Ltd., Southampton.

Dedicated to Constance and Karl

Preface

This book has been written to cover the level 2 Chemistry unit (U76/019) of the certificate courses of the Technician Education Council. A few additional topics have been included to meet the recommendations of the Royal Society of Chemistry. A knowledge of chemistry to the level 1 TEC standard unit is assumed. However, as some students beginning the level 2 course will have gained exemption from the level 1 unit by virtue of their C.S.E. and G.C.E. O-level examination results, some material has been included to allow for the difference in content of these other courses.

I am aware of the difficulties of both the teacher and student of day-release courses and one of the aims has been to reduce the time spent on note-taking. The book is self-contained and includes worked examples, end of chapter summaries and details of demonstrations, test-tube reactions and other practical work. It also contains more than two hundred short-answer questions which may be used for self-assessment, progress tests, homework etc. The wording of the specific objectives of the standard unit has been retained and these objectives are listed at the beginning of the relevant sections of the book so that the reader knows precisely what he, or she, is expected to achieve.

The International System of units (SI) and the nomenclature recommended by the International Union of Pure and Applied Chemistry (IUPAC) are used throughout (see also Appendices I and IV).

I wish to express my thanks to Griffin and George Ltd. and to British Petroleum for supplying photographs for use as illustrations; and to Dr Lester Crook and Christopher Coyer of Cassell for their encouragement and painstaking work in preparing the typescript for publication. Thanks are also due to Mrs E. M. Pickering for typing the manuscript and to my son, Karl, for his assistance in preparing the index.

April 1981   Malcolm D. Hawkins

Contents

Abbreviations and symbols

The following abbreviations and symbols are used in this book.

g = gram(s)
kg = kilogram(s)
mg = milligram (10^{-3} g)
m = metre
dm = decimetre (10^{-1} m)
cm = centimetre (10^{-2} m)
mm = millimetre (10^{-1} m)
nm = nanometre (10^{-9} m)
1 = litre (1 litre = 1 dm^3 = 10^{-3} m^3 = 1000 cm^3)
mol = mole
RAM or A_r = Relative atomic mass ('Atomic weight')
RMM or M_r = Relative molecular mass ('Molecular weight')
a = activity
M = concentration (mol of solute per litre of solution)
$[B]$ = molar concentration (mol 1^{-1}) in dilute solution
atm = atmosphere(s)
$mmHg$ = millimetres of mercury
K = kelvins (see Appendix I)
s = seconds
$t°$ = temperature (°C). *Unless otherwise stated temperatures in this book are in degrees Celsius*
R = the General Gas Constant (8.314 J mol^{-1} K^{-1})
F = Faraday constant (96 484.56 C)
N = newtons
J = joule(s)
Pa = pascal (Nm^{-2})
p = pressure
d = density
α (Greek letter alpha) = degree of ionisation
Z = Atomic number
A = mass number
ΔH = enthalpy change
E_H° = standard electrode potential
V = volts
e.m.f. = electromotive force
m.p. = melting point
b.p. = boiling point
pH = $-\log_{10}[H^+]$
pOH = $-\log_{10}[OH^-]$
K_{eq} or K_c = equilibrium constant
K_w = ionic product for water
(s) = solid
(l) = liquid
(g) = gas

(vap) = vapour
(aq) = in aqueous solution
1° = primary
2° = secondary
3° = tertiary
∝ = proportional to
> = greater than
< = less than
u.v. = ultra-violet
2,4-DNPH = 2,4-dinitrophenyl hydrazine
IMS = industrial methylated spirit

A Enthalpy changes

1 Energy and chemical reactions

General objective: *The expected learning outcome of this chapter is that the student is able to describe energy changes in chemical reactions.*

1.1
Energy and its interconversion

Specific objectives: *The expected learning outcome of this section is that the student: (i) States that energy changes occur in chemical reactions (ii) Recognises that these changes often appear in interconversions of chemical, heat or electrical energy.*

Energy is defined as the ability to do work. The SI unit of energy is the *joule*, which is given the symbol J. The kilojoule is a commonly used multiple of this unit, where

$$1 \text{ kilojoule (1 kJ)} = 1000 \text{ J.}$$

All chemical reactions are accompanied by a change in energy. This change is obvious in combustion processes, such as the burning of carbon or of methane ('natural gas') in air, where the energy of the reaction is given out in the form of heat:

$$C + O_2 \longrightarrow CO_2 + \text{heat}$$
$$CH_4 + 2O_2 \longrightarrow CO_2 + 2H_2O + \text{heat}$$

However, this energy can appear in forms other than heat. In the Daniell cell (see Section 5.6 and fig. 1.1), for example, the chemical energy of the displacement of copper from an aqueous solution of its ions by metallic zinc

$$Zn_{(s)} + Cu^{2+}_{(aq)} \longrightarrow Zn^{2+}_{(aq)} + Cu_{(s)}$$

is converted into electrical energy. If, however, the two reactants – powdered zinc and aqueous copper sulphate solution – are mixed in a test tube there is an immediate increase in temperature and the reaction energy appears as heat.

Chemical energy, heat energy and electrical energy are thus inter-convertible and the energy change which occurs in a reaction can appear

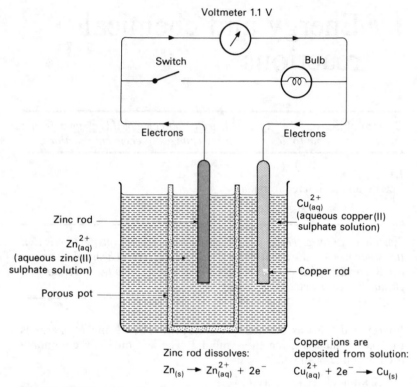

Fig. 1.1 The Daniell cell

in any of these forms. The explosive power of dynamite, or the propulsion of a rifle bullet, or a jet plane, are examples of mechanical, kinetic and sound energies from chemical reactions, while the bright incandescence of burning magnesium illustrates the conversion of chemical energy into light and heat. Photosynthesis is the process by which green plants convert the energy of sunlight into chemical energy for the synthesis of sugars, starch and other important compounds:

$$6CO_2 + 6H_2O \xrightarrow[\text{sunlight}]{\text{energy of}} C_6H_{12}O_6$$
$$\text{glucose}$$

The fact that oil and coal were formed from the fossilised remains or decomposition products of plant and animal tissues which were fed by products of this reaction many millions of years ago confirms the importance of the sun as a fuel source. Except for atomic fission and fusion processes, virtually all energy sources are derived either directly or indirectly from the energy of sunlight. Transport, industry, agriculture and even the vital processes which occur in our own bodies and in the tissues of all living organisms are dependent on the interconversion of the different forms of energy.

1.2
Exothermic and endothermic changes

Specific objective: *The expected learning outcome of this section is that the student states that in some chemical reactions heat energy is given out to the surroundings, and that in others heat is taken in, and uses the terms exothermic and endothermic.*

Combustion reactions and other processes in which heat is given out to the surroundings are said to be *exothermic*. These changes are accompanied by an *increase* in temperature. Examples include the reaction of a metal with acid, e.g.

$$Mg + 2HCl_{(aq)} \longrightarrow MgCl_{2(aq)} + H_{2(g)} + heat$$

the displacement of copper ions from their aqueous solution by zinc (see Sections 1.1 and 5.5), and the neutralisation of an acid by a base, e.g.

$$HCl_{(aq)} + NaOH_{(aq)} \longrightarrow NaCl_{(aq)} + H_2O_{(l)} + heat.$$

Reactions in which heat is taken in from the surroundings occur with a *decrease* in temperature and are said to be *endothermic*. The solution of ammonium nitrate in water is an example of an endothermic reaction:

$$NH_4^+ NO_{3(s)}^- \xrightarrow{\ H_2O\ } NH_{4(aq)}^+ + NO_{3(aq)}^- - heat$$

A drop in temperature of more than $10°$ is observed when a few grams of powdered ammonium nitrate are stirred into about 50 cm^3 of water in a beaker.

1.3
Conservation of energy

Specific objectives: *The expected learning outcome of this section is that the student: (i) States that the energy content of the products of an exothermic reaction is less than that of the reactants (ii) States that the energy content of the products of an endothermic reaction is greater than that of the reactants.*

The energy change which occurs in a chemical reaction stems from differences in the energies of the reactants and products. The internal energy of a compound consists mainly of the potential energy which results from the attractive forces between the atoms within the molecules. This energy is related to the strength of the chemical bonds linking the atoms. The internal energy of an element is largely determined by the attraction and arrangement of the sub-atomic particles (the electrons and protons) within the atom.

The energy change in a chemical reaction comes mainly from breaking and forming bonds of different strengths. In general, an exothermic reaction is one in which the bonds which are formed in the reaction products are stronger than those which were broken in the reactants. In an endothermic reaction the bonds formed are weaker than the bonds which were broken (see Example 2.3).

The energy difference is not lost as this would be contrary to the Law of the Conservation of Energy, but appears as heat which is given out or taken in from the surroundings respectively. *The Law of Conservation of Energy* (or the first law of thermodynamics) states:

Energy cannot be created nor destroyed in a chemical reaction.

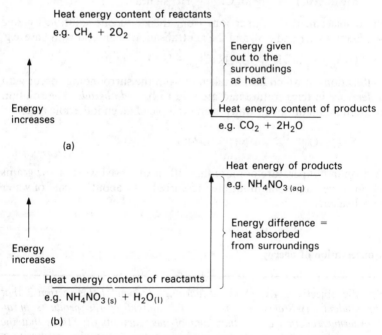

Fig. 1.2 Simple energy diagrams for (a) exothermic and (b) endothermic processes

However, as we saw in Section 1.1, energy may be transferred from one form to another, but the *total* energy remains constant. The total heat energy content of the products of an exothermic reaction is thus less than that of the reactants, as the simple energy diagram in fig. 1.2(a) indicates. For an endothermic process the heat energy content of the products is greater than that of the reactants, and energy in the form of heat must be supplied from the surroundings to raise the energy of the reactants to the higher level of the reaction products (see fig. 1.2(b)).

Demonstration 1.1
To demonstrate the conversion of the chemical energy of a reaction into heat and electricity

Apparatus and Materials
100 cm^3 beakers. 0–110° thermometers. 50 cm^3 measuring cylinders. Spatulas. Galvanometer. Wire. Crocodile clips. Distilled water. 2M hydrochloric acid. 2M sodium hydroxide. Powdered ammonium nitrate(V) or sodium thiosulphate–5–water. Sodium hydroxide pellets. (*Care! This substance is caustic. Do not allow the solid or its solution to come into contact with the skin or the eyes.*) Magnesium ribbon. Magnesium powder. Aqueous copper(II)sulphate(VI). A copper rod or a strip of copper foil. A carbon rod.

Method
(a) Using the thermometer as a stirrer, note the initial and final temperatures in the following:
(i) Mix equal volumes (about 25 cm^3) of 2M hydrochloric acid and 2M sodium hydroxide in a beaker.
(ii) Add *1.* powdered ammonium nitrate or sodium thiosulphate–5–water, *2.* half a dozen sodium hydroxide pellets (*Care!*) to about 30 cm^3 of distilled water in separate beakers.
(iii) Add powdered magnesium to about 25 cm^3 of *1.* 2M hydrochloric acid, *2.* aqueous copper(II)sulphate(VI) in separate beakers.
(b) Connect a strip of magnesium ribbon and a carbon rod to the galvanometer with crocodile clips and wire. Observe the deflection which occurs (indicating that an electric current is flowing) when the magnesium ribbon and carbon rod are dipped in a beaker containing about 25 cm^3 of 2M hydrochloric acid. Show that the direction of the current is reversed by reversing the connections to the galvanometer.

Replace the carbon rod with a copper rod or strip of copper foil and repeat the experiment using about 25 cm^3 of aqueous copper(II)-sulphate(VI) as the electrolyte.

Summary

1. Energy is defined as the ability to do work. The unit of energy is the joule (symbol, J).

2. An exothermic reaction is one in which heat is given out to the surroundings and is therefore accompanied by an increase in temperature.

3. An endothermic reaction is one in which heat energy is taken in from the surroundings and is therefore accompanied by a decrease in temperature.

4. The Law of the Conservation of Energy (or the First Law of Thermodynamics) states that energy cannot be created or destroyed in a chemical reaction. The total energy is therefore a constant; however energy may be converted into other forms.

5. The chemical energy liberated in a reaction may appear as interconversions of heat, light, chemical or electrical energy etc.

6. The heat energy content of the products of an exothermic reaction is less than that of the reactants. An exothermic reaction is one in which the bonds which are formed in the reaction products are stronger than those which were broken in the reactants.

7. The heat energy content of the products of an endothermic reaction is greater than that of the reactants. An endothermic reaction is one in which the bonds which are formed in the reaction products are weaker than those which were broken in the reactants.

Questions

1. Explain by reference to suitable examples what is meant by the term 'energy'.

2. Discuss two examples in each case of the conversion of the chemical energy of a reaction into heat, light, electrical and kinetic energy.

3. What is the difference between an exothermic and an endothermic reaction?

4. Draw and explain simple energy level diagrams for (a) an exothermic and (b) an endothermic reaction.

5. State the Law of the Conservation of Energy.

2 Enthalpy changes in chemical reactions

General objective: *The expected learning outcome of this chapter is that the student is able to define and use the concept of enthalpy.*

2.1
Enthalpy

Specific objective: *The expected learning outcome of this section is that the student defines enthalpy change for a reaction and uses the symbol ΔH.*

Enthalpy is the term used to describe the heat content of a system. It is given the symbol H. It is not possible to obtain absolute values of the enthalpies of elements and compounds, but the *enthalpy change* in a reaction is readily determined and defined as:

> the heat evolved or absorbed when the reaction is carried out at constant pressure.

The enthalpy change for a reaction is thus the difference in the enthalpy (or heat content) of the products and that of the reactants. It is given the symbol ΔH, where

$$\Delta H = H_2 - H_1.$$

$$\underset{\text{of products}}{\text{enthalpy}} \qquad \underset{\text{of reactants}}{\text{enthalpy}}$$

The symbol Δ is the Greek letter *delta* and is used to represent the change in a function.

For an exothermic reaction the enthalpy of the products is less than the enthalpy of the reactants, i.e. $H_2 < H_1$, and ΔH is negative. For an endothermic reaction the system has taken in heat from the surroundings and $H_2 > H_1$. ΔH thus has a positive sign for an endothermic reaction (see fig. 2.1).

The units of enthalpy change are usually kJ mol^{-1}, although occasionally the value is based on the amounts of material represented in the chemical equation for the reaction concerned. For example,

$$2HCl \longrightarrow H_2 + Cl_2 \qquad \Delta H_{\text{reaction}} = +184 \text{ kJ}$$

Here ΔH represents the energy liberated by the dissociation of two moles of hydrogen chloride and the enthalpy of dissociation is thus $+92$ kJ mol^{-1}. The positive sign indicates that the reaction is endothermic.

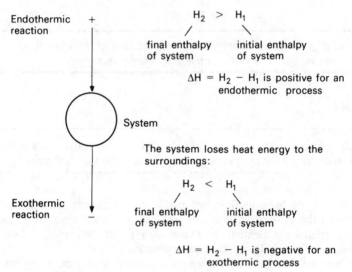

Fig. 2.1 Enthalpy changes: sign convention

The numerical value of an enthalpy change is affected by the conditions (i.e. the temperature, pressure and concentration of the reactants and products) at which it is measured and thus a standard for these conditions is defined for enthalpy changes. The energy required to raise the temperature of a substance from t_1° to t_2° is given by the relationship:

mass × specific heat capacity × temperature change

where the specific heat capacity of a substance is defined as the energy required to raise the temperature of unit mass of the material by 1°. For example, the specific heat capacities of water and copper are 4.2 and 0.38 kJ kg^{-1} K^{-1} respectively.

The standard conditions for enthalpy changes are a pressure of 101 325 Pa (Nm^{-2}) (1 atmosphere) at a temperature of 298 K (25°C) with solutions of unit concentration, or more accurately, of unit activity (see Section 5.3). Enthalpy changes under standard conditions are indicated by the addition of the superscript $^\circ$, thus ΔH° indicates that the enthalpy change refers to a pressure of 1 atm. The temperature is often written as a subscript, e.g. ΔH°_{298}.

It is also important to specify the physical states of the reactants and products as energy is required to change a solid to a liquid (enthalpy of fusion, ΔH_{fusion}) or to convert a liquid into a vapour (enthalpy of vaporisation, ΔH_{vapn}). For example, 334 kJ (the specific enthalpy of fusion of ice) are required to melt 1 kg of ice to water at 0°, while 2261 kJ (the specific enthalpy of vaporisation of water) are required to vaporise 1 kg of water at 100°C. The corresponding figures for 1 mole = 18 g of H_2O are 6.01 kJ and 40.7 kJ respectively:

$$H_2O_{(s)} \xrightarrow[-\Delta H_{fusion}]{+\Delta H_{fusion}} H_2O_{(l)} \xrightarrow[-\Delta H_{vaporisation}]{+\Delta H_{vaporisation}} H_2O_{(v)}$$

2.2
Specific enthalpy changes

Specific objectives: *The expected learning outcome of this section is that the student:* (i) *Defines the following specific enthalpy changes:*
(a) *enthalpy of formation*
(b) *enthalpy of combustion*
(c) *enthalpy of solution*
(d) *enthalpy of neutralisation*
(ii) *Performs an experiment to determine an enthalpy change for a suitable reaction* (iii) *Recognises the need for controlled conditions to obtain results of reasonable accuracy in such determinations.*

Enthalpy changes are defined according to the nature of the reaction to which they refer:

(a) *Enthalpy of formation*
The Enthalpy of formation ($\Delta H_{formation}$) *of a compound is defined as the enthalpy change of the reaction by which one mole of the compound is formed from its elements in the standard state, e.g.*

$2Al + 3/2O_2 \longrightarrow Al_2O_3$ ΔH_{298}° = standard enthalpy of formation of Al_2O_3 is -1669 kJ mol^{-1}

$\frac{1}{2}H_2 + \frac{1}{2}I_2 \longrightarrow HI$ $\Delta H_{formation}^{\circ}$ of HI = $+26$ kJ mol^{-1}.

By convention, the standard enthalpies of formation of elements in their stable form at the standard state are zero. The standard enthalpy change of any reaction is the difference between the sum of the enthalpies of formation of the products and that of the reactants, e.g.

$$CO + \frac{1}{2}O_2 \longrightarrow CO_2$$
ΔH_{298}° of formation kJ mol^{-1} -111 0 -394

$\Delta H_{reaction}^{\circ}$ $-394 - (-111) = -394 + 111 = -283$ kJ mol^{-1}

(b) Enthalpy of combustion
The enthalpy of combustion ($\Delta H^{\circ}_{combustion}$) *of an element or compound is defined as the enthalpy change which occurs when one mole of the substance is completely burnt in oxygen under standard conditions.* For example, the standard enthalpy of combustion of methane is -890 kJ mol^{-1}:

$$CH_{4(g)} + 2O_{2(g)} \longrightarrow CO_{2(g)} + H_2O_{(l)}$$
$$1 \text{ mol} \qquad\qquad \Delta H^{\circ} = -890 \text{ kJ mol}^{-1}$$

Determination of enthalpy of combustion
Enthalpies of combustion are determined using a bomb calorimeter (see fig. 2.2). A known mass of the substance is placed in the silica cup and the steel lid is screwed on tightly. Oxygen is pumped in under pressure (approx. 20 atm) and the vessel is immersed in water in an insulated calorimeter. The temperature of the system is noted and the sample is then ignited by passing an electric current through the heating filament. The heat evolved is determined from the temperature increase of the water/bomb calorimeter system and the enthalpy of combustion of the substance is calculated from the result:

$$\left.\begin{array}{l}\text{Heat produced by} \\ \text{combustion of} \\ w \text{ g of the} \\ \text{substance of} \\ \text{RMM, M}\end{array}\right\} = \left(\begin{array}{l}\text{Heat capacity of} \\ \text{calorimeter system}\end{array}\right) \times \left(\begin{array}{l}\text{Increase in} \\ \text{temperature}\end{array}\right)$$

$\Delta H_{combustion}$ = energy obtained by combustion of 1 mol of the substance.

$$\therefore \quad \Delta H_{combustion} = \frac{M}{w} \times \left(\begin{array}{l}\text{Heat capacity of} \\ \text{calorimeter system}\end{array}\right) \times \left(\begin{array}{l}\text{Increase in} \\ \text{temperature}\end{array}\right)$$

The heat capacity of the bomb calorimeter, water, stirrer, thermometer etc. (i.e. the calorimeter system) is found by noting the temperature increase which is obtained by the combustion of a known mass of a substance of known enthalpy of combustion. Benzoic acid, $C_6H_5CO_2H$, has a $\Delta H_{combustion}$ of -3228.4 kJ mol and is frequently used for this purpose. Alternatively, the temperature increase obtained when a steady current of i ampères is passed through the heating filament is noted and the heat capacity is calculated from the expression:

Vit = Heat capacity of calorimeter system × temperature increase

where Vit joules is the energy produced in t seconds by a current of i ampères at a voltage V.

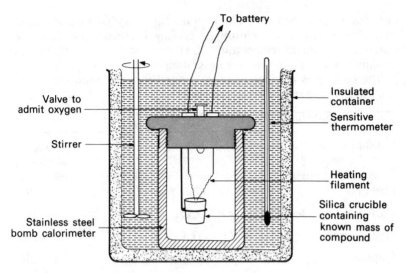

Fig. 2.2 The bomb calorimeter

Cooling corrections

In accurate determinations of enthalpy changes allowance should be made for the heat loss to the atmosphere which occurs once the calorimeter system is at a higher temperature than the surroundings. This correction may be made by noting the temperature of the water

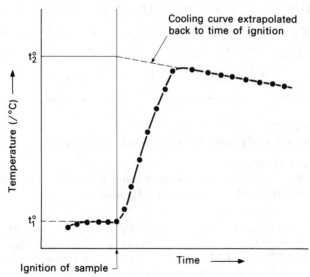

Fig. 2.3 A cooling curve to correct for heat losses

in the calorimeter tank at regular intervals (say every half minute), before and after ignition, and plotting a cooling curve (see fig. 2.3). The corrected maximum temperature, t_2°, is obtained by extrapolating the cooling curve back to the time of ignition.

The enthalpies of combustion of a number of common substances are listed in Table 2.1.

Table 2.1 Standard enthapies of combustion

Substance	Reaction	ΔH_{298}° (/kJ mol^{-1})
Carbon	$C_{(s)} + O_2 \rightarrow CO_2$	-394
Carbon monoxide	$CO_{(g)} + \frac{1}{2}O_2 \rightarrow CO_2$	-283
Hydrogen	$H_{2(g)} + \frac{1}{2}O_2 \rightarrow H_2O_{(l)}$	-286
Sulphur	$S_{(s)} + O_2 \rightarrow SO_2$	-297
Methane	$CH_{4(g)} + 2O_2 \rightarrow CO_2 + 2H_2O_{(l)}$	-890
Ethane	$C_2H_{6(g)} + 3\frac{1}{2}O_2 \rightarrow 2CO_2 + 3H_2O_{(l)}$	-1560
Ethene	$C_2H_{4(g)} + 3O_2 \rightarrow 2CO_2 + 2H_2O_{(l)}$	-1409
Ethyne	$C_2H_{2(g)} + 2\frac{1}{2}O_2 \rightarrow 2CO_2 + H_2O_{(l)}$	-1299
Methanol	$CH_3OH_{(l)} + 1\frac{1}{2}O_2 \rightarrow CO_2 + 2H_2O_{(l)}$	-726
Ethanol	$C_2H_5OH_{(l)} + 3O_2 \rightarrow 2CO_2 + 3H_2O_{(l)}$	-1367
Ethanoic acid	$CH_3CO_2H_{(l)} + 2O_2 \rightarrow 2CO_2 + 2H_2O_{(l)}$	-873
Benzoic acid	$C_6H_5CO_2H_{(s)} + 7\frac{1}{2}O_2 \rightarrow 7CO_2 + 3H_2O_{(l)}$	-3228
Glucose	$C_6H_{12}O_{6(s)} + 6O_2 \rightarrow 6CO_2 + 6H_2O_{(l)}$	-2816

Experiment 2.1
Determination of the enthalpy of combustion of methanol

Apparatus and materials
Small metal can. 250 cm^3 measuring cylinder. One 0–110° thermometer. Spirit lamp. Metal tripod and gauze. Methanol.

Method
Place the metal can on the gauze and tripod and pour in 200 cm^3 of cold water from the measuring cylinder. Half fill the spirit lamp with the alcohol (CH$_3$OH, RMM = 32) and weigh it (mass = m_1). Note the temperature of the water in the can (t_1°) and then light the lamp and place it under the can. Stir the water with the thermometer and extinguish

the spirit lamp when the temperature of the water has increased by 15–20°, noting the highest temperature attained (t_2°). Reweigh the spirit lamp (mass $= m_2$).

Calculation of enthalpy of combustion of methanol

Mass of methanol burned $= (m_1 - m_2)$ g
RMM of methanol, $CH_3OH = 32$

$$\left.\begin{array}{l}\text{Heat energy liberated} \\ \text{by combustion of} \\ (m_1 - m_2)/32 \text{ mol} \\ \text{of methanol}\end{array}\right\} \begin{array}{l}= \text{Mass of water} \times \text{specific heat} \\ \quad \text{capacity} \times (t_2 - t_1) \\ = 0.200 \times 4.2 \times (t_2 - t_1) \text{ kJ}\end{array}$$

$\Delta H_{\text{combustion}}$ of methanol = heat liberated by combustion of 1 mol of methanol $= 0.200 \times 4.2 \times (t_2 - t_1) \times 32/(m_1 - m_2)$ kJ mol^{-1}

This experiment is subject to considerable error because of heat losses from the burning alcohol to the atmosphere and, in addition, it is not possible to apply a cooling curve correction as described above. These errors are considerably reduced by using the apparatus shown in fig. 2.4.

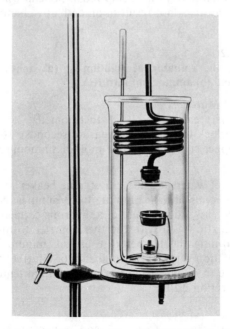

Fig. 2.4 Enthalpy of combustion apparatus. Photograph courtesy of Griffin and George Ltd.

The hot gases from the combustion of the liquid in the spirit lamp are drawn through the copper spiral immersed in the water. Sufficient suction for this is provided by connecting the end of the spiral to a water pump by a length of rubber tubing.

(c) Enthalpy of solution

The enthalpy of solution of a compound ($\Delta H_{solution}$) is defined as the enthalpy change which occurs when 1 mole of the substance is dissolved in a solvent to form a solution. Solution can be an exothermic or an endothermic process, e.g.

$$NH_4^+NO_{3(s)}^- \xrightarrow{H_2O} NH_{4(aq)}^+ + NO_{3(aq)}^-$$

ammonium nitrate(V) $\qquad\qquad\qquad \Delta H_{solution}^\circ = +25.8 \text{ kJ mol}^{-1}$

$$Na^+OH_{(s)}^- \xrightarrow{H_2O} Na^+OH_{(aq)}^-$$

sodium hydroxide $\qquad\qquad\qquad \Delta H_{solution}^\circ = -42.7 \text{ kJ mol}^{-1}$

The numerical value of the enthalpy of solution depends on the concentration of the solution obtained and increases to a maximum with increasing dilution. The enthalpy of solution usually refers to the formation of an infinitely dilute solution, i.e. one in which the addition of further solvent does not result in an enthalpy change.

Experiment 2.2
To determine the enthalpy of solution of (a) anhydrous copper(II) sulphate(VI) and (b) ammonium nitrate(V)

Apparatus and Materials
Expanded polystyrene beaker. 0–50° thermometer. 250 cm³ measuring cylinder. Stopclock (or watch to measure seconds). 16 g (0.1 mol) of anhydrous copper sulphate. 8 g (0.1 mol) of ammonium nitrate(V).

Method
Pour 150 cm³ of water into the polystyrene beaker and note its temperature at intervals of half a minute for 3 minutes. Noting the time of the addition, now add 0.1 mol of anhydrous copper(II)sulphate(VI) and stir the mixture well with the thermometer to dissolve the salt. Continue recording the temperature at half minute intervals while stirring the solution with the thermometer for a further 5 minutes. Plot a cooling curve to obtain the corrected maximum temperature, t_2°, as described in Section 2.2(b).

Calculation
The enthalpy change on the solution of 0.1 mol of anhydrous copper(II)-sulphate(VI) = Q joules, where

Q = mass × specific thermal capacity × temperature change

As an approximation, the specific heat capacity of the solution = 4.2 kJ $kg^{-1}K^{-1}$ (i.e. the same as that of water) and mass = mass of water = 0.150 kg.

(b) Repeat the experiment using 0.1 mol of ammonium nitrate(V) in 75 cm^3 of water. Again record the temperature at half minute intervals to allow for the heat *gained* from the surroundings.

(d) Enthalpy of neutralisation
The enthalpy of neutralisation ($\Delta H_{neutralisation}$) of an acid or base is defined as the enthalpy change which occurs when 1 mol of the substance is exactly neutralised at the stated temperature and pressure.

Neutralisation is invariably an exothermic process, e.g.

$$H^+Cl^-_{(aq)} + Na^+OH^-_{(aq)} \longrightarrow Na^+Cl^-_{(aq)} + H_2O_{(l)}$$
$$\Delta H^\circ_{298} = -57.1 \text{ kJ mol}^{-1}$$

The enthalpy of neutralisation of *any* strong acid by a strong base is virtually constant and is close to the value $(-57$ kJ mol$^{-1})$ reported for the hydrochloric acid/sodium hydroxide neutralisation. This constancy is a result of the fact that all strong acids (HCl, HBr, HNO_3 etc.), strong bases (e.g. NaOH and KOH) and salts are fully ionised in aqueous solution (see Section 4.1(b)). The overall reaction is therefore the same in each case: the neutralisation of one mole of $H^+_{(aq)}$ (hydrated protons) by one mole of hydrated hydroxyl ions to yield water for which the enthalpy change is -57 kJ mol^{-1}:

$$H^+_{(aq)} + OH^-_{(aq)} \longrightarrow H_2O_{(l)} \qquad \Delta H^\circ = -57 \text{ kJ mol}^{-1}$$

The enthalpy change when a weak acid or a weak base is neutralised is less than 57 kJ mol^{-1} as energy is required to dissociate the weakly ionised substance into its ions, e.g.

$$HCN + K^+OH^- \longrightarrow K^+CN^- + H_2O_{(l)}$$

hydrogen
cyanide

(a weak acid)   (a strong base) $\Delta H^\circ = -11.7$ kJ mol^{-1}

Experiment 2.3
To determine the enthalpy of neutralisation of a strong acid by a strong base

Apparatus and materials
Two expanded polystyrene beakers. Two 0–50° thermometers. Two 50 cm^3 measuring cylinders. Clock or watch for noting times to the nearest second. 2M hydrochloric acid. 2M sodium hydroxide.

Method

Using different measuring cylinders for each of the two solutions, transfer 50 cm^3 of 2M hydrochloric acid and 50 cm^3 of 2M sodium hydroxide solution into two separate polystyrene beakers. Place a thermometer in each and stir the solutions, noting their temperatures, t_1° and t_2° respectively, at half minute intervals. After 3 minutes pour the sodium hydroxide solution into the beaker containing the hydrochloric acid and stir the mixture with a thermometer (see fig. 2.5). Note the time when the solutions were mixed and continue to record the temperature every half minute for 5–6 minutes. Plot a cooling curve (see Section 2.2(b)) to obtain the corrected maximum temperature attained, t_3°.

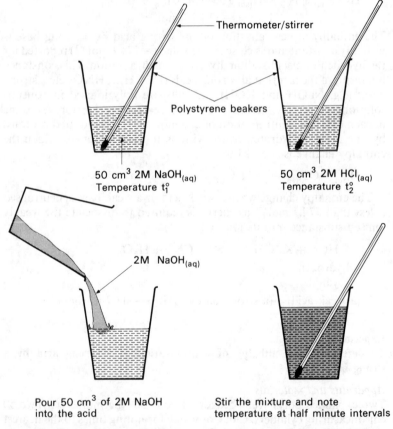

Fig. 2.5(a) Determination of enthalpy of neutralisation of hydrochloric acid

Calculation

$$\left.\begin{array}{l}\text{Heat liberated by}\\\text{neutralisation of}\\\text{50 cm}^3\text{ of 2M HCl by}\\\text{50 cm}^3\text{ of 2M NaOH}\end{array}\right\} = \left\{\begin{array}{l}\text{Heat gained in heating the 100 cm}^3\text{ of}\\\text{aqueous NaCl which is formed from a}\\\text{mean temperature of }(t_1+t_2)/2\text{ to }t_3^\circ\end{array}\right.$$

$$= \text{Mass} \times \text{specific heat capacity}$$
$$\times \text{temperature increase}$$

$$= 0.100 \times 4.2 \times t_3 - (t_1 + t_2)/2$$

$$= Q \text{ kJ}$$

The enthalpy of neutralisation is the enthalpy change which occurs when one mole of hydrochloric acid is neutralised. 50 cm^3 of 2M hydrochloric acid contains 0.1 mole of HCl.

∴   Enthalpy of neutralisation $= 10 \times Q \text{ kJ mol}^{-1}$

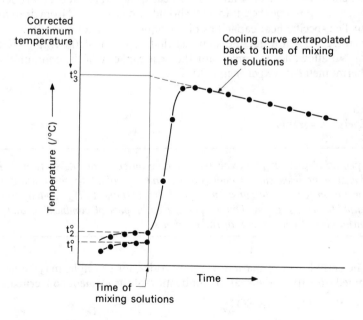

Fig. 2.5(b) Experiment to determine enthalpy of neutralisation: cooling curve

Experiment 2.4
To determine the enthalpy of neutralisation of a weak acid by a weak base

Method
Repeat Experiment 2.3 using 50 cm^3 of 2M ethanoic (acetic) acid and 50 cm^3 of 2M aqueous ammonia.

Sources of error in enthalpy change determinations
The standard conditions for enthalpy measurements were described in Section 2.1. Although many approximations were made and the results were subject to a number of sources of error, the experiments described in this section to measure specific enthalpy changes usually give satisfactory results with a minimum of practical skill. However, to obtain reliable results of reasonable accuracy the experimental conditions need to be carefully controlled. The chief sources of error are:
(a) Cooling losses. Some allowance was made for heat loss in Experiments 2.2–2.4 by plotting a cooling curve; however, this was not possible in the experiment to measure the enthalpy of combustion of methanol (see Experiment 2.1). Heat losses are minimised by lagging the calorimeter vessels or by using expanded polystyrene beakers (where the material itself provides effective insulation) or Thermos flasks as containers in the heat of solution and heat of neutralisation experiments. Wherever possible the equipment should also be shielded from draughts.
(b) The specific heat capacities of the aqueous salt solutions in Experiments 2.2–2.4 are not the same as that of water (4200 J kg^{-1} K^{-1}).
(c) No allowance was made for the heat capacity of the container and thermometer in Experiments 2.1–2.4.

2.3
Energy diagrams

Specific objective: *The expected learning outcome of this section is that the student uses simple energy diagrams to calculate the enthalpy of formation for simple substances, such as methane (CH$_4$) and hydrogen sulphide (H$_2$S), given their respective enthalpies of combustion and the enthalpies of combustion of the elements.*

The enthalpy of formation of some oxides, for example, may be determined directly as the heat of combustion of the element concerned, e.g.

$$S_{(s)} + O_{2(g)} \longrightarrow SO_{2(g)}$$

$\Delta H_{formation}$ of SO$_2$ = $\Delta H_{combustion}$ of sulphur = -297 kJ mol^{-1}

However, in most cases, compounds cannot be formed by direct combination of the elements of which they are composed and the enthalpy of formation of the substance has to be determined indirectly from the enthalpies of combustion of the compound and of its constituent elements. One method of calculating the result is to plot the energy changes for the combustion of one mole of the compound and the *total* enthalpy change for the combustion of the elements of which the substance is composed on an energy diagram (see Section 1.3).

Example 2.1
Calculate the enthalpy of formation of hydrogen sulphide,

(1) $\quad H_2 + S_{(s)} \longrightarrow H_2S \qquad\qquad \Delta H^c_{formation} = \Delta H^c_1$

from the enthalpies of combustion of hydrogen, sulphur and hydrogen sulphide:

(2) $\quad H_2 + \frac{1}{2}O_2 \longrightarrow H_2O_{(1)} \qquad\quad \Delta H^c_2 = -286$ kJ mol^{-1}

(3) $\quad S_{(s)} + O_2 \longrightarrow SO_2 \qquad\qquad \Delta H^c_3 = -297$ kJ mol^{-1}

(4) $\quad H_2S + 1\frac{1}{2}O_2 \longrightarrow H_2O + SO_2 \quad \Delta H^c_4 = -562$ kJ mol^{-1}

Solution
The energy diagram for the reaction is:

$H_2 + S + 1\frac{1}{2}O_2$

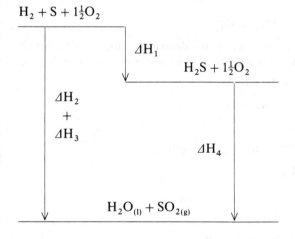

From which, it is apparent that:

$$\Delta H_2 + \Delta H_3 = \Delta H_1 + \Delta H_4$$

i.e.,
Enthalpy of formation of H_2S,

$$\Delta H_1 = \Delta H_2 + \Delta H_3 - \Delta H_4$$
$$= -286 + (-297) - (-562)$$
$$= -21 \text{ kJ mol}^{-1}$$

The negative sign indicates that the formation of hydrogen sulphide from its elements is an exothermic process.

Algebraically, this calculation is equivalent to saying that:

Equation (1) = Equation (2) + Equation (3) − Equation (4)

from which

$$\Delta H_1 = \Delta H_2 + \Delta H_3 - \Delta H_4$$

The energy diagram is a diagrammatic representation of Hess's Law (which is essentially a statement of the Law of Energy Conservation in terms of heat).

Hess's Law states that if a chemical change can be carried out by more than one route, the *total* enthalpy change is the same irrespective of the route taken.

In this example, the sum of the enthalpy changes for each of the two routes from hydrogen and sulphur to water and sulphur dioxide is the same:

Route 1: Combustion of the hydrogen and sulphur directly to water and sulphur dioxide

Enthalpy change $= \Delta H_2 + \Delta H_3$

Route 2: Formation of hydrogen sulphide from hydrogen and sulphur, followed by the combustion of the H_2S to water and sulphur dioxide

Enthalpy change $= \Delta H_1 + \Delta H_4$

i.e. $\Delta H_2 + \Delta H_3 = \Delta H_1 + \Delta H_4$

Example 2.2
Calculate the enthalpy of formation of ethyne

$$2C + H_2 \longrightarrow C_2H_2$$

from the data in Table 2.1.

Solution
From the energy diagram in fig. 2.6

$$2 \times (-394) + (-286) = \Delta H^{\circ}_{\text{formation}} + (-1299)$$
$$\Delta H^{\circ}_{\text{formation}} \text{ of } C_2H_2 = +225 \text{ kJ mol}^{-1}$$

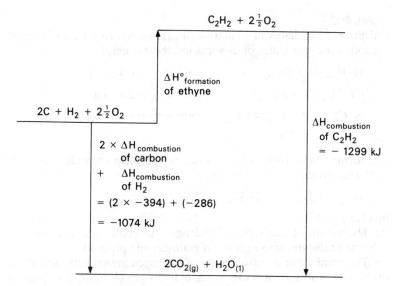

Fig. 2.6 Energy diagram to calculate $\Delta H^{\circ}_{\text{formation}}$ of ethyne

The positive sign indicates that the formation of ethyne from its elements is an endothermic process.

The enthalpy of formation of a simple compound may also be calculated from the bond energies, i.e. the enthalpies of dissociation, of the relevant molecules. The bond energy (or enthalpy) of the bond X—Y in a diatomic molecule is defined as the enthalpy change for the process:

$$X{-}Y_{(g)} \longrightarrow \underbrace{X\cdot_{(g)} + \cdot Y_{(g)}}_{\text{atoms}}$$

For a triatomic molecule, e.g. XY_2, the average bond enthalpy is defined as half the enthalpy change for the process:

$$Y{-}X{-}Y_{(g)} \longrightarrow X\cdot_{(g)} + 2Y\cdot_{(g)}$$

The enthalpy change in a chemical reaction is largely a result of the difference in bond enthalpies of the molecules of the reactants and those of the products (see Section 1.3 and Example 2.3). Bond fission is an endothermic process, e.g.

$$H_{2(g)} \longrightarrow 2H\cdot_{(g)} \qquad \Delta H = +436 \text{ kJ mol}^{-1}$$

while the reverse process (covalent bond formation) is exothermic and liberates considerable amounts of heat:

$$2H\cdot_{(g)} \longrightarrow H_{2(g)} \qquad \Delta H = -436 \text{ kJ mol}^{-1}$$

Example 2.3

Calculate the enthalpy of formation of gaseous hydrogen chloride from the following enthalpies of dissociation (bond energies):

$$H{-}H_{(g)} \longrightarrow 2H\cdot_{(g)} \qquad \Delta H = +436 \text{ kJ mol}^{-1}$$

$$Cl{-}Cl_{(g)} \longrightarrow 2Cl\cdot_{(g)} \qquad \Delta H = +242 \text{ kJ mol}^{-1}$$

$$H{-}Cl_{(g)} \longrightarrow H\cdot_{(g)} + Cl\cdot_{(g)} \qquad \Delta H = +431 \text{ kJ mol}^{-1}$$

Solution

The formation of two moles of gaseous hydrogen chloride according to the equation:

$$H_{2(g)} + Cl_{2(g)} \longrightarrow 2HCl_{(g)}$$

involves:

(a) The fission of one mole of hydrogen molecules and one mole of chlorine molecules into atoms (an endothermic process).

(b) The combination of two moles of hydrogen atoms with two moles of chlorine atoms to form two moles of hydrogen chloride. This process is exothermic.

The enthalpy change for the net reaction is equal to the the sum of the energy changes for these two processes:

$$H_{2(g)} \quad + \quad Cl_{2(g)} \longrightarrow 2HCl_{(g)}$$

energy required $= +436$ kJ $\quad = +242$ kJ $\quad$ energy liberated $2 \times -431 = -862$ kJ

$$2H\cdot_{(g)} \qquad 2Cl\cdot_{(g)}$$

$$+436 + 242 + (2 \times -431) = -184 \text{ kJ for the formation}$$

of *two* moles of hydrogen chloride. The enthalpy of formation of hydrogen chloride is thus $-184/2 = -92$ kJ mol^{-1}. The energy diagram for this reaction is shown in fig. 2.7. This reaction is an exothermic process as the energy obtained by the formation of the covalent bonds in two molecules of hydrogen chloride is greater than the energy required to break the covalent bonds in one molecule of hydrogen and one molecule of chlorine.

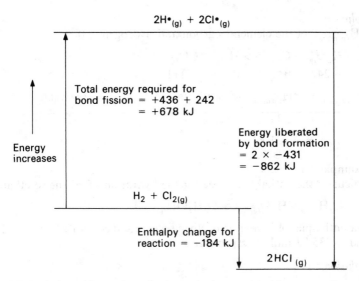

Fig. 2.7 Enthalpy of formation of gaseous hydrogen chloride: energy diagram

2.4
Calculation of enthalpy changes for chemical reactions

Specific objective: *The expected learning outcome of this section is that the student calculates enthalpy changes for simple reactions, given enthalpies of formation of reactants and products.*

The enthalpy change for any reaction is equal to the difference between the sum of the enthalpies of formation of the products and the sum of the enthalpies of formation of the reactants, i.e.

$$\Delta H_{reaction} = \text{Total } \Delta H_{formation} \text{ of products} -$$

$$\text{Total } \Delta H_{formation} \text{ of reactants.}$$

By convention, the standard enthalpy of formation of any element in its stable state at 298 K and 101.325 kN m^{-2}, ΔH°_{298}, is zero.

Example 2.4
Calculate the enthalpy change for the reaction

$$H_2O_{(g)} + C_{(s)} \longrightarrow H_{2(g)} + CO_{(g)}$$

The enthalpies of formation of steam and carbon monoxide are -242 and -111 kJ mol^{-1} respectively.

Solution

$\Delta H^{\circ}_{\text{formation}}$ of the elements carbon and hydrogen = 0

$$H_2O_{(g)} + C_{(s)} \longrightarrow H_{2(g)} + CO_{(g)}$$
$$\quad -242 \quad\quad 0 \quad\quad\quad 0 \quad\quad -111$$

$\Delta H^{\circ}_{\text{reaction}} = \Delta H^{\circ}_{\text{formation}}$ of products $- \Delta H^{\circ}_{\text{formation}}$ of reactants

$$= -111 - (-242)$$
$$= +131 \text{ kJ}$$

Example 2.5

Calculate the enthalpy change for the hydration of ethene to ethanol:

$$C_2H_{4(g)} + H_2O_{(g)} \longrightarrow C_2H_5OH_{(g)}$$

The enthalpies of formation of ethene, steam and ethanol are $+52$, -242 and -235 kJ mol^{-1} respectively.

Solution

$$\Delta H_{\text{reaction}} = \Delta H_{\text{formation}} \text{ of } C_2H_5OH_{(g)} - (\Delta H_{\text{formation}} \text{ of }$$
$$C_2H_4 + \Delta H_{\text{formation}} \text{ of } H_2O_{(g)})$$
$$= -235 - (+52 + -242)$$
$$= -45 \text{ kJ mol}^{-1}.$$

Summary

1. The symbol ΔH represents the enthalpy change of a chemical reaction, where

ΔH = Total enthalpy of the products of the reaction $-$ Total enthalpy of the reactants

$$= \quad \overset{\nearrow}{\underset{\text{final state}}{H_2}} - \overset{\nwarrow}{\underset{\text{initial state}}{H_1}}$$

2. The enthalpy change in a reaction is defined as the heat evolved or absorbed (in kJ mol^{-1}) when the reaction is carried out at constant pressure.

3. ΔH is negative for an exothermic reaction ($H_2 < H_1$) and positive for an endothermic reaction ($H_2 > H_1$).

4. The standard conditions for enthalpy changes are a pressure of 101 325 Pa (1 atm) at 298 K. Standard enthalpy changes are denoted by the symbol ΔH° or ΔH°_{298}.

5. The enthalpy of formation of a compound is defined as the enthalpy change of the reaction by which one mole of the compound is formed from its elements in the standard state.

6. The standard enthalpies of formation of elements in their stable form at the standard state are zero.

7. The enthalpy change of any reaction is equal to the difference between the sum of the enthalpies of formation of the products of the reaction and the sum of the enthalpies of formation of the reactants.

8. The enthalpy of combustion of an element or compound is defined as the enthalpy change which occurs when one mole of the substance is completely burnt in oxygen under standard conditions.

9. The enthalpy of solution of a compound is defined as the enthalpy change which occurs when one mole of the substance is dissolved in a solvent to form a solution.

10. The enthalpy of neutralisation of an acid or base is defined as the enthalpy change which occurs when one mole of the substance is exactly neutralised by a base or acid.

11. The enthalpy of neutralisation of a strong acid by a strong base is a constant owing to the virtually complete ionisation of these substances in aqueous solution. The net reaction is:

$$H^+_{(aq)} + OH^-_{(aq)} \longrightarrow H_2O_{(l)} \qquad \Delta H = -57 \text{ kJ mol}^{-1}$$

12. Hess's Law states that if a chemical change can be carried out by more than one route, the *total* enthalpy change is the same, irrespective of the route taken.

Questions

1. What is meant by the enthalpy change of a chemical reaction? Deduce the signs (i.e. positive or negative) for endothermic and exothermic reactions.

2. Why is it important to specify the physical state of the reactants or products when stating enthalpy changes for a chemical reaction?

3. What are the conditions for the measurement of standard enthalpy changes?

4. Define the enthalpy of formation of a compound. Describe how

enthalpies of formation may be used to calculate the enthalpy change of a chemical reaction.

5. Define enthalpy of combustion.

6. Describe how you would determine the enthalpy of combustion of a solid and show how the result is calculated.

7. Describe one method of correcting for cooling losses in experiments to measure enthalpy changes.

8. Define enthalpy of solution. Describe how you would determine the enthalpy of solution of ammonium nitrate(V).

9. Explain why the enthalpy of neutralisation of a strong acid by a strong base is approximately constant ($\Delta H = -57$ kJ mol^{-1}).

10. The enthalpy of combustion of methane (CH_4) is -890 kJ mol^{-1}. Use the data in Table 2.1 to calculate its enthalpy of formation.

11. Calculate the enthalpies of formation of ethane (C_2H_6) and ethene (C_2H_4) from the data in Table 2.1. Are these reactions exothermic or endothermic? Draw energy diagrams for these reactions.

12. The enthalpy of combustion of carbon disulphide (CS_2) is -1078 kJ mol^{-1}. Use the data in Table 2.1 to calculate its enthalpy of formation.

13. The bond dissociation energies of hydrogen, fluorine and hydrogen fluoride are $+436$, $+158$ and $+562$ kJ mol^{-1} respectively. Calculate the enthalpy of formation of hydrogen fluoride.

14. In the Thermite process aluminium is used to reduce iron(III)oxide to iron:

$$2Al + Fe_2O_3 \longrightarrow Al_2O_3 + 2Fe$$

Calculate the enthalpy change for this reaction if the enthalpies of formation of Fe_2O_3 and Al_2O_3 are -822 and -1669 kJ mol^{-1} respectively.

15. Describe an experiment to determine the enthalpy of reaction of (i) zinc and (ii) zinc oxide (ZnO) with hydrochloric acid. How would you use your results to deduce the enthalpy of formation of zinc oxide?

16. Describe experiments to determine enthalpies of (i) combustion and (ii) neutralisation. What precautions would you take to obtain reason-

ably accurate results?

17. A temperature increase of 6.6° was observed when 50 cm^3 of 1M nitric acid was neutralised with 50 cm^3 of 1M potassium hydroxide solution. Calculate the enthalpy of neutralisation. Specific heat capacity of water $= 4.2$ kJ kg^{-1} K^{-1}.

18. A temperature increase of 4.7° was observed after adding 0.01 mole of powdered zinc to 100 cm^3 of aqueous copper sulphate(VI) solution. Calculate the enthalpy change for the reaction:

$$Zn_{(s)} + Cu^{2+}_{(aq)} \longrightarrow Zn^{2+}_{(aq)} + Cu_{(s)}$$

19. The enthalpy of formation of methanol, $CH_3OH_{(l)}$, is -240 kJ mol^{-1}. The enthalpies of combustion of carbon and hydrogen are -394 and -286 kJ mol^{-1} respectively. Calculate the enthalpy of combustion of methanol:

$$CH_3OH_{(l)} + 1\tfrac{1}{2}O_{2(g)} \longrightarrow CO_{2(g)} + 2H_2O_{(l)}$$

20. Use the information in Table 2.1 to deduce the enthalpy of formation of benzoic acid, $C_6H_5CO_2H$, from its elements.

21. The enthalpies of formation of propane (C_3H_8), carbon dioxide and water ($H_2O_{(l)}$) are -104, -394 and -286 kJ mol^{-1} respectively. Calculate the enthalpy of combustion of propane.

22. The standard enthalpies of combustion of carbon$_{(graphite)}$ and carbon$_{(diamond)}$ are -393.5 and -395.4 kJ mol^{-1} respectively. Calculate the enthalpy change for the process:

$$C_{(graphite)} \longrightarrow C_{(diamond)}$$

Draw an energy diagram for the transition.

B Equilibrium

3 Reversible reactions and equilibrium

General objective: *The expected learning outcome of this chapter is that the student is able to describe and use some ideas of chemical equilibrium.*

3.1
Introduction

The rate of a chemical reaction is defined *either* in terms of the number of moles of reactant which are consumed in one second, *or* as the number of moles of product which are formed each second. The factors which can affect reaction rates were discussed in greater detail at Level 1, or as part of your C.S.E. or G.C.E. chemistry course. These factors may be summarised as follows:

(a) The degree of subdivision of the reactants
Substances react at a much faster rate if they are in solution or in the form of a fine powder. For example, 1 g of magnesium powder or finely divided calcium carbonate dissolves more rapidly in a given volume of dilute hydrochloric acid than the same mass of the material in the form of a single lump:

$$Mg_{(s)} + 2HCl_{(aq)} \rightarrow MgCl_{2(aq)} + H_{2(g)}$$

$$CaCO_{3(s)} + 2HCl_{(aq)} \rightarrow CaCl_{2(aq)} + H_2O_{(l)} + CO_{2(g)}$$

The results of such an experiment are listed in Table 3.1. Similarly, the brilliant flashes of light when iron filings are sprinkled into the flame of a Bunsen burner indicate an immediate reaction, while there would be little or no change if an iron nail is placed in the flame. These rate

Table 3.1   *Effect of particle size on the rate of solution of iron in 2M hydrochloric acid (t = 24°)*

Form	Time required for iron to dissolve (seconds)
Fine powder	7
Coarse filings	68
Wire	174
Lump	580

differences are due to the enormous increase in the surface area of the solid when it is in powdered form.

Substances also react faster when they are in solution. For example, dry crystals of silver nitrate and potassium chromate may be mixed in a test-tube at room temperature without any apparent chemical change as the ions of which these substances are composed are firmly fixed in the crystal. But if these substances are first dissolved in water and then mixed, an immediate reaction to form a red precipitate of silver chromate takes place:

$$2Ag^+_{(aq)} + CrO_{4(aq)}^{2-} \rightarrow Ag_2CrO_{4(s)}$$

colourless   yellow   red precipitate

This is because the silver ions and chromate ions are free to move and react with one another when they are in solution.

(b) Concentration of the reactants

In general, an increase in concentration produces an increase in reaction rate. The times required for a strip of magnesium ribbon to dissolve in hydrochloric acid solutions of different strengths are shown in fig. 3.1. The ions or molecules of a reactant in solution must 'collide' with

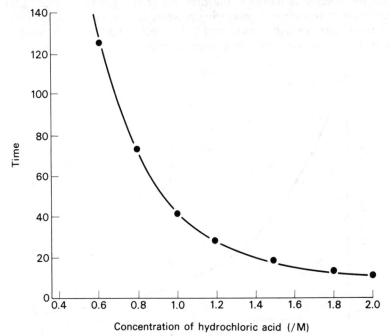

Fig. 3.1 Effect of hydrochloric acid concentration on the time (seconds) required to dissolve a 3 cm length of magnesium ribbon at 24°

one another in order to react. An increase in the concentration (i.e. an increase in the number of ions or molecules present in unit volume of the solution) increases the number of collisions which occur in each second and hence increases the reaction rate. For simple, single-stage reactions the reaction rate is directly proportional to concentration, thus a tenfold increase in concentration results in a tenfold increase in reaction rate. The decrease in concentration of the reactants with time explains why there is a gradual decrease in reaction rate in the course of a chemical reaction (see fig. 3.2).

(c) Pressure

An increase in pressure has little or no effect on the volumes of solids or liquids and thus does not appreciably alter the rates of chemical reactions between substances in these two phases. However, pressure changes have an enormous effect on the volume of a gas. *At constant temperature the volume of a gas is inversely proportional to the pressure (Boyle's Law)*, thus

$$V \propto \frac{1}{p} \text{ (at constant temperature)}$$

or $pV = a$ *constant*

i.e. the volume is halved if the pressure of the gas is doubled. This decrease in volume with increasing pressure compresses the same mass of a gas into a smaller space and is thus equivalent to an increase in concentration and results in a faster reaction rate.

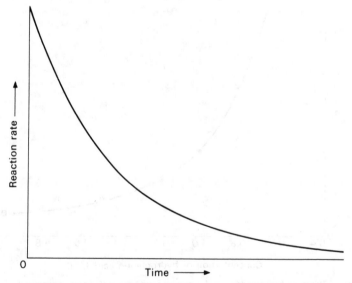

Fig. 3.2 Variation in reaction rate in the course of a chemical reaction

(*d*) *Temperature*

An increase in temperature generally produces a considerably faster reaction rate. The effect of temperature on the time required for a strip of magnesium ribbon to dissolve in 0.5M hydrochloric acid is given in Table 3.2 as an example. For many reactions the rate is approximately doubled by every 10° temperature increase. This does not always apply in the case of enzyme catalysed reactions (see Section 3.1(e)) where

Table 3.2   *Effect of temperature on the time required for a strip of magnesium ribbon to dissolve in 0.50 M hydrochloric acid*

Temperature (/°C)	Time (/s)
23.5	260
29.0	208
38.0	135
44.5	100
49.1	88
61.0	55

increasing the temperature beyond the optimum value at which the rate is a maximum (see fig. 3.3) produces a decrease in reaction rate.

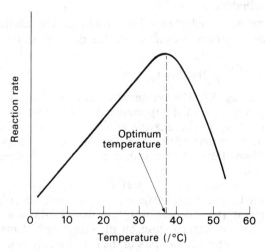

Fig. 3.3 Effect of temperature on the rate of an enzyme catalysed reaction

Further temperature increases cause a dramatic drop in the rate as the protein molecule of the enzyme is denatured and rendered inactive.

(e) Catalysts
A catalyst is a substance which influences the rate of a chemical reaction, but which is unchanged chemically at the end of the reaction. Catalysts are often specific for a single reaction or particular type of reaction. For example, finely divided nickel or platinum are effective catalysts for the addition of hydrogen to the double bond of an alkene to yield an alkane (see Section 9.6(c)(i)):

$$\underset{\text{an alkene}}{\diagdown C = C \diagup} \xrightarrow[\text{hydrogenation}]{\text{H}_2/\text{Ni/pressure}/140^\circ} \underset{\text{an alkane}}{-\overset{\overset{\displaystyle H}{|}}{C}-\overset{\overset{\displaystyle H}{|}}{C}-}$$

or for the reduction of an aldehyde or ketone to an alcohol (see Section 10.6(d)(i)4).

The highly efficient catalysts known as *enzymes*, which are produced in the tissues of plants, animals, bacteria and other living organisms, are sometimes effective for only one particular substance and reaction. For example, the enzyme *urease* catalyses the breakdown of carbamide (urea) into carbon dioxide and ammonia:

$$\underset{\text{carbamide}}{O = C\overset{\displaystyle \diagup NH_2}{\diagdown NH_2}} + H_2O \xrightarrow{\text{urease}} CO_{2(aq)} + 2NH_{3(aq)}$$

This enzyme has no effect on other substances. The relative efficiencies of a number of different catalysts on the decomposition of hydrogen peroxide:

$$2H_2O_2 \xrightarrow{\text{catalyst}} 2H_2O + O_2$$

are shown in fig. 3.4. The greater efficiency of catalysts in powdered form again emphasises the importance of surface area on reaction rate (see Section 3.1(a)). The enzyme *catalase* is highly effective in this reaction and it is estimated that a single molecule of the enzyme catalyses the breakdown of tens of thousands of molecules of hydrogen peroxide every second.

Catalysts are extremely important in industry as they enable substances to be manufactured faster, in higher yield and at considerably lower temperatures and pressures than would otherwise be possible. They thus have a marked effect on the economics of many chemical processes. A number of examples of the use of catalysts in industry are described in Section 3.7.

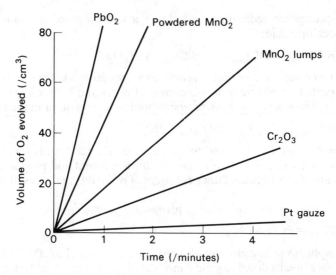

Order of catalytic efficiency:
PbO_2 > MnO_2 (powder) > MnO_2 (lumps) > Cr_2O_3 > Pt gauze

Fig. 3.4 Relative efficiency of catalysts on the decomposition of hydrogen peroxide

3.2
Reversible reactions

Specific objectives: *The expected learning outcome of this section is that the student: (i) Recognises a reversible reaction as one in which the products can react to form the original substances (ii) Uses the symbol* ⇌.

A *reversible reaction* is one which can proceed in either direction according to the reaction conditions, i.e. the products of the reaction can react to reform the original substances.

For example, a white precipitate of bismuth(III)chloride oxide (bismuth oxychloride) is obtained when water is added to a solution of bismuth(III) chloride in aqueous hydrochloric acid:

$$BiCl_{3(aq)} + H_2O_{(l)} \longrightarrow BiOCl_{(s)} + 2HCl_{(aq)} \qquad \text{(i)}$$
bismuth(III) chloride bismuth(III) chloride oxide

This precipitate redissolves on adding a few drops of concentrated hydrochloric acid:

$$BiOCl_{(s)} + 2HCl_{(aq)} \longrightarrow BiCl_{3(aq)} + H_2O_{(l)}$$

thus reversing the reaction represented in equation (i). This cycle can be repeated on adding further amounts of water and hydrochloric acid in turn. The reaction is thus reversible and may be written in the form:

$$BiCl_{3(aq)} + H_2O_{(l)} \rightleftharpoons BiOCl_{(s)} + 2HCl_{(aq)}$$

where the symbol $\rightleftharpoons$ is used to indicate that the reaction is reversible and is proceeding in both directions and the reactant and products are in a state of equilibrium. Other examples of reversible reactions include:

(a) *The thermal decomposition of phosphorus pentachloride:*

$$PCl_5 \rightleftharpoons PCl_3 + Cl_2$$

If phosphorus pentachloride is heated in a sealed vessel to 200–300° the substance breaks down to yield a mixture of phosphorus trichloride and chlorine. If the experiment is repeated using a 1 : 1 mixture of phosphorus trichloride and chlorine, the substances react to form phosphorus pentachloride. In each case the mixture which is obtained contains all three substances – phosphorus pentachloride, phosphorus trichloride and chlorine. Provided the vessel is heated at the same temperature each time until no further change is apparent, the composition of the mixture is the same irrespective of the direction in which the reaction is carried out. This state at which there is no apparent change in the amount of the reactants and products is known as *equilibrium*.

(b) *The esterification of alcohols (see Section 10.2(c)(iii))*
Alcohols react with organic acids to yield pleasant-smelling liquids known as *esters*. The reaction is reversible and is catalysed by sulphuric(VI) acid or other strong acids. For example, the ester ethyl ethanoate (acetate) is obtained by the reaction between ethanol (ethyl alcohol) and ethanoic (acetic) acid:

$$\underset{\text{ethanoic acid}}{CH_3CO_2H} + \underset{\text{ethanol}}{C_2H_5OH} \xrightleftharpoons[]{H^+_{(aq)} \text{ catalyst}} \underset{\text{ethyl ethanoate}}{CH_3CO_2C_2H_5} + H_2O$$

In general,

$$acid + alcohol \xrightleftharpoons[\text{ester hydrolysis}]{\text{esterification}} ester + water$$

The reverse reaction represents the hydrolysis of the ester to yield the organic acid (ethanoic acid) and the alcohol (ethanol). These reactions are discussed in greater detail in Sections 10.2(c)(iii) and 10.4(c)(iii).

(c) The thermal decomposition of hydrogen iodide
Hydrogen iodide decomposes into its elements on heating:

$$2HI_{(g)} \underset{\longleftarrow}{\overset{\text{heat}}{\longrightarrow}} H_{2(g)} + I_{2(g)}$$

The reaction is reversible and the reverse reaction represents the formation of hydrogen iodide from hydrogen and iodine in the gas phase.

In general, any reversible reaction may be expressed in the form:

$$\underbrace{A + B}_{\text{reactants}} \rightleftharpoons \underbrace{C + D}_{\text{products}}$$

in which the products C and D are formed initially by the reaction of substances A and B. As soon as some C and D are formed they react together and immediately begin to reform compounds A and B.

To a certain extent all reactions are reversible, although under normal conditions of temperature and pressure the contribution of the reverse reaction in many changes, such as the combustion of carbon or hydrogen or the solution of magnesium in an acid, is negligible and the reaction proceeds essentially to completion.

3.3
Chemical equilibrium

Specific objectives: *The expected learning outcome of this section is that the student: (i) Defines chemical equilibrium in terms of there being no bulk change of reactants or products (ii) States that chemical equilibrium is a dynamic condition with the rate of the forward reaction equal to the rate of the reverse reaction.*

Eventually a stage is reached in any reversible reaction at which no further chemical change is apparent. The reaction has not gone to completion as both reactants and products are present in the mixture, but their concentrations are now constant, i.e. there is no further bulk change in the reactants and products. This condition is known as the *equilibrium state*. Although no change is apparent at equilibrium the reaction has not stopped. Equilibrium is not a static state, but a *dynamic process* in which the reactants (e.g. A and B) are being consumed at the same rate as they are reformed from the products (C and D):

$$A + B \underset{\text{reverse reaction}}{\overset{\text{forward reaction}}{\rightleftharpoons}} C + D$$

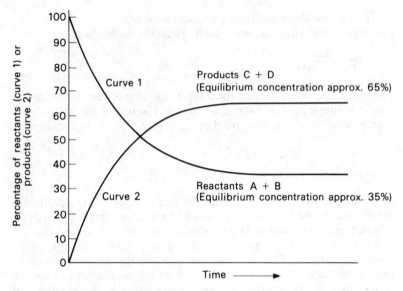

Fig. 3.5 Attainment of equilibrium in a reversible reaction

i.e. it is the state at which the rate of the forward reaction is equal to the rate of the reverse reaction.

The attainment of the equilibrium state is shown graphically in fig. 3.5. At the beginning of the reaction the concentration of the products C and D is zero, but this concentration gradually increases (curve 2) with time as the reactants A and B are consumed (curve 1). Finally a stage is reached when the curves level off and there is no further change in the concentration of any of the substances present. In this example the equilibrium state is attained when the forward reaction is 65% completed.

3.4
The Equilibrium Law

Specific objectives: *The expected learning outcome of this section is that the student: (i) Writes an equation for the equilibrium constant K_c given the equation for the reaction (ii) Uses the symbol [ ] for molar concentration in dilute solution (iii) Calculates K_c for a given reaction, given equilibrium concentrations of reactants and products (iv) States that the larger the value of K_c, the more the products will predominate in the equilibrium mixture, and conversely, the smaller the value of K_c, the more the reactants will predominate in the equilibrium mixture.*

The relationship between the concentrations of the reactants and of the products in the equilibrium mixture at a particular temperature is provided by the *Equilibrium Law*. If the stoichiometric equation (i.e. the chemical equation which indicates the *proportions* in which the substances react and in which the molecules of product are formed) for a general reversible reaction is written as:

$$aA + bB \rightleftharpoons cC + dD$$

the Equilibrium Law may be expressed as:

$$K_{eq} = \frac{(\text{Concentration of } C)^c \times (\text{Concentration of } D)^d}{(\text{Concentration of } A)^a \times (\text{Concentration of } B)^b}$$

at constant temperature

Where K_{eq} is the *equilibrium constant*. The numerical value of the equilibrium constant for a reversible reaction is dependent upon the temperature (see Section 3.5(c)), but is unaffected by the presence of a catalyst (see Section 3.6).

By convention, the product of the concentrations of the products is always written as the numerator (or upper part of the fraction) and the product of the concentrations of the reactants as the denominator (i.e. the lower part). The concentration of each of the reactants or products is raised to the power of the relevant numerical coefficient (a, b, c or d) in the stoichiometric equation for the reaction. For example, the equilibrium constant for the formation of ammonia by the Haber process:

$$N_2 + 3H_2 \rightleftharpoons 2NH_3$$

is:

$$K_{eq} = \frac{(\text{Concentration of } NH_3)^2}{(\text{Concentration of } N_2) \times (\text{Concentration of } H_2)^3}$$

Similarly, for the thermal decomposition of hydrogen iodide:

$$2HI \rightleftharpoons H_2 + I_2$$

$$K_{eq} = \frac{(\text{Concentration of hydrogen}) \times (\text{Concentration of iodine})}{(\text{Concentration of hydrogen iodide})^2}$$

The equilibrium constant is given the symbol K_c when the concentrations of the substances are expressed in $mol\,l^{-1}$, i.e. for the general equation for the reversible reaction:

$$K_c = \frac{[C]^c[D]^d}{[A]^a[B]^b} \text{ at constant temperature}$$

where the brackets [] are used to indicate the concentration of a substance in mol l^{-1} in dilute solution. For example, the equilibrium constant for the formation of ethyl ethanoate by the esterification of ethanol:

$$CH_3CO_2H + C_2H_5OH \rightleftharpoons CH_3CO_2C_2H_5 + H_2O$$

is

$$K_c = \frac{[CH_3CO_2C_2H_5][H_2O]}{[CH_3CO_2H][C_2H_5OH]} = 4.0 \text{ at } 100° \text{ (373K)}$$

The application of the equilibrium law to substances in dilute aqueous solution is particularly important in the case of weak electrolytes. These ionic equilibria are discussed in Chapter 4.

The concentrations of substances in the gas phase are usually expressed in terms of the pressure which a particular component exerts in a mixture and the corresponding equilibrium content is given the symbol K_p. For example, the equilibrium constant for the Haber process may be written as:

$$K_p = \frac{(P_{NH_3})^2}{(P_{N_2})(P_{H_2})^3} \text{ at a constant temperature}$$

where P_{NH_3}, and P_{H_2} are the pressures exerted by ammonia, nitrogen and hydrogen in the equilibrium mixture respectively. K_c and K_p values are related, but are not identical. The values of the equilibrium constants for a number of reversible reactions are listed in Table 3.3. As the concentrations of the products appear in the numerator of the expression for the equilibrium constant, it follows that: *the larger the numerical value of K_c, the more the products will predominate in the equilibrium mixture*, i.e. the further the equilibrium position will be to the right-hand

Table 3.3   Equilibrium constants

Reaction	$t(/°C)$	Equilibrium constant
$CH_3CO_2H + C_2H_5OH \rightleftharpoons CH_3CO_2C_2H_5 + H_2O$	100	4.00
$N_2O_4 \rightleftharpoons 2NO_2$ (in $CHCl_3$ solution)	10	1.1×10^{-5}
$H_{2(g)} + I_{2(g)} \rightleftharpoons 2HI_{(g)}$	425	55
$CH_3CO_2H_{(aq)} + H_2O \rightleftharpoons CH_3CO_{2(aq)}^- + H_3O_{(aq)}^+$	25	1.8×10^{-5}
$HNO_3 + H_2O \rightleftharpoons H_3O_{(aq)}^+ + NO_{3(aq)}^-$	25	40

side of the equation. This is represented as:

$$aA + bB \xrightleftharpoons{\qquad} cC + dD$$

Conversely, a small numerical value of the equilibrium constant indicates that the equilibrium position is towards the left-hand (reactant) side of the equation and the reactants predominate in the equilibrium mixture:

$$aA + bB \xrightleftharpoons{\qquad} cC + dD$$

Equilibrium constants are readily calculated if the concentrations of all the substances in the equilibrium mixture are known. In some cases it is not possible to determine all these concentrations directly, but – provided the initial concentrations of the reactants are known and the concentration of one of the reactants or products in the equilibrium mixture can be measured – the concentrations of the others may be calculated from the stoichiometric equation for the reaction.

Example 3.1
0.114 mol of ethyl ethanoate was present in the equilibrium mixture obtained by the reaction of 0.150 mol of ethanol with 0.20 mol of ethanoic acid. Calculate the equilibrium constant for the reaction.

Solution
From the equation for the reaction:

$$CH_3CO_2H + C_2H_5OH \rightleftharpoons CH_3CO_2C_2H_5 + H_2O$$

Concentrations: $\dfrac{a-x}{V} \qquad \dfrac{b-x}{V} \qquad \dfrac{x}{V} \qquad \dfrac{x}{V}$

it follows that if a mol of ethanoic acid were reacted with b mol of ethanol to yield x mol of ethyl ethanoate, the equilibrium concentrations are as indicated, where V is the volume of the mixture. Thus,

$$K_c = \frac{[CH_3CO_2C_2H_5][H_2O]}{[CH_3CO_2H][C_2H_5OH]} = \frac{\left(\dfrac{x}{V}\right)^2}{\dfrac{(a-x)}{V}\dfrac{(b-x)}{V}}$$

$$= \frac{(x^2)}{(a-x)(b-x)}$$

$$x = 0.114 \text{ mol}$$

$$\therefore (a - x) = 0.20 - 0.114 = 0.086 \text{ mol}$$
$$(b - x) = 0.150 - 0.114 = 0.036 \text{ mol.}$$
$$K_c = \frac{(0.114)^2}{0.086 \times 0.036} = 4.2$$

3.5
Factors affecting the composition of the equilibrium mixture

Specific objectives: *The expected learning outcome of the following section is that the student: (i) Predicts, using the equation for K_c, how alteration of the concentration will affect the composition of the equilibrium mixture (ii) Predicts how the alteration of pressure will affect the composition of the equilibrium mixture (iii) Predicts the effect of changing temperature on the equilibrium composition, given the sign of ΔH for the reaction.*

The effect of any change on a system in equilibrium may be predicted from *Le Chatelier's Principle*. This important concept was first formulated in 1888 and applies to many physical systems as well as to chemical equilibria. *Le Chatelier's Principle states that if any change is applied to a system in equilibrium, then the equilibrium will adjust itself in such a direction as to counteract that change or the effects of that change.*

The principal changes which can affect the composition of the equilibrium mixture which is obtained in a reversible reaction are changes in concentration, pressure or temperature. These effects will now be considered in turn.

(a) Concentration
We saw in Section 3.2, in the experiment in which first water and then hydrochloric acid was added to a solution of bismuth(III)chloride, that the 'overall' direction of a reversible reaction was affected by the concentration of the reactants or products:

$$BiCl_{(aq)3} + H_2O_{(l)} \underset{\text{excess of } HCl_{(aq)}}{\overset{\text{excess of } H_2O}{\rightleftharpoons}} BiOCl_{(s)} + 2HCl_{(aq)}$$

The effect of a change in the concentration of any of the substances present in the equation for the reversible reaction on the composition of the equilibrium mixture may be deduced from Le Chatelier's Principle: an increase in the concentration of one of the substances present in the equilibrium favours the reaction in which the added compound is consumed. A decrease in the concentration of one of the substances present in the equilibrium favours the reaction in which that compound is formed.

For example, the addition of hydrochloric acid to the bismuth trichloride—bismuth(III)chloride oxide equilibrium favours the reverse reaction, i.e. the solution of the white bismuth(III)chloride oxide precipitate to yield bismuth trichloride, as this is the reaction which lowers the hydrochloric acid concentration in the mixture and thus decreases the change which has been made to the equilibrium system. This result may also be deduced from the equilibrium law. The equilibrium constant for this reaction is:

$$K_c = \frac{[BiOCl][HCl]^2}{[BiCl_3][H_2O]} \text{ at constant temperature}$$

An increase in the concentration of hydrochloric acid which was not accompanied by changes in the concentrations of the other substances in the equilibrium mixture would cause the value of the equilibrium constant to be exceeded. This is contrary to the Equilibrium Law which requires that the value of K_c should remain constant at a particular temperature.

An increase in the hydrochloric acid concentration must be accompanied therefore by a decrease in [BiOCl] and an increase in [BiCl$_3$] and [H$_2$O] (these changes also serve to lower the hydrochloric acid concentration) in order that K_c should remain constant. The effect of adding an excess of water to the system can be predicted in the same way:

To keep K_c constant

concentrations increase

$$K_c = \frac{[BiOCl][HCl]^2}{[BiCl_3][H_2O]} \text{ at constant temperature}$$

concentration   water added to
decreased by   the equilibrium
hydrolysis   mixture

An excess of one of the reagents is frequently employed in preparations which proceed by a reversible reaction in order to increase the yield of the product in the equilibrium mixture. For example, an excess of air (the cheaper of the two reactants) is used to increase the yield of sulphur(VI)oxide (sulphur trioxide) from sulphur dioxide in the contact process (see Section 3.7(b)):

$$2SO_{2(g)} + O_{2(g)} \rightleftharpoons 2SO_{3(g)}$$
air

Similarly, esters are usually prepared by the action of an alcohol with an excess of the organic acid (see Section 10.2(c)(iii) and Experiment 10.1(c)):

$$\text{Organic acid} + \text{alcohol} \xrightleftharpoons[]{H^+_{(aq)}\ \text{catalyst}} \text{ester} + \text{water}$$

concentration increased in equilibrium mixture

$$K_c = \frac{[\text{ester}]\,[\text{water}]}{[\text{Organic acid}]\ [\text{alcohol}]} \quad \text{at constant temperature}$$

large initial concentration

low concentration in equilibrium mixture

The yield of the product is further improved by removing the ester from the reaction mixture as it is formed by distillation wherever possible. The effect of increasing the concentration of one of the reactants on the yield of ethyl ethanoate is shown in Table 3.4

Table 3.4 Effect of reactant concentration on the equilibrium yield of ethyl ethanoate

Ratio of initial concentrations Ethanol : Ethanoic acid	Equilibrium concentration of ester	Yield (%) (based on ethanol)
1 : 1	0.667	66.7
1 : 10	0.974	97.4
1 : 100	0.998	99.8

Experiment 3.1
To investigate the effect of concentration changes on a system in equilibrium

An aqueous solution of an iron(III)salt reacts with thiocyanate ions to yield a deep red coloration. The reaction between iron(III)chloride and ammonium thiocyanate may be represented by the equation:

$$FeCl_{3(aq)} + NH_4CNS_{(aq)} \rightleftharpoons Fe(CNS)^{2+}_{(aq)} + NH_4Cl_{(aq)} + 2Cl^-_{(aq)}$$

yellow   colourless   red   colourless

Dilute the solution obtained by adding a few drops of dilute iron(III)-chloride solution to an equal volume of aqueous ammonium thio-cyanate and divide the mixture into four portions. Keep one sample as a reference and compare the changes in intensity of the red colour which occur on adding one of the following substances to each of the remaining three samples: a small amount of solid ammonium chloride,

1–2 cm^3 of concentrated ammonium thiocyanate solution, 1 cm^3 of iron(III)chloride solution.

Interpret your observations in terms of (a) the equilibrium constant, K_c, for the reaction; (b) Le Chatelier's Principle.

Experiment 3.2
To investigate the effect of concentration changes on a system in equilibrium

Bromine reacts with aqueous sodium hydroxide according to the equation:

$$Br_{2(aq)} + OH^-_{(aq)} \rightleftharpoons Br^-_{(aq)} + OBr^-_{(aq)} + H^+_{(aq)}$$

$\quad$ brown $\quad$ colourless $\quad$ colourless $\quad$ colourless

Add a few drops of aqueous sodium hydroxide to 2–3 cm^3 of bromine water (*Care: Do not inhale bromine vapour or allow the substance to come into contact with the eyes or skin*) and note the change in colour. Interpret the changes in colour which occur on adding 1–2 cm^3 of concentrated sodium bromide solution to the mixture followed by 2–3 cm^3 of aqueous sodium hydroxide. Finally acidify the mixture with dilute hydrochloric acid.

(b) Pressure
Pressure changes will affect the composition of an equilibrium mixture only if there is a difference in the number of moles of gases between the reactant and product sides of the chemical equation. From Le Chatelier's Principle it may be predicted that an *increase in pressure* will favour that reaction which results in a reduction of pressure within the system, i.e. the equilibrium composition will be displaced in favour of the reaction which proceeds with a *decrease in volume*. The Haber process is an example of this type of reaction:

$$N_{2(g)} + 3H_{2(g)} \rightleftharpoons 2NH_{3(g)}$$

$\quad$ 1 mole $\qquad$ 3 moles $\qquad$ 2 moles

$\quad$ 1 volume $\quad$ 3 volumes

$\underbrace{\qquad\qquad\qquad}$

$\quad$ 4 volumes of gas $\qquad$ 2 volumes of gas

decrease in volume
$\longrightarrow$

increase in pressure
favours formation of NH$_3$
$\longrightarrow$

So too is the hydration of ethene by steam in the vapour phase to yield ethanol:

$$C_2H_{4(g)} + H_2O_{(g)} \rightleftharpoons C_2H_5OH_{(g)}$$

ethene	steam	ethanol
1 mole	1 mole	1 mole

$\underbrace{2 \text{ volumes of gas}}$ 1 volume of gas

increase in pressure favours ethanol formation
⟶

Equal numbers of moles of any gas under the same conditions of temperature and pressure occupy the same volume (Avogadro's Law). Thus, volumes may be used instead of moles to represent the amount of any substance in the gas phase. At s.t.p. (standard temperature and pressure: 273K (0°C) and 101 325 Pa (or 1 atmosphere = 760 mm of mercury)) one mole of any gas occupies 22 414 cm^3. The volume (V_2) occupied by a given amount of gas (volume, V_1 at temperature T_1 and pressure P_1) at any other temperature (T_2) or pressure (P_2) may be calculated from the equation: $\dfrac{P_1 V_1}{T_1} = \dfrac{P_2 V_2}{T_2}$

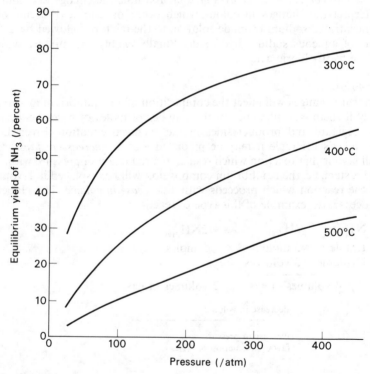

Fig. 3.6 The Haber process: effect of pressure on the equilibrium yield of ammonia

These two reactions are accompanied by a *decrease* in the number of moles of gas and an increase in pressure will therefore favour the forward reaction, i.e. the formation of ammonia or ethanol. The increasing yield of ammonia with increasing pressure is shown in fig. 3.6. In practice the Haber process is carried out at pressures as high as 350 atm (see Section 3.7(a)).

Reactions which proceed with an *increase* in the number of moles of gas will be favoured by a *decrease* in pressure. The dissociation of calcium carbonate on heating provides an example of this type of reaction. The volume occupied by one mole of substances in the solid or liquid state (e.g. $CaCO_3$ (density = 2.71 g cm^{-3}; R.M.M. = 100), molar volume = 36.9 cm^3; H_2O, molar volume = 18 cm^3) is negligible compared with the molar volume of gases (22 414 cm^3 at s.t.p.), thus the dissociation of calcium carbonate proceeds with an enormous increase in volume and is therefore promoted by a low pressure:

$$CaCO_{3(s)} \rightleftharpoons CaO_{(s)} + CO_{2(g)}$$

calcium carbonate   calcium oxide   carbon dioxide
1 mole   1 mole   1 mole
negligible volume   negligible volume   1 volume of gas

increase in volume
$\longrightarrow$

By Le Chatelier's Principle:

reaction favoured by a low pressure
$\longrightarrow$

reaction favoured by a high pressure
$\longleftarrow$

Pressure changes have no effect on the composition of the equilibrium mixtures obtained in the hydrogen iodide dissociation:

$$2HI_{(g)} \xrightarrow{\text{heat}} H_{2(g)} + I_{2(g)}$$

2 volumes $\longleftarrow$ 1 volume   1 volume

or in the production of hydrogen from the reaction between carbon monoxide and steam:

1 atm/800 K/catalyst
of Fe and Cr oxides

$$CO_{(g)} + H_2O_{(g)} \rightleftharpoons CO_{2(g)} + H_{2(g)}$$

1 volume   1 volume   1 volume   1 volume

2 volumes of gas   2 volumes of gas

as the reactions do not involve a change in the number of moles of gas between the reactant and product sides of the chemical equation.

(c) Temperature

Equilibrium constants are temperature dependent. The effect of temperature changes on the composition of an equilibrium mixture (and hence on K_c) may be predicted from Le Chatelier's Principle if the sign of the enthalpy change (see Section 2.1) for the reaction is known. For example, if the change applied to the system is an increase in temperature, then the position of equilibrium will alter so as to counteract it and the reaction which absorbs heat from the surroundings and produces a decrease in temperature will be favoured.

The effects may be summarised:

In any reversible process in equilibrium, the endothermic reaction (i.e. the one for which ΔH is positive) is favoured by an *increase in temperature*. The exothermic reaction (i.e. the one for which ΔH is negative) is favoured by a *temperature decrease*.

The general equation is:

$$\underset{\text{favoured by temperature increase}}{\xleftarrow{\hspace{4cm}}} \overset{\text{favoured by temperature decrease}}{\xrightarrow{\hspace{4cm}}}$$

$$\underbrace{aA + bB}_{\text{reactants}} \rightleftharpoons \underbrace{cC + dD}_{\text{products}} + \text{heat} \quad (\Delta H \text{ reaction is negative})$$

where the forward reaction:

$$aA + bB \longrightarrow cC + dD + \text{heat}$$

is exothermic (ΔH negative); and the reverse reaction:

$$cC + dD + \text{heat} \longrightarrow aA + bB$$

which may be written as:

$$cC + dD \longrightarrow aA + bB - \text{heat}$$

is endothermic (ΔH positive).

The equilibrium constant, K_c, for a reversible exothermic reaction *decreases* with temperature. The equilibrium constant for a reversible endothermic reaction *increases* with temperature. The effect of temperature on chemical reactions in equilibrium is illustrated by:

(i) The dinitrogen tetroxide – nitrogen dioxide equilibrium

Dinitrogen tetroxide, N_2O_4, yields a pale yellow vapour in which the compound is in equilibrium with the dark brown gas, nitrogen dioxide, NO_2.

The reaction:

$$N_2O_4 \rightleftharpoons 2NO_2 \qquad \Delta H = +58 \text{ kJ mol}^{-1}$$

colourless –   dark brown

pale yellow

is endothermic, thus an increase in temperature will favour the dissociation of dinitrogen tetroxide. The equilibrium content increases with temperature and the proportion of nitrogen dioxide in the equilibrium mixture rises from about 25% at 25° to over 90% at 100°. The shift in equilibrium composition is demonstrated by the change in the intensity of the brown colour when sealed tubes containing the gaseous mixture are placed in beakers of hot or cold water.

Dinitrogen tetroxide for this demonstration may be prepared by condensing the gases evolved on heating lead nitrate in a test-tube cooled in ice:

$$Pb(NO_3)_{2(s)} \xrightarrow{\text{heat}} PbO_{(s)} + 2NO_{2(g)} + O_{2(g)}$$

$$\big\updownarrow$$

$$N_2O_{4(l)}$$

b.p.21°

collect in tube cooled in ice

(ii) The Haber process

The formation of ammonia from its elements is an exothermic process:

$$\xrightarrow{\text{exothermic reaction}}$$

$$N_2 + 3H_2 \rightleftharpoons 2NH_3 \qquad \Delta H = -92 \text{ kJ mol}^{-1}$$

$$\xleftarrow{\text{endothermic reaction}}$$

An increase in temperature thus favours the reverse reaction – the endothermic decomposition of ammonia into nitrogen and hydrogen – and decreases the equilibrium constant:

$$K_p = \frac{(P_{NH_3})^2}{(P_{N_2})(P_{H_2})^3}$$

The effect of temperature on the proportion of ammonia in the equilibrium mixture is shown in Table 3.5 and fig. 3.6 (see also Sections 3.5(b) and 3.7(a)).

Table 3.5   Haber process: Effect of temperature on the proportion of ammonia in the equilibrium mixture

Temperature (/°C)	Equilibrium percentage of ammonia at	
	25 atm	200 atm
100	91.7	98.4
200	63.6	89.0
300	27.4	66.7
400	8.7	38.8
500	2.9	18.3

(iii) The esterification of ethanol by ethanoic acid

This reaction (see Section 10.2(c)(iii)) takes place with little or no enthalpy change, thus – although equilibrium is achieved more quickly at a higher temperature – the composition of the equilibrium mixture (and hence the equilibrium constant, K_c) is virtually unchanged on heating.

Table 3.6   Uses of sulphur(VI)oxide (sulphur trioxide), ammonia and nitric acid

Compound	Use
Sulphur(VI)oxide	Manufacture of sulphuric(VI)acid and, hence, of fertilizers (e.g. $(NH_4)_2SO_4$), paints, pigments, man-made fibres, detergents, dyestuffs, plastics, cleaning steel and other metallurgical uses, explosives, batteries, insecticides, pharmaceuticals.
Ammonia	Preparation of ammonium salts, nitric acid, fertilizers etc. Production of nylon.
Nitric(V)acid	Manufacture of fertilizers and explosives.

3.6
Catalysis

Specific objectives: *The expected learning outcome of the following sections is that the student:* (i) *States that the rate of the forward and reverse reactions of a system in equilibrium are equally affected by a catalyst* (ii) *Deduces that catalysts do not affect the equilibrium composition.*

Many substances of great economic importance, such as ammonia, sulphur(VI)oxide, ethanol and nitric(V)acid, are obtained as products of reactions which are reversible. Hundreds of thousands of tonnes of these compounds are produced every year and, in addition to their own specific uses, these substances act as the starting materials for the manufacture of an enormous range of other essential products (see Table 3.6). A study of the effects of the factors which influence the rates of reaction and the composition of the equilibrium mixture which is obtained is thus an important part of the design of any large-scale manufacturing process. In an era of high energy costs the use of elevated temperatures and pressures is very expensive and is to be avoided wherever possible, but frequently these conditions have to be employed in order to obtain the product in high yield and at a reasonable reaction rate. Examples of the application of these principles to help to determine the optimum conditions for a reaction are described in Section 3.7.

Catalysts (see Section 3.1(e)) also play an important part in decreasing reaction times. Many chemical changes would take many months or years to attain equilibrium if left to themselves. However, in the presence of a suitable catalyst satisfactory yields are frequently obtained within the time required for the reactants to flow through the catalyst chamber at the optimum temperature and pressure. The rates of both the forward and the reverse reactions in the equilibrium system are affected to the same extent by the catalyst, so there is no change in the composition of the equilibrium mixture or in the equilibrium constant: *the equilibrium state is simply achieved at a faster rate.*

(a) Activators, inhibitors and catalyst poisons
The efficiency of a catalyst is frequently increased by the presence of another substance known as an *activator* or *promoter* (see Section 3.7(a)) or decreased by an *inhibitor*. Occasionally catalytic activity is stopped altogether by the presence of substances known as *catalyst poisons*. Examples of activators, inhibitors and catalyst poisons are described in Sections 3.7(a) and 3.7(b).

The effects of the various changes on the position of equilibrium in a reversible reaction are summarised in Table 3.7.

Table 3.7 Reversible reactions: Effect of changes in conditions on the position of equilibrium

Change	Position or direction of equilibrium shifted in favour of:
Addition of reactant	Reaction in which added reactant is consumed
Removal of reactant	Reaction in which added reactant is formed
Increase in pressure	Reaction which occurs with a decrease in the number of gaseous molecules
Decrease in pressure	Reaction which occurs with an increase in the number of gaseous molecules
Increase in temperature	The endothermic reaction
Decrease in temperature	The exothermic reaction
Addition of catalyst	No change in equilibrium position. Catalyst affects the rates of the forward and reverse reactions to the same extent

3.7
Important industrial processes

Common examples of the application of Le Chatelier's Principle to chemical equilibria in industry include:

(a) The manufacture of ammonia

The equation for the synthesis of ammonia by the Haber process is:

$$N_{2(g)} + 3H_{2(g)} \rightleftharpoons 2NH_{3(g)} \qquad \Delta H = -92 \text{ kJ mol}^{-1}$$
$$\text{1 volume} \quad \text{3 volumes} \quad \text{2 volumes}$$

The reaction is exothermic and is accompanied by a decrease in volume. Ammonia formation is therefore favoured by: (i) a low temperature (see Section 3.5(c)) and (ii) a high pressure (see Section 3.5(b)). The effect of these two variables on the yield of ammonia in the equilibrium mixture was shown in fig. 3.6 and Table 3.5.

In practice, pressures in the range 200–350 atm are employed, but as the reaction would be too slow at low temperatures the process is carried out at 400–500° in the presence of a catalyst. The catalyst consists of iron which is in the form of a fine powder to provide an enormous surface area for contact with the gaseous reagents (see Section 3.1(a) and (e)) and is activated with potassium hydroxide and alumina. The catalyst is susceptible to hydrogen sulphide, water vapour and other catalyst poisons. The gases are therefore purified before use, or the effective life of the catalyst is considerably reduced. The conversion to ammonia is increased by removing the ammonia from the mixture by condensation and then re-cycling the unchanged nitrogen and hydrogen through the catalyst chamber.

(b) *The manufacture of sulphur(VI)oxide* (*The Contact Process*)
Sulphur(VI)oxide (sulphur trioxide) for the manufacture of sulphuric(VI) acid is obtained from the reaction:

$$2SO_{2(g)} + O_{2(g)} \rightleftharpoons 2SO_{3(g)}$$

2 volumes   1 volume   2 volumes $\Delta H = -196$ kJ reaction

or -98 kJ mol^{-1}

The reaction is exothermic and takes place with a decrease in volume. From Le Chatelier's Principle it may be predicted that sulphur(VI)oxide ‚ formation is favoured by:

(i) a low temperature
and (ii) a high pressure.

Owing partly to the difficulty of containing a highly compressed acid gas, it is uneconomic (and – as the conversion is so high – unnecessary) to use high pressures for this reaction. The process is carried out at 420° at atmospheric pressure in the presence of a vanadium(V)oxide catalyst. The gases must be pure and dry otherwise the catalyst is poisoned – particularly by the presence of arsenic compounds.

Sulphuric(VI)acid is manufactured by absorbing the sulphur(VI)oxide in an aqueous solution of sulphuric(VI)acid, in which it dissolves more readily than in water alone. A solution of sulphur(VI)oxide in sulphuric(VI)acid ('fuming sulphuric acid') is obtained which is diluted with water to yield 98% sulphuric acid.

(c) *The production of ethanol*
Although some ethanol, especially that in whisky, brandy, beer, wine and other alcoholic beverages, is still obtained by fermentation (see Section 10.2(a)), the principal industrial source is now the hydration of ethene from cracked petroleum (see Section 9.4) by steam:

$$\begin{array}{c} H \\ \diagdown \\ C \end{array} = \begin{array}{c} H \\ \diagup \\ C \end{array} + H_2O_{(g)} \rightleftharpoons C_2H_5OH_{(g)} \qquad \Delta H = -45 \text{ kJ mol}^{-1}$$

ethene	steam	ethanol
1 volume of gas	1 volume of gas	1 volume of gas

The conditions employed (approximately 70 atm at 320°) are a compromise with the high pressure and low temperature suggested by the application of Le Chatelier's Principle. Figure 3.7 shows the distillation section of an industrial ethanol plant. Phosphoric(V)acid supported on Celite is used as the catalyst.

Fig. 3.7 Distillation section of the 42 000 tonnes/year ethanol plant at BP Chemicals, Grangemouth. Photograph by BP Oil Limited

Summary

1. The main factors which can influence the rate of a chemical reaction are: (i) the degree of subdivision of the reactants (e.g. as finely powdered solids or dissolved in a solution), (ii) concentration, (iii) pressure (applies only to reactions where a gas is present), (iv) temperature, (v) catalysts.

2. A reversible reaction is one which can proceed in either direction according to the reaction conditions, i.e. the products can react to reform the original substances.

3. Chemical equilibrium is a dynamic condition in which the rate of the forward reaction is equal to the rate of the reverse reaction, i.e. there is no bulk change of reactants or products.

4. The composition of an equilibrium mixture may be affected by concentration, pressure and temperature changes. The effect of these changes are summarised in Table 3.7. A catalyst does not affect the composition of the equilibrium mixture as it influences the forward and reverse reactions to an equal extent.

5. The larger the value of the equilibrium constant, K_c, (see Section 3.4), the more the products will predominate in the equilibrium mixture, and conversely.

Questions

1. What is meant by the following terms: (a) reversible reaction, (b) equilibrium, (c) a catalyst, (d) optimum reaction conditions?

2. List the factors which influence (a) the rate of a chemical reaction, and (b) the composition of the equilibrium mixture obtained in a reversible reaction.

3. What is an enzyme? Give two examples.

4. Why does a solid react more rapidly if it is in the form of a powder.

5. Why do pressure changes have little effect on the rate of reaction of liquids or solids?

6. Give three examples of a reversible reaction.

7. Write an expression for the equilibrium constant, K_c, for a reversible reaction.

8. What is the effect of (a) an increase in temperature, (b) the addition of a catalyst, (c) an increase in the concentration of one of the reactants on the equilibrium constant of a reversible exothermic process?

9. Describe three methods of increasing the yield of a substance pre-pared by a reversible endothermic reaction.

10. Describe the effect of pressure changes on the composition of the following equilibria:

(a) $H_{2(g)} + I_{2(g)} \rightleftharpoons 2HI_{(g)}$

(b) $2NO_{2(g)} \rightleftharpoons N_2O_{4(g)}$

(c) $BiCl_{3(aq)} + H_2O_{(l)} \rightleftharpoons BiOCl_{(s)} + 2HCl_{(aq)}$

11. Why does a large numerical value of K_c indicate that the products of the reversible reaction will predominate in the equilibrium mixture?

12. What information is conveyed by the equation:

$$CaCO_{3(s)} \xrightleftharpoons[7]{500} CaO_{(s)} + CO_{2(g)}$$

13. Why is it important to specify the temperature at which an equi-librium constant is determined?

14. What is meant by the stoichiometric equation for a chemical reaction?

15. What are (a) a poison, (b) an inhibitor and (c) a promoter (or activator) when applied to a catalysed reaction?

16. Dinitrogen tetroxide is 25% dissociated at 25° and 90% dissociated at 100°. State whether the reaction:

$$2NO_2 \rightleftharpoons N_2O_4$$

is exothermic or endothermic.

17. How do you account for the fact that a small amount of a catalyst will often catalyse the reaction of large amounts of a substance?

18. Calculate the volume occupied by 36 g of water as (a) a liquid at 25° and (b) a gas at 200° (473 K).

19. To what extent are the conditions employed in (a) the Haber process, (b) the contact process, and (c) the manufacture of ethanol determined by Le Chatelier's Principle?

20. 0.086 mol of ethyl ethanoate was present in the equilibrium mixture obtained by the action of 0.5 mol of ethanoic acid on 0.09 mol of ethanol at 15°. Calculate the concentration equilibrium constant, K_c.

4　Ionic equilibria

General objective: *The expected learning outcome of this chapter is that the student is able to apply the concepts of equilibrium to electrolytes.*

4.1
Strong and weak electrolytes

Specific objective: *The expected learning outcome of this section is that the student recognises the differences between strong and weak electrolytes with regard to degree of ionisation.*

(a) Conductivity of materials
Substances are classified as *conductors* or *insulators* according to whether they will permit the passage of an electric current. Typical non-conductors (or insulators) include sulphur, petrol, plastic, rubber, paraffin wax, tetrachloromethane, alcohol and other covalently bonded materials. The conductors are of two types: *electronic* conductors or *electrolytic* conductors, depending on whether the current is carried through the substance by the electrons or by the ions.

Metals such as copper, silver, sodium and mercury or metal amalgams (i.e. solutions of gold, silver, zinc, sodium or other metals in mercury) are the principal examples of electronic conductors, although carbon in the form of graphite also conducts in this manner (see Section 8.6). The high conductivity of metals (i.e. the easy movement of electrons through the material) is readily explained by their structure (see Section 8.1(*d*)).

(b) Electrolytes
As the ions must be free to move before an electric current can pass, the conductivity of electrolytic conductors is only apparent when the substance is in solution or in the molten state. Solid potassium iodide, for example, will not conduct, but a current will pass immediately if the substance is dissolved in water or is heated until it melts to form a liquid.

The passage of a current through an electrolytic conductor is accompanied by chemical decomposition at the electrodes (i.e. *electrolysis* occurs). In general: metals are deposited (or hydrogen is evolved) at the cathode, while non-metals (except hydrogen) are evolved at the anode or the metal anode dissolves. Oxidation and reduction are defined in terms of the loss and gain of electrons respectively, e.g.

$$Cl^- \xrightarrow{\text{at anode}} \tfrac{1}{2}Cl_2 + e^- \qquad \text{(oxidation)}$$

$$Mg^{2+} + 2e^- \xrightarrow{\text{at cathode}} Mg \qquad \text{(reduction)}$$

$$Cu \xrightarrow{\text{at anode}} Cu^{2+}_{(aq)} + 2e^- \qquad \text{(oxidation)}$$

copper anode dissolves

$$Cu^{2+} + 2e^- \xrightarrow{\text{at cathode}} Cu \qquad \text{(reduction)}$$

copper deposited

The *anode* is thus the electrode associated with *oxidation* in electrolysis, while the *cathode* is associated with *reduction*. A number of examples of electrolysis are listed in Table 4.1.

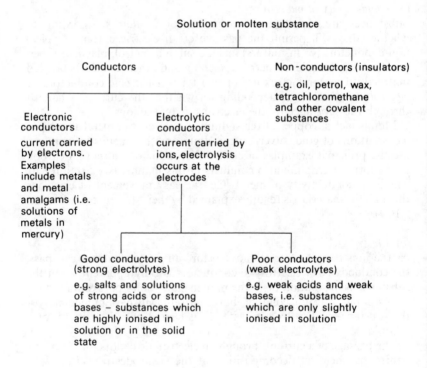

Fig. 4.1 Conductivity of substances in solution or in molten state

Table 4.1 *Examples of electrolysis*

Cathode	Anode	Electrolyte	Reaction at cathode	Reaction at anode
Carbon	Carbon	Aqueous hydrochloric acid	Hydrogen evolved $H^+_{(aq)} + e^- \longrightarrow \frac{1}{2}H_{2(g)}$	Chlorine evolved $Cl^-_{(aq)} \longrightarrow \frac{1}{2}Cl_2 + e^-$
Steel	Carbon	Fused magnesium chloride	Magnesium deposited $Mg^{2+} + 2e^- \longrightarrow Mg$	Chlorine evolved $Cl^- \longrightarrow \frac{1}{2}Cl_2 + e^-$
Carbon	Carbon	Fused lead bromide	Lead deposited $Pb^{2+} + 2e^- \longrightarrow Pb$	Bromine evolved $Br^- \longrightarrow \frac{1}{2}Br_2 + e^-$
Steel	Carbon	Fused Al_2O_3 in Na_3AlF_6	Aluminium deposited $Al^{3+} + 3e^- \longrightarrow Al$	Oxygen evolved $O^{2-} \longrightarrow \frac{1}{2}O_2 + 2e^-$
Silver	Silver	Aqueous silver nitrate	Silver deposited $Ag^+_{(aq)} + e^- \longrightarrow Ag$	Silver dissolves $Ag \longrightarrow Ag^+_{(aq)} + e^-$
Platinum	Platinum	Water containing a trace of sulphuric acid	Hydrogen evolved $H^+_{(aq)} + e^- \longrightarrow \frac{1}{2}H_{2(g)}$	Oxygen evolved $4OH^- \longrightarrow 2H_2O + O_2 + 4e^-$

Substances which conduct electricity in this way when they are in solution or in the molten state are known as *electrolytes* and are classed as *strong electrolytes* or *weak electrolytes* depending on whether they are good or poor conductors of electricity respectively. The different types of conductor are summarised in fig. 4.1.

Strong electrolytes are *either* ionic (or electrovalent) compounds such as salts or the strong bases and some oxides which are fully ionised even in the solid state (see Section 8.1(*a*)): e.g.

$$
\left.
\begin{array}{l}
Na^+Cl^- \\
K^+NO_3^- \\
Mg^{2+}Cl_2^- \\
Pb^{2+}Br_2^- \\
NH_4^+NO_3^-
\end{array}
\right\} \text{salts}
\qquad
\left.
\begin{array}{l}
Na^+OH^- \\
K^+OH^-
\end{array}
\right\} \text{strong bases}
$$

$$
\left.
\begin{array}{l}
Ca^{2+}O^{2-} \\
Al_2^{3+}O_3^{2-}
\end{array}
\right\} \text{oxides}
$$

or like the strong acids (such as hydrochloric, nitric(V) and sulphuric(VI) acids) react with water to yield high concentrations of ions in aqueous solution, e.g.

$$
\underset{\substack{\text{hydrogen chloride} \\ \text{(covalent)}}}{H{-}Cl} + H_2O \longrightarrow \underset{\substack{\text{hydroxonium ion} \\ \text{or oxonium ion}}}{H_3O^+ + Cl^-}
$$

H_3O^+ (the hydroxonium or oxonium ion) is the hydrated proton. The reaction may also be written as:

$$
H{-}Cl \xrightarrow{H_2O} H^+_{(aq)} + Cl^-_{(aq)}
$$

Table 4.2   Reaction of strong acids with water

Strong acid	Reaction
HNO_3	$HNO_3 + H_2O \longrightarrow H_3O^+_{(aq)} + NO_{3(aq)}^-$
H_2SO_4	$H_2SO_4 + H_2O \longrightarrow H_3O^+_{(aq)} + HSO_{4(aq)}^-$
	$HSO_{4(aq)}^- + H_2O \longrightarrow H_3O^+_{(aq)} + SO_{4(aq)}^{2-}$
HBr	$HBr + H_2O \longrightarrow H_3O^+_{(aq)} + Br^-_{(aq)}$

Other examples are listed in Table 4.2. Evidence for the complete ionisation of strong acids and strong bases in aqueous solution is provided by the constancy of the enthalpy of neutralisation of any strong acid by a strong base (see Section 2.2(d)). Weak electrolytes are only slightly ionised in solution. This explains their poor conductivity as the electric current is carried by the ions and the concentration of these particles in a solution of a weak electrolyte is very low. The principal classes of weak electrolyte are the weak acids (e.g. ethanoic acid) and the weak bases (e.g. aqueous ammonia):

$$CH_3CO_2H_{(aq)} + H_2O \xrightleftharpoons{} CH_3CO_{2(aq)}^- + H_3O_{(aq)}^+$$
ethanoic acid ethanoate
anion

i.e.

$$CH_3CO_2H_{(aq)} \xrightleftharpoons{} CH_3CO_{2(aq)}^- + H_{(aq)}^+$$

and

$$NH_{3(aq)} + H_2O \xrightleftharpoons{} NH_{4(aq)}^+ + OH_{(aq)}^-$$

The symbol $\rightleftharpoons$ indicates that the equilibrium position in these reversible reactions is well over to the left-hand side of the equation and that weak acids and weak bases yield only a low concentration of hydrated protons and hydroxyl ions in aqueous solution. The *degree of ionisation* is denoted by the Greek letter *alpha*, α, and is defined as the fraction of the substance which is ionised. The amounts of un-dissociated weak acid or weak base in the equilibrium mixture obtained from one mole of the compound is thus $(1 - \alpha)$, while the amount of positive and negative ions is α mol in each case:

$$HY_{(aq)} \rightleftharpoons H_{(aq)}^+ + Y_{(aq)}^-$$
weak acid

$(1 - \alpha)$ α α

$$B + H_2O \rightleftharpoons BH_{(aq)}^+ + OH_{(aq)}^-$$
weak base

$(1 - \alpha)$ α α

The degrees of ionisation of a number of common electrolytes in aqueous solution are listed in Table 4.3. Ionisation increases with increasing dilution. This effect resulting from a decrease in the concentration of the weak electrolyte or an increase in the amount of water present in the equilibrium mixture may be predicted from the application of Le Chatelier's Principle (see Section 3.5), e.g.

$$HY + H_2O \rightleftharpoons H_3O_{(aq)}^+ + Y_{(aq)}^-$$
weak acid

increase in $[H_2O]$ favours forward reaction
$\longrightarrow$

Table 4.3   Degree of ionisation of common electrolytes in aqueous solution

Compound	Formula	Concentration (/mol l^{-1})	Percentage ionisation
Ethanoic acid	CH_3CO_2H	0.1	1.3
		0.01	4.2
Benzoic acid	$C_6H_5CO_2H$	0.01	7.9
Phenol	C_6H_5OH		
	($C_6H_5OH + H_2O \rightleftharpoons C_6H_5O^- + H_3O^+$)	0.01	0.01
Ammonia	NH_3		
	($NH_3 + H_2O \rightleftharpoons NH_4^+ + OH^-$)	0.1	1.3
Pure water	H_2O		
	($2H_2O \rightleftharpoons H_3O^+ + OH^-$)	—	1.8×10^{-7}

4.2
Ionisation of water

Specific objectives: *The expected learning outcome of this section is that the student: (i) states the value of the ionic product for water (K_w) at 298 K, and hence states the values of $[H_{(aq)}^+]$ and $[OH_{(aq)}^-]$ in water, (ii) states the range of values for $[H_{(aq)}^+]$ and $[OH_{(aq)}^-]$ for acidic and basic aqueous solutions, and (iii) recognises that in these solutions K_w remains constant.*

Water is a very poor conductor of electricity. Its conductivity is increased by the presence of salts or other electrolytes as impurities, but even the purest distilled or ion exchange water has a small, measurable conductivity. It is thus an extremely weak electrolyte. Water is ionised to a slight extent into protons and hydroxyl ions. This self-ionisation of the solvent molecules:

$$H_2O + H_2O \longleftarrow H_3O_{(aq)}^+ + OH_{(aq)}^-$$

may be expressed as:

$$H_2O \rightleftharpoons H_{(aq)}^+ + OH_{(aq)}^-$$

The following expression for the equilibrium constant, K_c, is obtained by applying the equilibrium law (see Section 3.4) to this ionisation:

$$K_c = \frac{[H_{(aq)}^+][OH_{(aq)}^-]}{[H_2O]} \text{ at constant temperature}$$

The degree of ionisation is so very small that ten thousand tonnes of pure water would contain only 1 g of free hydrogen ions (protons), thus the concentration of undissociated water $[H_2O]$ is effectively unchanged by this ionisation and may be regarded as a constant.[1] The equation for the equilibrium constant may be rearranged thus:

$$[H^+_{(aq)}][OH^-_{(aq)}] = K_c \times [H_2O] \text{ at constant temperature}$$

a constant   constant
at constant
temperature

The product of the concentrations of the protons and hydroxyl ions in aqueous solution is thus a constant at a given temperature. This constant is known as the *ionic product for water* and is given the symbol K_w:

$$[H^+_{(aq)}][OH^-_{(aq)}] = K_w$$

The units of K_w are (concentration)^2 or $mol^2 \, l^{-2}$, but these are generally omitted. The numerical values of K_w at a series of temperatures are listed in Table 4.4. K_w increases with temperature, thereby confirming that the ionisation of water is an endothermic reaction (see Le Chatelier's Principle, Section 3.5):

$$H_2O \longrightarrow H^+ + OH^- \qquad \varDelta H = +57 \text{ kJ mol}^{-1}$$

At 298 K (25°C), the value of K_w is 1×10^{-14}.

It must be emphasised that K_w is not an equilibrium constant. As its name indicates, the constant K_w refers to the *product* of the concentrations of protons and hydroxyl ions in aqueous solution. The concept is an important one for it means that whatever the concentration of either of these ions in a solution of an acid, base or salt in water at a particular

Table 4.4 Numerical values of ionic product of water, K_w, at various temperatures

| | Temperature (/°C) | | | | | |
	0	10	20	25	30	40
$K_w(/mol^2 \, l^{-2})$	0.114	0.293	0.681	1.008	1.471	2.916

[1] The density of pure water (H_2O, RMM = 18) is 1 kg dm^{-3}. As 1 mole of water weighs 18 g and the mass of 1 litre of water is 1000 g, $[H_2O]$, i.e. the number of moles of water in one litre of pure water is $\frac{1000}{18} = 55.55$.

temperature, the concentration of the other is immediately defined by the expression:

$$[H^+_{(aq)}] \times [OH^-_{(aq)}] = K_w$$

Thus at 298 K (25°C):

$$[H^+_{(aq)}] = \frac{10^{-14}}{[OH^-_{(aq)}]} \quad \text{and} \quad [OH^-_{(aq)}] = \frac{10^{-14}}{[H^+_{(aq)}]}$$

In a neutral solution $[H^+_{(aq)}] = [OH^-_{(aq)}] = \sqrt{K_w}$

$$= \sqrt{10^{-14}} = 10^{-7} \text{ mol } l^{-1} \text{ at 298 K}$$

The effect may be deduced from Le Chatelier's Principle: the addition of an acid, for example, to pure water lowers the concentration of hydroxyl ions by the formation of water:

$$H^+_{(aq)} \quad + \quad OH^-_{(aq)} \rightleftharpoons H_2O$$

concentration   concentration
increased by   decreased
addition of
acid

A solution is acidic if $[H^+_{(aq)}] > [OH^-_{(aq)}]$ and alkaline if $[OH^-_{(aq)}] > [H^+_{(aq)}]$ (see Table 4.5) thereby maintaining the equilibrium and the constancy of the ionic product, K_w.

Table 4.5   Range of values of $[H^+_{(aq)}]$ and $[OH^-_{(aq)}]$ for acidic and basic aqueous solutions

Solution	$[H^+_{(aq)}]$ (/mol l^{-1})	$[OH^-_{(aq)}]$ (/mol l^{-1})
Acidic	$> 10^{-7}$	$< 10^{-7}$
Neutral	10^{-7}	10^{-7}
Basic	$< 10^{-7}$	$> 10^{-7}$

Example 4.1
Calculate the concentrations of hydrogen ions and hydroxyl ions in (a) 0.01 M hydrochloric acid, and (b) 0.2 M sodium hydroxide at 25°.

Solution
(a) Aqueous hydrochloric acid is a strong electrolyte (see Section 4.1(b)) and is therefore fully ionised and exists in solution as $H^+_{(aq)}$ and $Cl^-_{(aq)}$.
    0.01 M hydrochloric acid contains 0.01 mole of HCl per litre of solution:

$$\text{HCl}_{(aq)} \xrightarrow{\text{H}_2\text{O}} \text{H}^+_{(aq)} + \text{Cl}^-_{(aq)}$$

0.01 mol   0.01 mol   0.01 mol

thus, the hydrogen ion concentration in the solution, $[\text{H}^+] = 0.01$ or 10^{-2} mol l^{-1}.

The small concentration of hydrogen ions from the water may be ignored.

Hydroxyl ion concentration,

$$[\text{OH}^-] = \frac{K_w}{[\text{H}^+]} = \frac{10^{-14}}{10^{-2}} = 10^{-12} \text{ mol } l^{-1}$$

(b) Sodium hydroxide is a strong electrolyte and exists in solution as $\text{Na}^+_{(aq)}$ and $\text{OH}^-_{(aq)}$. A 0.2 M solution of sodium hydroxide therefore contains 0.2 mole of $\text{Na}^+_{(aq)}$ and 0.2 mole of $\text{OH}^-_{(aq)}$ in each litre of solution. If the small concentration of hydroxyl ions from the dissociation of water is ignored, $[\text{OH}^-_{(aq)}]$ in the solution = 0.2, or 2×10^{-1} mol l^{-1} and the hydrogen ion concentration, $[\text{H}^+] = \dfrac{K_w}{[\text{OH}^-]} = \dfrac{10^{-14}}{2 \times 10^{-1}} = 5 \times 10^{-14} \text{ mol } l^{-1}$

4.3
The pH scale

Specific objective: *The expected learning outcome of this section is that the student is able to calculate whole number values of pH and pOH from the relationship pH = $-log[H^+]$ and pOH = $-log[OH^-]$*

The pH scale was first proposed by Sorensen in 1909 as a convenient method of representing the degree of acidity or basicity of an aqueous solution. The pH of a solution may be defined mathematically by the equation:

$$\text{pH} = -\log[\text{H}^+]$$

Similarly, the hydroxide ion concentration of a solution and the ionic product of water, K_w, may be represented as pOH and pK_w respectively where:

$$\text{pOH} = -\log[\text{OH}^-]$$
$$\text{and, } pK_w = -\log K_w$$

This notation avoids the use of such awkward figures as the negative exponents of numbers (e.g. 10^{-7}) or their decimal equivalents (e.g. 0.000 000 1). pH or pK_w etc. are simply the negative *powers* (the p in pH, pK_w etc.) to which the number 10 is raised to express $[H^+]$ or K_w, thus

$$[H^+] = 10^{-pH}$$

$$K_w = 10^{-pK_w}$$

For example, the hydrogen ion concentration, $[H^+_{(aq)}]$, in a neutral aqueous solution at $25°$ is 10^{-7} mol l^{-1}, thus

$$pH = -\log 10^{-7} = -(\bar{7}.00) = -(-7.00) = 7.00$$

Similarly,

$$pK_w = -\log 10^{-14} = 14.00 \text{ at } 25°C.$$

In any aqueous solution at $25°C$:

$$[H^+_{(aq)}][OH^-_{(aq)}] = 10^{-14}$$

$$\text{therefore, } -\log[H^+_{(aq)}] - \log[OH^-_{(aq)}] = -\log 10^{-14}$$

$$\text{i.e. pH} + pOH = 14.00$$

A solution is acidic if its pH is less than 7 and alkaline (basic) if its pH is greater than 7. A neutral aqueous solution has a pH of exactly 7. The pH scale extends from approximately 0–14. The *smaller* the numerical value of the pH, the higher the hydrogen ion concentration and the more acidic the solution. Similarly, the *higher* the pH value the lower is the hydrogen ion concentration (and the higher the hydroxyl ion concentration) in the solution.

The $[H^+_{(aq)}]$, $[OH^-_{(aq)}]$, pH and pOH values of a number of aqueous solutions at $25°$ are listed in Table 4.6. As the scale is a logarithmic one, a change of one unit in the pH is equivalent to a tenfold change in the hydrogen ion concentration. The neutralisation of a 0.1 M solution of hydrochloric acid changes its pH from 1 to 7, and thus decreases the hydrogen ion concentration in the solution to one millionth of its original value.

The hydrogen ion or hydroxyl ion concentrations in saliva (pH = 6.8 approximately), blood (pH = 7.4) and in many other tissue fluids are extremely small. Nevertheless even at these small concentrations, the actual values are highly important, partly because these ions can act as catalysts themselves, or can influence the efficiency of other catalysts present in solution, such as enzymes. An example of the effect of pH on the rate of an enzyme-catalysed reaction is shown in fig. 4.2.

Example 4.2
Calculate (i) the hydrogen ion concentration, (ii) the hydroxyl ion concentration, (iii) the pH and (iv) the pOH of (a) 10^{-3} M nitric(V)acid and (b) 0.01 M potassium hydroxide.

Table 4.6 The pH and pOH scales

Solutions	pH	pOH	$[H^+]$ (/mol l^{-1})	$[OH^-]$ (/mol l^{-1})
	0	14	1	10^{-14}
0.1M HCl gastric juice	1	13	10^{-1}	10^{-13}
0.01M HCl lemon juice	2	12	10^{-2}	10^{-12}
	3	11	10^{-3}	10^{-11}
0.01M ethanoic acid	4	10	10^{-4}	10^{-10}
	5	9	10^{-5}	10^{-9}
rain water, milk	6	8	10^{-6}	10^{-8}
NEUTRAL	7	7	10^{-7}	10^{-7}
blood (pH = 7.4 approx.)	8	6	10^{-8}	10^{-6}
	9	5	10^{-9}	10^{-5}
	10	4	10^{-10}	10^{-4}
0.1M aqueous NH$_3$	11	3	10^{-11}	10^{-3}
0.01M NaOH or KOH	12	2	10^{-12}	10^{-2}
0.1M NaOH or KOH	13	1	10^{-13}	10^{-1}
	14	0	10^{-14}	1

acidity increases

alkaline strength increases

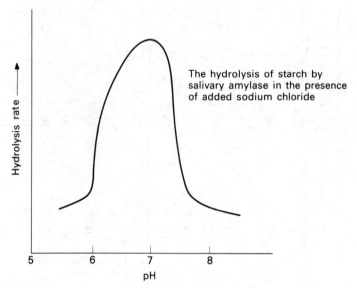

Fig. 4.2 Effect of pH on the rate of an enzyme catalysed reaction

Solution

(a) Nitric(V)acid is a strong electrolyte and is fully ionised in aqueous solution:

$$HNO_3 + H_2O \longrightarrow H_3O^+_{(aq)} + NO^-_{3(aq)}$$

(i) $[H^+_{(aq)}]$ in $10^{-3}M$ $HNO_3 = 10^{-3}$ mol l^{-1}

(ii) $[OH^-] = \dfrac{K_w}{[H^+]} = -\dfrac{10^{-14}}{10^{-3}} = 10^{-11}$ mol l^{-1}

(iii) pH of $10^{-3}M$ $HNO_3 = -\log[H^+] = -\log 10^{-3} = 3.00$

(iv) pOH of $10^{-3}M$ $HNO_3 = 14.00 - pH = 11.00$

$$\text{or } pOH = -\log[OH^-] = -\log 10^{-11} = 11.00$$

(b) Potassium hydroxide is a strong base and is fully ionised as $K^+_{(aq)}$ and $OH^-_{(aq)}$ ions in aqueous solution

(i) $[H^+]$ in 0.01M $KOH = \dfrac{K_w}{[OH^-]} = \dfrac{10^{-14}}{10^{-2}} = 10^{-12}$ mol l^{-1}

(ii) hydroxyl ion concentration in 0.01M KOH $= 10^{-2}$ mol l^{-1}

(iii) pH $= -\log[H^+] = -\log 10^{-12} = 12.00$

(iv) pOH $= 14.00 - 12.00 = 2.00$

   or pOH $= -\log[OH^-] = -\log 10^{-2} = 2.00$

Example 4.3

Calculate (a) the pH and (b) the pOH of a 0.030M solution of sodium hydroxide.

Solution

(a) As NaOH is a strong electrolyte the hydroxyl ion concentration in a 0.030 M solution of sodium hydroxide, $[OH^-] = 0.030$, or 3×10^{-2} mol l^{-1}.

$$[H^+] = \frac{K_w}{[OH^-]} = \frac{10^{-14}}{3 \times 10^{-2}} = 3.333 \times 10^{-13} \text{ mol } l^{-1}$$

$$\text{pH} = -\log[H^+] = -\log(3.333 \times 10^{-13})$$

$$= (\overline{13}.523) = -(-13 + 0.523) = 12.477$$

(b) pOH $= -\log[OH^-] = -\log 3 \times 10^{-2} = -(\overline{2}.477)$

$$= -(-2 + 0.477) = -(-1.523) = 1.523$$

or pOH $= 14.00 - \text{pH}$

$$= 14.00 - 12.477$$

$$= 1.523$$

4.4
Measurement of pH

Specific objective: *The expected learning outcome of this section is that the student will be able to determine pH both by indicator methods and by using a pH meter.*

Biologists, agriculturalists, chemists and other scientists frequently need to know the degree of acidity or alkalinity of a soil, or the pH of a solution or aqueous suspension. The principal methods used for the measurement of pH are:

   (a) Indicators

and (b) a pH meter

(*a*) *Indicators*

An acid-base indicator is a substance which changes colour over a particular pH range. Many indicators, e.g. litmus and blackberry juice, are naturally occurring compounds, while others, such as methyl orange and phenolphthalein are synthetic substances. Indicators are usually weak acids in which the undissociated acid and its anion are of different colours:

$$HIn_{(aq)} \rightleftharpoons H^+_{(aq)} + In^-_{(aq)}$$

Colour A Colour B

(acid colour) (alkaline colour)

where HIn and In$^-$ represent the undissociated indicator and its anion respectively.

It may be deduced from Le Chatelier's Principle (see Section 3.5) that the addition of an acid (i.e. $H^+_{(aq)}$) will promote the reverse reaction and colour A (the acid colour of the indicator) will appear. The addition of a base, e.g. $OH^-_{(aq)}$, will increase the concentration of the indicator anion In$^-$ as a result of the reaction:

$$HIn_{(aq)} + OH^-_{(aq)} \longrightarrow In^-_{(aq)} + H_2O$$

colour A colour B

and the indicator will change to colour B (the alkaline colour). The pH at which a particular indicator changes colour is determined by its acid strength, i.e. by the degree of ionisation of HIn. The pH ranges and colour changes of a number of common indicators are shown in Table 4.7.

Table 4.7 Acid-base indicators

Indicator	pH range	Acid colour	Alkaline colour
Screened methyl orange	3.2–4.2	Pink	Green
Methyl orange	3.1–4.4	Red	Yellow
Methyl red	4.2–6.3	Red	Yellow
Phenolphthalein	8.3–10.0	Colourless	Red
Litmus	5.0–8.0	Red	Blue
Congo red	3.0–5.0	Violet	Red

(i) Universal indicators

By mixing a number of different indicators universal indicators are obtained which undergo a series of colour changes at various points in the pH scale. The approximate pH of a solution or aqueous suspension may be found by dipping a small strip of *universal* or *full-range indicator paper* into it and comparing the colour of the paper with a reference chart. The colour usually takes about 30 seconds to develop. A more accurate pH (to within about 0.5 of a pH unit) may be found by using the appropriate *narrow range paper*.

Experiment 4.1
To determine the pH of aqueous solutions using indicator papers

Use wide range (universal) and narrow range indicator papers to determine the pH of the following solutions: (a) approximately 0.1 M hydrochloric acid, (b) tap water, (c) approximately 0.1 M aqueous ammonia, (d) approximately 0.1 M ethanoic acid, (e) approximately 0.1 M sodium carbonate.

(ii) Choice of indicator for an acid-base titration

The correct indicator for an acid-base titration is one which will change colour when the titration reaction is completed. The aqueous solution of a salt obtained by the reaction of an acid with a base is not necessarily exactly neutral (i.e. pH = 7). Ammonium chloride, ammonium sulphate and other salts of a weak base (aqueous ammonia) and a strong acid (e.g. hydrochloric acid and sulphuric(VI)acid) give an acid solution in water. The pH values of 0.1 M solutions of ammonium chloride and ammonium sulphate for example, are 4.6 and 5.5 respectively at room temperature. This is due to *salt hydrolysis*. Ammonium chloride, for example, is fully ionised in solution but the presence of hydroxyl ions from the ionisation of water sets up an equilibrium with the ammonium ions to form the weak base. This reduces the concentration of hydroxyl ions in the solution and makes it acidic (i.e. the pH is considerably less than 7):

$$NH_4Cl_{(aq)} \longrightarrow NH_{4(aq)}^+ + Cl_{(aq)}^-$$

$$H_2O \rightleftharpoons H_{(aq)}^+ + OH_{(aq)}^-$$

$$NH_{4(aq)}^+ + OH_{(aq)}^- \rightleftharpoons NH_{3(aq)} + H_2O$$

$$[H^+][OH^-] = K_w$$

The concentration of hydroxyl ions is reduced, so therefore $[H^+] > [OH^-]$ and the solution is acidic.

Methyl orange changes colour over the range pH 3–4.5 and is therefore used as the indicator for titrations of a strong acid against a weak base. The change in pH in the course of the reaction between 0.1 M

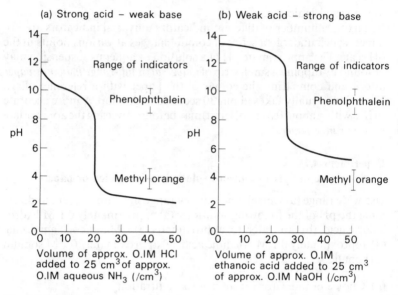

Fig. 4.3 Titration curves

hydrochloric acid and 0.1 M aqueous ammonia is shown in the titration curve in fig. 4.3(a).

Salts of a weak acid and a strong base yield an alkaline solution when they are dissolved in water. Common examples include sodium ethanoate, sodium carbonate, potassium cyanide and borax. The pH of 0.1 M solutions of sodium ethanoate and sodium carbonate are 8.9 and 11.5 respectively. The hydrogen ion concentration in the solution is reduced by the formation of small amounts of the weak acid by combination of the anion from the salt with protons from water, e.g.

$$CH_3CO_2Na_{(aq)} \longrightarrow CH_3CO_{2(aq)}^- + Na_{(aq)}^+$$

Sodium ethanoate

$$H_2O \rightleftharpoons H_{(aq)}^+ + OH_{(aq)}^-$$

$$CH_3CO_{2(aq)}^- + H_{(aq)}^+ \rightleftharpoons CH_3CO_2H_{(aq)}$$

$$[H^+][OH^-] = K_w$$

The $[H^+]$ is reduced by formation of ethanoic acid and therefore $[OH^-] > [H^+]$ and the solution is alkaline.

Phenolphthalein changes colour over the range pH 8–10 approximately and is therefore used as the indicator in titrations of a weak acid against a strong base (see fig. 4.3(b)). Virtually any indicator can be used for the titration of a strong acid against a strong base as there is a large and sudden pH change at the equivalence point (see fig. 4.4).

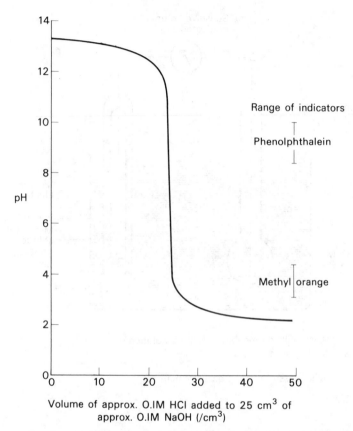

Fig. 4.4 Titration curve of a strong acid against a strong base

(b) The pH-meter

The pH-meter uses a glass electrode whose potential depends on the hydrogen ion concentration in which it is placed (see fig. 4.5). By measuring the voltage relative to a reference electrode, the pH of the solution may be determined and read directly on a potentiometric (millivolt) scale calibrated in pH units. A saturated calomel electrode (potential = 0.2444 V at 25°) is commonly used as the reference for pH measurements. The instrument is first set using a buffer solution of known pH which is close to the pH of the solution which is being measured (see Demonstration 4.1 and Section 4.5). A 0.05 M solution of potassium hydrogen phthalate is generally used for this purpose. By definition this solution has a pH of 4.000 at 15°. These meters provide the quickest and most convenient method of determining the pH of a solution and are now available with digital read-out and built-in

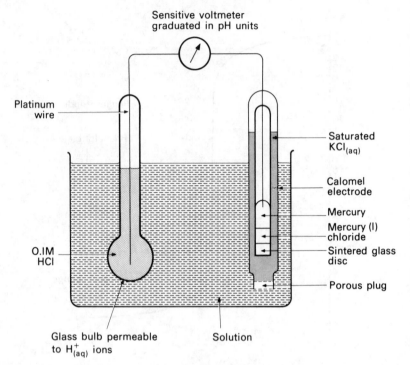

Fig. 4.5 The glass electrode: measurement of pH

temperature compensators for operation at other temperatures (see fig. 4.6 and the cover). Combined electrodes which incorporate the glass electrode and a silver–silver chloride reference electrode in a single probe (see fig. 4.7) are commonly employed.

Demonstration 4.1
Determination of titration curves using a pH-meter

Materials and apparatus
0.1 M hydrochloric acid. 0.1 M sodium hydroxide. 0.05 M sodium carbonate. Distilled water. Phenolphthalein. Methyl orange (or screened methyl orange). A pH-meter. Magnetic stirrer. pH 4.00 or pH 7.00 buffer. 2×25 cm^3 pipettes. 1×50 cm^3 burette and stand. 3×100 cm^3 beakers.

Method
Wash the glass and reference electrodes well in distilled water (*Care:* the glass electrode is extremely fragile) and then lower them into a beaker

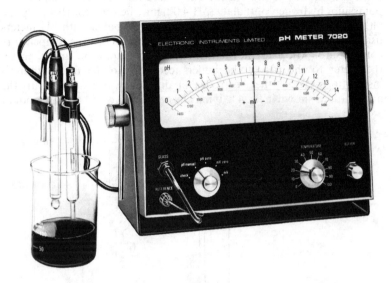

Fig. 4.6 A pH meter. Photograph courtesy of Griffin and George Ltd.

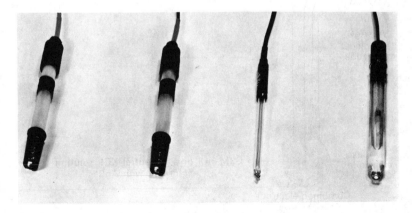

Fig. 4.7 Combined electrode for pH measurements. Photograph courtesy of Griffin and George Ltd.

containing about 40 cm³ of the buffer solution. A 0.05 M solution of potassium hydrogen phthalate (pH 4.00) may be used for this purpose, although manufacturers recommend a pH 7.00 buffer with pH meters using a silver–silver chloride reference electrode. Turn the temperature compensator knob to the temperature of the solution and then set the meter to the pH of the buffer according to the manufacturer's instructions. Wash the electrodes in distilled water and set up the apparatus as shown in fig. 4.8. It may be necessary to add a small amount

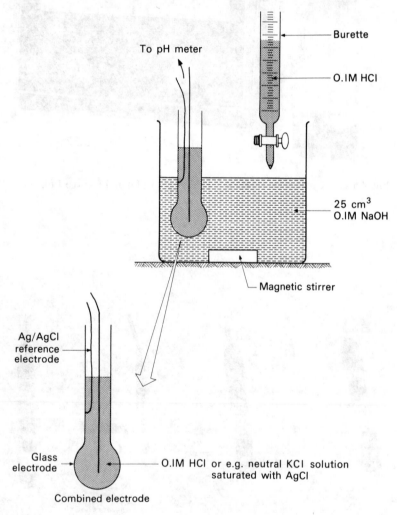

Fig. 4.8 Determination of titration curves using a pH meter and combined electrode

of distilled water to the 25 cm³ of sodium hydroxide solution in the beaker to ensure that the glass and reference electrodes are beneath the surface of the liquid. Note the pH reading. Add two drops of methyl orange and then plot pH values directly on a graph as the 50 cm³ of 0.1 M hydrochloric acid is added progressively. The solution should be stirred continuously. The acid may be added 3–4 cm³ at a time for the 0–22 and 28–50 cm³ ranges and 0.1 to 0.5 cm³ at a time for the range close to the end-point. Compare the curve obtained with fig. 4.4.

Repeat the experiment using 25 cm³ of 0.05 M sodium carbonate in place of the sodium hydroxide. Add 2–3 drops of phenolphthalein as indicator and then run in the hydrochloric acid 0.5–1 cm³ at a time for the first half of the titration (up to 30 cm³), noting the pH after each addition. Add 2–3 drops of methyl orange as soon as the phenolphthalein is colourless. Note the burette and pH readings when the indicators change colour and when carbon dioxide is evolved. How do you account for the shape of the titration curve which is obtained?

Experiment 4.2
To determine the pH of aqueous solutions using a pH-meter

Calibrate the pH meter using a pH 4 or pH 7 buffer solution as described above. Use the instrument to measure the pH of a number of the following solutions: (a) approx. 0.1 M sodium chloride, (b) approx. 0.1 M sodium ethanoate, (c) approx. 0.1 M ammonium chloride, (d) distilled water, (e) tap water, (f) rain water, (g) 0.1 M borax, (h) approx. 0.1 M sodium hydrogen carbonate (sodium bicarbonate), (i) approx. 0.1 M sodium carbonate, (j) fresh milk, (k) sour milk. How do you account for the pH values of these solutions?

4.5
Buffer solutions

Specific objectives: *The expected learning outcome of this section is that the student: (i) defines a buffer solution in terms of pH stability (ii) describes the composition of a simple buffer solution (iii) explains the action of a buffer solution in terms of the equilibrium concept.*

The pH of pure water and of most aqueous solutions changes slowly on standing. The absorption of carbon dioxide from the atmosphere lowers the pH by formation of the weak acid, carbonic acid:

$$CO_{2(g)} + H_2O_{(l)} \rightleftharpoons {}^{\cdot}H_2CO{}^{\cdot}{}_{3(aq)} \rightleftharpoons H^+_{(aq)} + HCO_{3(aq)}^-$$
$$\text{carbonic acid}$$
$$\text{(moderately stable in aqueous solution,}$$
$$\text{but has not been isolated in the pure state)}$$

$$HCO_{3(aq)}^- \rightleftharpoons H_{(aq)}^+ + CO_{3(aq)}^{2-}$$

while solutions in glass containers may slowly dissolve trace amounts of alkali from the glass and thereby increase their pH.

$$[H_{(aq)}^+][OH_{(aq)}^-] = K_w$$

The $[OH_{(aq)}^-]$ is increased by solution of alkalis from glass so therefore: $[OH_{(aq)}^-] > [H_{(aq)}^+]$ and the solution is alkaline.

Sometimes it is necessary to control the pH of a solution within fine limits. For example, the rates of many chemical reactions are strongly dependent on the pH of the solution. This is particularly true of many enzyme-catalysed reactions (see fig. 4.2) and the pH must be maintained close to the optimum value if the efficiency of the process is to be sustained. The pH of blood, for example, is 7.4. A variation of as much as 0.3 of a pH unit would certainly be fatal.

The hydrogen ion concentration of a solution is controlled by adding a buffer. A buffer solution is defined as *a solution of constant pH which is able to maintain its pH stability in the presence of traces of added acids or alkalis*. Most buffer solutions consist of a mixture of the sodium (or potassium) salt of a weak acid and the weak acid itself.

For example:

    sodium ethanoate and ethanoic acid

    sodium citrate and citric acid

    sodium tetraborate (borax, $Na_2B_4O_7$) and boric acid (H_3BO_3).

Potassium hydrogen phthalate is a special case as this salt contains a free acid group:

so both components of a buffer are present within the single molecule. An aqueous solution of potassium hydrogen phthalate buffer may be prepared by simply dissolving the salt in pure water. A 0.05 M solution has a pH of 4.00 at 15°.

The pH of a buffer solution is determined by the strength of the weak acid and by the relative amounts of the free acid and its salt which are present in solution. The composition and pH of a number of common buffer solutions are listed in Table 4.8.

Action of a buffer solution

Small amounts of acid or alkali have an enormous effect on the pH of pure water. For example, the addition of a few drops of 0.1 M hydro-

Table 4.8   Common buffer solutions

Composition of buffer	pH at 25°
0.1 M potassium dihydrogen citrate	5.72
0.05 M potassium hydrogen phthalate	4.005
0.1 M ethanoic acid + 0.1 M sodium ethanoate	4.64
0.01 M KH_2PO_4 + 0.01 M Na_2HPO_4	6.85
0.05 M borax	9.18
0.025 M sodium bicarbonate + 0.025 M sodium carbonate	10.00

chloric acid or 0.1 M sodium hydroxide is sufficient to change the pH of a beaker of water by three units from pH 7 to about pH 4 or 10 respectively. This is equivalent to a thousandfold change in the hydrogen or hydroxyl ion concentration. To maintain its constant pH a buffer solution must 'absorb' protons or hydroxyl ions from added traces of acids or bases. The method by which this is achieved may be explained using the sodium ethanoate–ethanoic acid (sodium acetate–acetic acid) buffer as an example:

The salt, sodium ethanoate, CH_3CO_2Na, is fully ionised and exists in solution as $CH_3CO_{2(aq)}^-$ and $Na_{(aq)}^+$ (or more simply, as $Na_{(aq)}^+$ and $OAc_{(aq)}^-$ ions). Ethanoic acid or acetic acid (CH_3CO_2H or more simply, HOAc) is a weak acid and yields only a small concentration of ions. in solution:

$$HOAc_{(aq)} \rightleftharpoons H_{(aq)}^+ + OAc_{(aq)}^-$$

(i) Addition of an acid
If a small amount of acid, e.g. $HCl_{(aq)}$, is poured into the buffer solution, the added protons combine with the ethanoate (acetate) anions from the salt to form the feebly ionised weak acid, HOAc, thereby removing most of the added hydrogen ions from solution and maintaining a constant pH:

$$\underset{\text{sodium ethanoate}}{Na^+OAc^-} \xrightarrow{\text{in solution}} Na_{(aq)}^+ + OAc_{(aq)}^-$$

$$\underset{\substack{\text{added hydrochloric}\\\text{acid (a strong acid –}\\\text{fully ionised in solution)}}}{HCl_{(aq)}} \longrightarrow H_{(aq)}^+ + Cl_{(aq)}^-$$

$$H^+_{(aq)} \qquad + OAc^-_{(aq)} \;\rightleftharpoons HOAc_{(aq)}$$

added protons   from salt
from $HCl_{(aq)}$

The added protons also suppress the ionisation of ethanoic acid in the buffer by displacing this equilibrium to the right (see Le Chatelier's Principle, Section 3.5) which further reduces the effect of the addition of hydrochloric acid to the system. The overall effect is thus a slight *increase* in the concentration of the weak acid and an equivalent *decrease* in the amount of the salt in the buffer:

$$H^+Cl^-_{(aq)} \qquad + Na^+OAc^-_{(aq)} \longrightarrow HOAc_{(aq)} \qquad + Na^+Cl^-_{(aq)}$$

small amounts of	amount of salt	amount of	x mol
hydrochloric acid	in the buffer	weak acid in	
added, x mol	*decreased* by	the buffer	
	amount, x mol	*increased* by	
		amount, x mol	

But the hydrogen ion concentration (and hence the pH of the solution) is effectively unchanged.

(ii) Addition of base

The buffer resists changes in pH on the addition of small amounts of alkali by the reaction of the added hydroxyl ions with the weak acid in the buffer:

$$HOAc_{(aq)} \quad + OH^-_{(aq)} \longrightarrow H_2O_{(l)} \qquad + OAc^-_{(aq)}$$

weak acid in   a very
the buffer   weak electrolyte

The products are ethanoate anions and water. Water is an extremely weak electrolyte:

$$H_2O_{(l)} \rightleftharpoons H^+_{(aq)} + OH^-_{(aq)}$$

so the change in the concentrations of hydrogen ions and hydroxyl ions in solution by its formation is negligible. The overall effect of adding a small amount, x mol, of sodium hydroxide to the buffer is thus to *decrease* the weak acid concentration slightly while the salt concentration is slightly *increased*:

$$Na^+OH^- \qquad + HOAc \longrightarrow Na^+OAc^- + H_2O$$

small amount,	amount of	amount of	
x mol, of	weak acid	salt in	
sodium hydroxide	in buffer	buffer	
added to buffer	decreased by	increased by	
	x mol	x mol	

The $H^+_{(aq)}$ and $OH^-_{(aq)}$ concentrations in the solution are virtually unchanged, thus maintaining the constant pH of the buffer.

Experiment 4.3
To demonstrate the action of a buffer solution

Materials and apparatus
Approx. 0.1 M hydrochloric acid. Approx. 0.1 M sodium hydroxide. A sodium ethanoate – ethanoic acid buffer. (This may be prepared by mixing equal volumes of approximately 1 M solutions of sodium ethanoate and ethanoic acid.) Distilled water. 0.05 M potassium hydrogen phthalate buffer (pH = 4.00). pH-meter and combined electrode. Beakers. Pasteur (dropping) pipette.

Method
Calibrate the pH-meter against the 0.05 M potassium hydrogen phthalate buffer as described in Demonstration 4.1 and then use the instrument to determine the pH of about 30 cm^3 of distilled water in a beaker. Add 3 separate drops of 0.1 M hydrochloric acid to the beaker, stir the solution and note the pH of the mixture after the addition of each drop. Now add 5 drops of the approximately 0.1 M sodium hydroxide, again noting the pH of the solution after each addition.

Repeat this experiment with about 40 cm^3 of the sodium ethanoate–ethanoic acid buffer.

Note: This experiment can be carried out using indicator papers (see Experiment 4.1) if a pH-meter is not available.

Summary

1. Salts, strong acids (e.g. HCl, HNO$_3$ and H$_2$SO$_4$) and strong bases (e.g. NaOH and KOH) are highly ionised in solution. These substances are known as *strong electrolytes.*

2. Weak acids (e.g. ethanoic acid and carbonic acid) and weak bases (e.g. aqueous ammonia) are only slightly (approx. 1–3%) ionised in solution. These substances are known as *weak electrolytes.*

3. Aqueous solutions of strong electrolytes are considerably better conductors of electricity than aqueous solutions of weak electrolytes.

4. The degree of ionisation, α, of a weak electrolyte is defined as the fraction of the amount of the substance which is present as ions.

5. Water is an extremely weak electrolyte:

$$H_2O \rightleftharpoons H^+_{(aq)} + OH^-_{(aq)}$$

The product of the concentrations of hydrogen ions (protons) and hydroxyl ions in any aqueous solution is a constant:

$$[H^+_{(aq)}][OH^-_{(aq)}] = K_w = 10^{-14} \text{ at } 25°$$

where K_w is the ionic product of water.

6. $pH = -\log[H^+]$ and $pOH = -\log[OH^-]$. For any aqueous solution at 25° $pH + pOH = 14.00$.

7. The range of values of $[H^+]$, $[OH^-]$, pH and pOH for aqueous solutions is listed in Tables 4.5 and 4.6. A neutral solution has a pH of 7; acidic and alkaline solutions have a pH of <7 and >7 respectively.

8. The pH of a solution may be determined using indicators or a pH-meter.

9. A buffer solution is a solution of constant pH which is able to maintain this pH stability in the presence of added traces of acids or alkalis.

10. A buffer solution usually contains a mixture of a salt of a weak acid and the weak acid itself.

Questions

1. Classify the following liquids as electronic conductors, electrolytic conductors or insulators: liquid paraffin, acidified distilled water, fused calcium chloride, solid calcium chloride, molten wax, an aqueous solution of gaseous hydrogen chloride, molten silver, gold amalgam, fused aluminium oxide, an aqueous solution of sugar, a mixture of alcohol and water.

2. What is meant by the term 'electrolysis'? Give three examples.

3. 'Electrolysis is a redox (reduction–oxidation) process'. Discuss this statement with reference to suitable examples.

4. What are the differences between strong and weak electrolytes? Give three examples of each class of compound.

5. 'Aqueous solutions of strong acids and strong bases are almost completely ionised.' Describe two experiments which provide evidence in support of this statement.

6. How do you account for the fact that the conductivity of an aqueous solution of a weak acid increases with dilution?

7. What is meant by the term 'the ionic product of water'? What is its numerical value at 25° (298 K)?

8. Is K_w the same as the equilibrium constant for the ionisation of water?

9. How do you account for the fact that K_w is a constant for virtually any aqueous solution at constant temperature?

10. State the range of values of $[H^+_{(aq)}]$ and $[OH^-_{(aq)}]$ for (a) acidic and (b) alkaline aqueous solutions.

11. What is meant by the pH of an aqueous solution?

12. What is meant by the term 'pOH'?

13. What is the relationship between the pH and the pOH of an aqueous solution at 25°?

14. Calculate (i) the hydrogen ion concentration, (ii) the hydroxyl ion concentration, (iii) the pH and (iv) the pOH values of (a) a neutral aqueous solution, (b) 0.1 M sodium hydroxide and (c) 10^{-4} M hydrochloric acid.

15. State whether solutions with the following $[H^+]$, $[OH^-]$, pH or pOH values are acidic, alkaline or neutral: (a) pOH = 6.72, (b) pH = 0.01, (c) $[H^+] = 10^{-12}$ mol l^{-1}, (d) $[H^+] = 1$ mol l^{-1}, (e) $[OH^-] = 10^{-7}$ mol l^{-1}, (f) pOH = 13, (g) pH = 10.

16. The pH of two aqueous solutions are 3.89 and 12.42 at 25°. Calculate the pOH values of these solutions.

17. Describe how you would determine the pH of an aqueous solution using full-range (universal) and narrow-range indicator papers.

18. What is a glass electrode?

19. Outline the procedure for measuring the pH of an aqueous solution using a pH meter.

20. How do you account for the fact that an aqueous solution of ammonium chloride is acidic?

21. What is a buffer solution? Give two examples.

22. Why is it important to control the pH of a solution?

23. Explain the action of an aqueous potassium hydrogen phthalate buffer in resisting changes in pH on the addition of traces of aqueous sodium hydroxide or hydrochloric acid.

24. Blood is buffered by the presence of dissolved carbon dioxide and hydrogen carbonate (HCO_3^-) ions:

$$H_2O + CO_{2(aq)} \rightleftharpoons H_2CO_{3(aq)} \rightleftharpoons H^+_{(aq)} + HCO^-_{3(aq)}$$

Write equations to explain the buffering effect of blood on the addition of small amounts of an acid or a base.

25. Describe two reasons why the pH of an aqueous solution of a substance could change during prolonged storage.

C Electrode potentials

5 Electrochemical cells

General objective: *The expected learning outcome of this chapter is that the student describes and uses some basic electrochemical concepts.*

5.1
Half-cells

Specific objectives: *The expected learning outcome of this section is that the student:* (i) *states that an equilibrium is set up when a metal is placed in a solution containing its ions i.e.,*

$$M_{(s)} \rightleftharpoons M^{n+}_{(aq)} + ne^-$$

(ii) *recognises that the equilibrium in* (i) *results in a potential difference between the metal and the solution, and that this system is called a half-cell.*

If a metal rod is placed in contact with a solution of its ions, an equilibrium is established in which the rate at which the solid metal dissolves is equal to the rate at which the ions are deposited from solution (see fig. 5.1):

$$M_{(s)} \xrightleftharpoons[\text{metal ions deposited}]{\text{metal dissolves}} M^{n+}_{(aq)} + ne^-$$

metal   metal ions
in aqueous
solution

The position of this equilibrium varies enormously and is a measure of the reactivity of the metal. With highly reactive metals much as sodium or calcium the equilibrium position is far over to the right-hand side of the equation, while silver and gold have little tendency to dissolve in a solution of their ions and the position of equilibrium is well over to the left. The dynamic nature of this equilibrium (see Section 3.3) may be demonstrated by immersing the metal, e.g. magnesium, in a solution containing ions of a radioactive isotope of the metal, e.g. an aqueous solution of $MgSO_4$:

$$Mg_{(s)} \rightleftharpoons {}^*Mg^{2+}_{(aq)} + 2e^-$$

radioactive
magnesium
ions in
solution

The detection of radioactivity on the surface of the metal after thorough

83

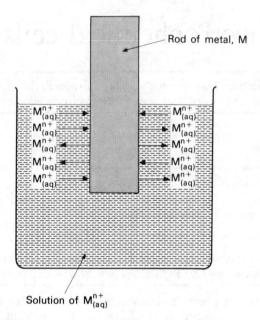

Fig. 5.1 Equilibrium between a metal and a solution of its ions

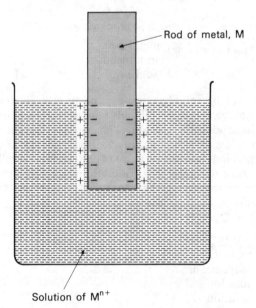

Fig. 5.2 Helmholtz double layer

washing with distilled water indicates that ions have been deposited from solution.

The electrons produced when a metal dissolves are left behind on the metal surface. The metal thus becomes negatively charged relative to the cations in solution in contact with it and two oppositely charged layers (known as the *Helmholtz double layer* (see fig. 5.2)) are obtained. This separation of charges produces a potential difference between the metal and the ions in solution. The magnitude of this potential is a measure of the position of equilibrium in the reaction:

$$M_{(s)} \rightleftharpoons M^{n+}_{(aq)} + ne^-$$

and hence of the reactivity of the metal.

A metal in contact with a solution of its ions is known as a *metal electrode* or, as an electrochemical cell (see Section 5.6) is obtained by the combination of two such electrodes, it is also referred to as a *half-cell*. The electrode is written as $M|M^{n+}_{(aq)}(c_1)$, where the vertical line represents the phase boundary (e.g. solid–liquid) across which the electrons are transferred and is the site of the redox (reduction and oxidation) process:

$$M_{(s)} \underset{\text{reduction – gain of electrons}}{\overset{\text{oxidation – loss of electrons}}{\rightleftharpoons}} M^{n+}_{(aq)} + ne^-$$

and c_1 is the concentration of the metal ions in the solution in contact with the metal.

Other electrodes or half-cells are obtained when a gas is in contact both with a solution of its ions and an inert metal much as platinum or gold. This half-cell is known as a *gas electrode*. A hydrogen electrode is shown in fig. 5.3 and is written as:

$$\text{Pt, H}_2\,(p_1)|H^+_{(aq)}\,(\text{concentration, c})$$

where p_1 is the pressure of gaseous hydrogen. The reversible reaction occurring at the electrode is:

$$H^+_{(aq)} + e^- \underset{\text{oxidation}}{\overset{\text{reduction}}{\rightleftharpoons}} \tfrac{1}{2}H_{2(g)}$$

The platinum surface is coated with a finely divided form of platinum known as platinum black which catalyses this electrode reaction.

5.2
Electrode potentials

Specific objective: *The expected learning outcome of this section is that the student recognises that the potential difference between a metal and a solution of its ions can only be measured relative to a second half-cell.*

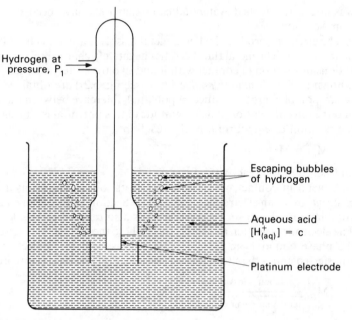

Hydrogen at pressure, P_1

Escaping bubbles of hydrogen

Aqueous acid $[H^+_{(aq)}] = c$

Platinum electrode

Fig. 5.3 The hydrogen electrode

It is not possible to measure the potential of a single electrode or half-cell. Just as the height of a mountain, or town, or the level of the floor of the ocean is represented in terms of the height above or below mean sea level, a standard or reference point is required. The potential of a single electrode can only be measured relative to a second half-cell. The voltage of the combination is determined using a valve voltmeter or poten-tiometer. The measurement of the potentials of a number of metal electrodes relative to the copper half-cell is described in Section 5.2(a) and Demonstration 5.1. The values obtained are a measure of the extent to which the potential of the electrode is more or less positive than the potential of the reference electrode. It is also a measure of the relative ease with which the two metals will yield cations in solution (see Section 5.5).

The two half-cell reactions are separate, but dependent. Thus in the example shown in fig. 5.4, the discharge of copper ions:

$$Cu^{2+}_{(aq)} + 2e^- \xrightarrow{\text{reduction}} Cu_{(s)}$$
$$\text{oxidising agent}$$

at one electrode cannot occur without the presence of an electron donor (i.e. a reducing agent) to provide the electrons at the other electrode:

$$\text{Mg}_{(s)} \xrightarrow{\text{oxidation}} \text{Mg}^{2+}_{(aq)} + 2e^-$$

reducing agent

The overall reaction:

$$\text{Mg}_{(s)} + \text{Cu}^{2+}_{(aq)} \longrightarrow \text{Mg}^{2+}_{(aq)} + \text{Cu}_{(s)}$$

is the sum of the two half-cell reactions.

An inverted U-tube containing an aqueous solution of potassium chloride, ammonium nitrate(V), or some other suitable electrolyte which does not react with the solutions in the cell, is used to prevent the two electrolytes mixing while providing electrical contact between the two half-cells. This arrangement is known as a *salt bridge* (see fig. 5.4). The use of cotton wool plugs is avoided by filling the U-tube with a saturated solution of the electrolyte in agar jelly. In many experiments a strip of filter paper soaked in ammonium nitrate solution may be used as a salt bridge. Alternatively, the electrolytes in the two half-cells may be separated by a sintered glass disc, a plug of plaster or some other suitable porous material.

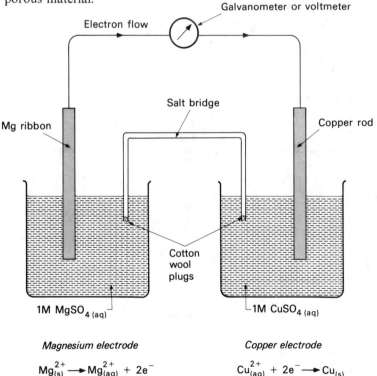

Fig. 5.4 The magnesium–copper cell

(a) Measurement of relative electrode potentials
The potential difference between two electrodes (for example, the combination of the copper and magnesium half-cells shown in fig. 5.4) may be measured directly using a valve voltmeter or, alternatively, the potentiometer circuit shown in fig. 5.5 may be employed. The sliding contact X is applied at points along the uniform potentiometer wire AB until the position is found at which the galvanometer reading is zero, i.e. when no current is flowing through the galvanometer circuit. At this point the electromotive force or e.m.f. of the cell, C, is equal and opposite to the potential difference between the end of the wire A and the sliding contact X. This potential difference is proportional to the length of wire AX. The cell is then switched out of the circuit and replaced by a cell of known voltage, S, such as the Standard Weston Cell (e.m.f. = 1.0181 V at 25°) and the new balance point, Y, at which no current is flowing through the galvanometer is found. The e.m.f. of the experimental cell (and hence the potential of the magnesium half-cell relative to the copper electrode) is found from:

e.m.f. of cell, $C \propto AX$

e.m.f. of standard cell, $S \propto AY$

$$\therefore \frac{C}{S} = \frac{AX}{AY}$$

and $C = S \times \dfrac{AX}{AY}$

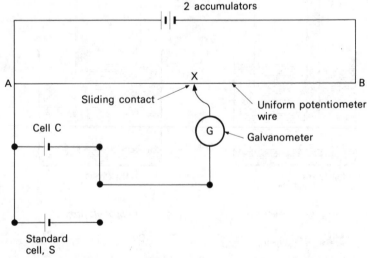

Fig. 5.5 Measurement of cell e.m.f.

Demonstration 5.1
To measure the potential of a number of half-cells relative to that of the copper electrode

Materials
Strips of foil or rods of a number of suitable metals, e.g. magnesium, copper, zinc, iron, lead and silver. Approx. 50 cm^3 of 1 M aqueous solutions of soluble salts of the corresponding metals, e.g. magnesium sulphate, copper sulphate, zinc sulphate, iron(II)sulphate, lead nitrate and silver nitrate. Distilled water.

Apparatus
A voltmeter or the potentiometer circuit shown in fig. 5.5. Two accumulators or three NiFe cells in series. Galvanometer. Sliding contact. Salt bridges or strips of filter paper soaked in aqueous ammonium nitrate solution. A standard Weston Cell. 5–6 100 cm^3 beakers.

Method
Place the metal rods or strips of foil in the beakers containing the solution of the corresponding metal ion. Link the beakers in turn with a salt bridge, or strip of filter paper soaked in ammonium nitrate solution, to the beaker containing the copper rod in aqueous copper sulphate solution and determine the voltage of the cells obtained using a voltmeter or potentiometer. Reverse the connections on the cells if a balance point or voltmeter reading is not obtained. List your results in order of decreasing electrode potential.

Link the following electrodes together with a salt bridge and measure the e.m.f. of the cell obtained: (a) zinc and silver (b) magnesium and lead. Compare your results with the corresponding half-cell potentials measured relative to the copper electrode in the first part of the experiment.

5.3
The standard hydrogen electrode

Specific objective: *The expected learning outcome of this section is that the student: (i) Defines electrode potential and relates values to that of the standard hydrogen electrode; (ii) States that if the metal has a greater tendency to form cations than has hydrogen, then the electrode potential will have a negative sign.*

The *standard hydrogen electrode* is used as the ultimate reference for the measurement of all electrode potentials. It consists of a gas electrode (see fig. 5.3) in which hydrogen at a pressure of 1 atmosphere (101 325 Nm^{-2}) is in contact with a solution of hydrogen ions of unit activity at a temperature of 298 K (25°C). By convention the standard electrode potential, or E_H°, of this electrode is zero:

$$E_H^\circ = 0.000 \text{ V}$$

The electrode potential of any other half-cell is defined as the voltage of the cell obtained when the standard hydrogen electrode is linked to it. For example, the arrangement used to measure the potential of a metal electrode:

$$\text{Pt, H}_2(p = 101\ 325\ \text{Nm}^{-2})|\text{H}^+_{(aq)}(a = 1)\ ||\ \text{M}^{n+}_{(aq)}(\text{concentration} = c_1)|\text{M}_{(s)}$$

$$\underbrace{\text{standard hydrogen electrode}} \qquad \underbrace{\text{metal electrode}}$$

$$\text{salt bridge}$$

is shown in fig. 5.6. The double vertical line in the cell diagram represents the junction between the two electrolyte solutions which are joined by a salt bridge.

The activity of a dilute aqueous solution is virtually the same as its concentration in mol l^{-1}. However, with more concentrated solutions (especially of electrolytes) the term *activity*, in which allowance has been made for the interaction of the ions in solution with one another, is preferred to concentration.

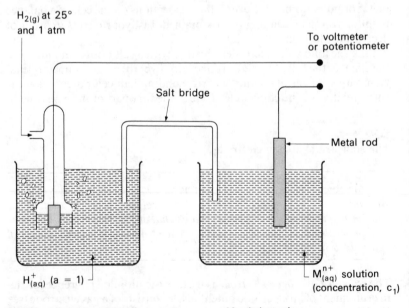

Fig. 5.6 Measurement of electrode potential

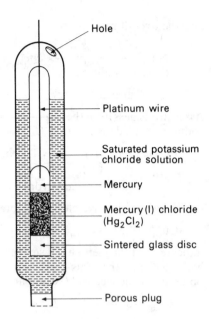

Hole

Platinum wire

Saturated potassium chloride solution

Mercury

Mercury (I) chloride (Hg$_2$Cl$_2$)

Sintered glass disc

Porous plug

Fig. 5.7 The calomel electrode

(a) *Use of a calomel electrode as a secondary standard*

The standard hydrogen electrode is not an easy standard to set up, nor is it readily portable as it requires a cylinder of pure hydrogen with all the accompanying gauges and reducing valves. Other electrodes are therefore used as a reference for measuring half-cell potentials. The calomel electrode (see fig. 5.7) is the most important of these secondary standards. Its electrode potential at 25° is 0.2444 V. The electrode potential of a half-cell is found by adding this value to the e.m.f. of the cell obtained when this reference electrode is linked to it.

(b) *Sign of electrode potential*

By convention the standard hydrogen electrode is always written on the left-hand side of the cell diagram and the sign of the cell voltage is that of the right-hand electrode. Any metal which has a greater tendency to form cations than hydrogen has a negative electrode potential. For example, the standard electrode potential of sodium ($Na^+_{(aq)}|Na$) is -2.71 V. This indicates that sodium loses an electron (i.e. is oxidised) more easily than hydrogen ($H^+_{(aq)}|\frac{1}{2}H_{2(g)}$, $E^\circ_H = 0.000$ V). The electrons produced when metallic sodium dissolves in water reduce protons in solution to gaseous hydrogen:

$$Na \rightleftharpoons Na^+_{(aq)} + e^-$$

$$H^+_{(aq)} + e^- \rightleftharpoons \frac{1}{2}H_{2(g)}$$

and the overall reaction is:

$$Na_{(s)} + H^+_{(aq)} \longrightarrow Na^+_{(aq)} + \tfrac{1}{2}H_{2(g)}$$

oxidised   reduced

As electrons pass from the negative electrode to the positive electrode the sodium electrode is negative (E°_H for $Na^+_{(aq)}|Na_{(s)} = -2.71$ V):

$$Pt, H_2 \text{ (1 atm)}|H^+_{(aq)} \text{ (a = 1)}\|Na^+_{(aq)} \text{ (a = 1)}|Na_{(s)}$$

(+)   (−)

Similarly, a positive electrode potential, e.g.

$$Cu^{2+}_{(aq)} + 2e^- \rightleftharpoons Cu_{(s)} \qquad E^\circ_H = +0.34 \text{ V}$$

indicates that the metal has a smaller tendency to yield cations than has hydrogen and that this tendency decreases with increasing positive potential of the electrode. Compare,

$$K^+_{(aq)} + e^- \rightleftharpoons K \qquad E^\circ_H = -2.92 \text{ V}$$

$$H^+_{(aq)} + e^- \rightleftharpoons \tfrac{1}{2}H_{2(g)} \qquad E^\circ_H = 0.000 \text{ V}$$

$$Ag^+_{(aq)} + e^- \rightleftharpoons Ag_{(s)} \qquad E^\circ_H = +0.80 \text{ V}$$

Silver has virtually no tendency to yield cations compared with hydrogen and (especially) potassium and is thus a fairly unreactive metal (see Section 5.5).

5.4
Standard electrode potentials

Specific objectives: *The expected learning outcome of this section is that the student: (i) recognises that in a given electrode system the temperature and concentration of the ion affect the electrode potential; (ii) states the temperature and the concentration of the ion required for the standard electrode potential.*

The potential of a half-cell is a measure of the position of equilibrium between the ions in solution and the metal:

$$M^{n+}_{(aq)} + ne^- \rightleftharpoons M_{(s)}$$

or non-metal, e.g.

$$H^+_{(aq)} + e^- \rightleftharpoons \tfrac{1}{2}H_{2(g)}$$

$$\tfrac{1}{2}Cl_{2(g)} + e^- \rightleftharpoons Cl^-_{(aq)}$$

The position of this equilibrium for a particular half-cell, and hence the magnitude of its electrode potential, is dependent on a number of factors of which the most important are the concentration of the ions in solution and the temperature. An increase in the concentration of cations in solution promotes the deposition process and makes the electrode potential of a metal more positive. An increase in temperature has the same effect.

The influence of temperature and concentration on the electrode potential of a metal is given by the *Nernst equation*:

$$E = E^\circ_H + 2.303 \frac{RT}{nF} \log [M^{n+}]$$

where E is the measured electrode potential at a temperature T and cation concentration $[M^{n+}]$. R is the General Gas constant ($8.314\,J\,K^{-1}$ mol^{-1}), F is the Faraday constant ($96\,500$ coulombs) and n is the numerical charge on the cation. The potential of a gas electrode is also strongly dependent on the pressure of the gas.

Standard conditions
The conditions shown for the measurement of *standard electrode potentials* are a pressure of 1 atmosphere ($101\,325\,Nm^{-2}$) with solutions of ions at unit concentration (or, more accurately, unit activity) at a temperature of 298 K (25°C). Standard electrode potentials are denoted by the symbol E°_H in which the subscript H indicates that these values are measured on a scale for which the standard hydrogen electrode (see Section 5.3) is the primary standard or reference. The standard electrode potential of the copper electrode ($Cu^{2+}_{(aq)}|Cu$, $E^\circ_H = +0.34\,V$), for example, is the e.m.f. of the cell:

$$Pt,\ H_2\ (p = 1\ atm)|H^+_{(aq)}\ (conc.^n = 1M)\|Cu^{2+}_{(aq)}\ (conc.^n = 1M)|Cu$$

The standard electrode potentials of a number of common electrodes are listed in Table 5.1. These values are also known as *standard reduction potentials* as the reactions to which they refer, e.g.

$$Cu^{2+}_{(aq)} + 2e^- \rightleftharpoons Cu_{(s)}$$

involve the addition of electrons and are thus reduction processes.

Table 5.1   Standard electrode (reduction) potentials

Electrode	Electrode reaction	E_H° (/volts)
Li^+/Li	$Li^+ + e^- \rightleftharpoons Li$	-3.04
K^+/K	$K^+ + e^- \rightleftharpoons K$	-2.92
Ba^{2+}/Ba		-2.90
Ca^{2+}/Ca		-2.87
Na^+/Na		-2.71
Mg^{2+}/Mg		-2.37
Al^{3+}/Al	$M^{n+} + ne^- \rightleftharpoons M$	-1.66
Mn^{2+}/Mn		-1.18
Zn^{2+}/Zn		-0.76
Cr^{3+}/Cr		-0.74
Fe^{2+}/Fe		-0.44
Cr^{3+}/Cr^{2+}	$Cr^{3+} + e^- \rightleftharpoons Cr^{2+}$	-0.41
Ni^{2+}/Ni		-0.25
Sn^{2+}/Sn	$M^{2+} + 2e^- \rightleftharpoons M$	-0.14
Pb^{2+}/Pb		-0.13
$H^+/\frac{1}{2}H_2$	$H_{(aq)}^+ + e^- \rightleftharpoons \frac{1}{2}H_2$	0.00
Cu^{2+}/Cu^+	$Cu^{2+} + e^- \rightleftharpoons Cu^+$	$+0.15$
Sn^{4+}/Sn^{2+}	$Sn^{4+} + 2e^- \rightleftharpoons Sn^{2+}$	$+0.15$
Cu^{2+}/Cu	$Cu^{2+} + 2e^- \rightleftharpoons Cu$	$+0.34$
Cu^+/Cu	$Cu^+ + e^- \rightleftharpoons Cu$	$+0.52$
I_2/I^-	$\frac{1}{2}I_2 + e^- \rightleftharpoons I^-$	$+0.54$
Fe^{3+}/Fe^{2+}	$Fe^{3+} + e^- \rightleftharpoons Fe^{2+}$	$+0.76$
Ag^+/Ag	$Ag^+ + e^- \rightleftharpoons Ag$	$+0.80$
Br_2/Br^-	$\frac{1}{2}Br_2 + e^- \rightleftharpoons Br^-$	$+1.07$
O_2/H_2O	$\frac{1}{2}O_2 + 2H^+ + 2e^- \rightleftharpoons H_2O$	$+1.23$
$Cr_2O_7^{2-}/H^+/Cr^{3+}$	$Cr_2O_7^{2-} + 14H^+ + 6e^- \rightleftharpoons 2Cr^{3+} + 7H_2O$	$+1.33$
Cl_2/Cl^-	$\frac{1}{2}Cl_2 + e^- \rightleftharpoons Cl^-$	$+1.36$

Table 5.1 (continued)

Electrode	Electrode reaction	E°_H (/volts)
Ce^{4+}/Ce^{3+}	$Ce^{4+} + e^- \rightleftharpoons Ce^{3+}$	$+1.45$
$MnO_4^-/H^+/Mn^{2+}$	$MnO_4^- + 8H^+ + 5e^- \rightleftharpoons Mn^{2+} + 4H_2O$	$+1.52$
MnO_4^-/MnO_2	$MnO_4^- + 4H^+ + 3e^- \rightleftharpoons MnO_2 + 2H_2O$	$+1.69$
F_2/F^-	$\frac{1}{2}F_2 + e^- \rightleftharpoons F^-$	$+2.80$

5.5
The electrochemical series

Specific objectives: *The expected learning outcome of this section is that the student: (i) Describes the electrochemical series as a list of elements in order of standard electrode potentials; (ii) Uses the electrochemical series to predict the feasibility of displacement reactions at 298 K; (iii) States that displacement is an example of a redox process.*

The electrochemical series of the elements is obtained by arranging the metals (or non-metals) in order of increasing standard electrode potential (see Table 5.2(a) and (b)). The principal applications of the electrochemical series are:

(a) *As a summary of the relative reactivities of the elements*
The electrochemical series is essentially an activity series with the most reactive metals, e.g. sodium, potassium and calcium, at the top of the list and the least reactive, e.g. copper, silver and gold, at the bottom. The list also helps to correlate the properties of the elements. The principal trends in the properties and reactivity of the metals and their compounds according to their position in the electrochemical series are summarised in Tables 5.3(a) and 5.3(b) respectively for reference.

(b) *The prediction of displacement reactions*
Metals above hydrogen in the electrochemical series will yield hydrogen on treatment with an acid, e.g.

$$Fe_{(s)} + H_2SO_{4(aq)} \longrightarrow FeSO_{4(aq)} + H_{2(g)}$$

$$Sn_{(s)} + 2HCl_{(aq)} \longrightarrow SnCl_{2(aq)} + H_{2(g)}$$

Table 5.2   The electrochemical series

(a) **The metals**	(b) **The non-metals**
K	
Na	
Ca	I_2
Mg	Br_2
Al	
Zn	Cl_2
Fe	F_2
Cr	
Ni	
Sn	
Pb	
(H_2)	
Cu	
Hg	
Ag	
Pt	
Au	

Reactivity increases (metals, upward)   *Reactivity increases* (non-metals, downward)

Metals below hydrogen in the series do not yield hydrogen and if they are attacked by an acid some other reaction occurs, e.g.

$$Cu_{(s)} + 4HNO_{3(aq)} \longrightarrow Cu(NO_3)_2 + 2H_2O + 2NO_{2(g)}$$

The same principle applies to the displacement of metals: any metal will displace one lower in the series from a solution of its ions. The exothermic displacement of copper from copper sulphate(VI) solution by the addition of metallic zinc was discussed in Section 1.1. Similarly iron will displace lead ions:

$$Fe_{(s)} + Pb(NO_3)_{2(aq)} \longrightarrow Fe(NO_3)_{2(aq)} + Pb_{(s)}$$

and copper will displace silver ions:

$$Cu_{(s)} + 2AgNO_{3(aq)} \longrightarrow Cu(NO_3)_{2(aq)} + 2Ag_{(s)}$$

from suitable solutions.

All these displacement reactions are redox processes and involve transfer of electrons from the *reducing agent* (or *electron donor*) to the *oxidising agent* (or *electron acceptor*). The net reaction is the sum of the oxidation and reduction steps, e.g.

$$Fe_{(s)} \longrightarrow Fe^{2+}_{(aq)} + 2e^- \qquad \text{oxidation step}$$
$$\underline{Cu^{2+}_{(aq)} + 2e^- \longrightarrow Cu_{(s)}} \qquad \text{reduction step}$$

Overall reaction:

$$\underset{\substack{\text{reducing agent}\\\text{oxidised}}}{Fe_{(s)}} + \underset{\substack{\text{oxidising agent}\\\text{reduced}}}{Cu^{2+}_{(aq)}} \rightarrow Fe^{2+}_{(aq)} + Cu_{(s)} \qquad \text{redox reaction}$$

electrons
transferred

It should be noted that in the course of the reaction the reducing agent is oxidised by donation of its electrons to the oxidising agent and the oxidising agent (or electron acceptor) is reduced.

The displacement reactions of the halogens may be used to distinguish between the chloride, bromide and iodide anions (see Table 5.4). A halogen will displace a less reactive halogen, i.e. one *higher* in the electrochemical series, from a solution of its ions. Thus chlorine will displace bromine or iodine from an aqueous solution of bromide or iodide ions:

$$Cl_{2(aq)} + 2Br^-_{(aq)} \longrightarrow 2Cl^-_{(aq)} + Br_{2(aq)}$$
$$Cl_{2(aq)} + 2I^-_{(aq)} \longrightarrow 2Cl^-_{(aq)} + I_{2(aq)}$$

and bromine will displace iodine from an aqueous solution of iodide ions:

$$Br_{2(aq)} + 2I^-_{(aq)} \longrightarrow 2Br^-_{(aq)} + I_{2(aq)}$$

These reactions are redox processes, e.g.

$$\tfrac{1}{2}Cl_{2(aq)} + e^- \xrightarrow{\text{reduction}} Cl^-_{(aq)}$$

$$Br^-_{(aq)} \xrightarrow{\text{oxidation}} \tfrac{1}{2}Br_{2(aq)} + e^-$$

Table 5.3(*a*)   *Trends in electrochemical series: reactivity of metals*

Metal	E_H (/V)	(Electrode)	Pauling electronegativity (see Section 8.3)	Reaction of metal with air
K	-2.92	(K^+/K)	0.8	
Na	-2.71	(Na^+/Na)	0.9	Burn vigorously in air or oxygen
Ca	-2.87	(Ca^{2+}/Ca)	1.0	
Mg	-2.37	(Mg^{2+}/Mg)	1.2	
Al	-1.66	(Al^{3+}/Al)	1.5	
Zn	-0.76	(Zn^{2+}/Zn)	1.6	Burn if strongly heated in air or oxygen
Fe	-0.44	(Fe^{2+}/Fe)	1.8	
Pb	-0.13	(Pb^{2+}/Pb)	1.8	
Cu	$+0.34$	(Cu^{2+}/Cu)	1.9	Form oxide when heated in air
Hg	$+0.79$ $+0.85$	(Hg_2^{2+}/Hg) (Hg^{2+}/Hg)	1.9	
Ag	$+0.80$	(Ag^+/Ag)	1.9	
Pt	$+1.20$	(Pt^{2+}/Pt)	2.2	Unaffected by air or oxygen
Au	$+1.50$	(Au^{3+}/Au)	2.4	

Ease of reduction of metal cation increases

Reducing power of metal increases

Reactivity of metal decreases

Increasing electropositivity

	Reaction with water	Action of aqueous acids		Displacement of metals from aqueous solutions
K				
Na	Liberate H_2 from cold water e.g. $Na + 2H_2O \rightarrow 2NaOH + H_2$			React with water
Ca				
Mg	Burns in steam $Mg + H_2O \rightarrow MgO + H_2$	Displace hydrogen from non-oxidising acids e.g. HCl or H_2SO_4 $Fe + H_2SO_4 \rightarrow FeSO_4 + H_2$		
Al				
Zn	React with steam on heating, e.g. $3Fe + 4H_2O \rightarrow Fe_3O_4 + 4H_2$			
Fe				Displace a metal lower in the series from an aqueous solution of its salts, e.g. $Mg_{(s)} + Pb^{2+}_{(aq)} \rightarrow Mg^{2+}_{(aq)} + Pb_{(s)}$ $Cu_{(s)} + 2Ag^{+}_{(aq)} \rightarrow Cu^{2+}_{(aq)} + 2Ag_{(s)}$
Pb				
Cu		React only with oxidising acids e.g. $3Cu + 8HNO_3 \rightarrow 3Cu(NO_3)_2 + 2NO + 4H_2O$	Do not displace hydrogen from an acid	
Hg				
Ag	Do not react with water			
Pt		Do not react with acid		
Au				

Table 5.3(b)   Trends in electrochemical series: reactivity of compounds

Metal	Oxides			Hydroxides
K	Strongly basic oxides	React with water to yield an alkaline solution e.g. $Na_2O + H_2O \rightarrow 2NaOH$	Oxides not affected by heat	Soluble in water and stable to heat
Na				
Ca				Slightly soluble in water
Mg		Oxides do not react with water		
Al	Amphoteric oxides			Hydrated oxides insoluble in water
Zn				Decompose to yield oxide + water on heating
Fe	Basic			
Pb	Amphoteric			
Cu	Basic oxides			
Hg			Oxides decompose on heating e.g. $2HgO \rightarrow 2Hg + O_2$	Do not form stable hydroxides
Ag				
Pt				

100

Metal	Carbonates	Nitrates
K Na	Soluble in water and stable to heat	Yield nitrate(III) (nitrite) on heating, e.g. $2KNO_3 \rightarrow 2KNO_2 + O_2$ On strong heating yield oxide + NO_2 + O_2
Ca Mg Al Zn Fe Pb Cu	Insoluble in water. Yield oxide + CO_2 on heating, e.g. $CaCO_3 \xrightarrow{\text{heat}} CaO + CO_2$	Yield oxide + NO_2 + O_2 on heating: $M(NO_3)_2 \rightarrow$ $ MO + 2NO_2 + O_2$
Hg Ag Pt	Carbonates unstable or do not exist	Yield metal + NO_2 + O_2 on heating, e.g. $2AgNO_3 \rightarrow 2Ag + 2NO_2 + O_2$

Table 5.4   Chemical tests to distinguish the halide ions

Test	Chloride
Add a few drops of chlorine water to 2–3 cm^3 of the halide solution in a test-tube and shake with 2 cm^3 of trichloromethane (chloroform).	Colourless No reaction

$$\tfrac{1}{2}Cl_{2(aq)} \quad + \quad Br^-_{(aq)} \quad \rightarrow Cl^-_{(aq)} + \tfrac{1}{2}Br_{2(aq)}$$

oxidising agent   reducing agent
(reduced)   (oxidised)   Redox equation

↑___ electrons ___|

Both half-cell reactions in a redox process are reversible, so the direction in which a given reaction proceeds is determined by which is the stronger oxidising or reducing agent. For example, the $Fe^{2+}_{(aq)}/Fe$ electrode ($E^{\circ}_H = -0.44$ V) has a more negative electrode potential than the $Cu^{2+}_{(aq)}/Cu$ redox couple ($E^{\circ}_H = 0.34$ V) and iron is thus a weaker oxidising agent or more powerful reducing agent than copper. The oxidation of iron to iron(II) is able therefore to reverse the corresponding oxidation of copper, and copper(II) ions are reduced to metallic copper:

direction of reaction
———————————→

$$Fe \; \rightleftharpoons Fe^{2+}_{(aq)} + 2e^-$$
oxidised

$$Cu \rightleftharpoons Cu^{2+}_{(aq)} + 2e^-$$
reduced

←———————
direction of reaction

However the silver electrode ($Ag^+_{(aq)}/Ag$, $E^{\circ}_H = +0.80$ V) has a more positive electrode potential than that of copper and is thus a stronger oxidising agent. This means that $Ag^+_{(aq)}$ is more easily reduced than $Cu^{2+}_{(aq)}$ and in the reaction between the $Ag^+_{(aq)}/Ag$ and $Cu^{2+}_{(aq)}/Cu$ redox couples metallic copper is oxidised:

Appearance of lower ($CHCl_3$) layer	
Bromide	Iodide
Yellow–brown or orange $Cl_2 + 2Br^- \rightarrow 2Cl^- + Br_2$	Pink or purple $Cl_2 + 2I^- \rightarrow 2Cl^- + I_2$

direction of reaction
$\longrightarrow$

$$Cu \rightleftharpoons Cu^{2+}_{(aq)} + 2e^-$$
oxidised

$$Ag \rightleftharpoons 2Ag^+_{(aq)} + 2e^-$$
reduced

$\longleftarrow$
direction of reaction

These predictions of the feasibility of a displacement reaction refer to the conditions of the standard state and do not necessarily apply at temperatures considerably higher or lower than 298 K or with concentrations far greater or smaller than 1 M. It should also be emphasised that such predictions refer only to the *thermodynamic favourability* of the reaction and do not indicate that the reaction will proceed at a measurable rate at room temperature. For example, bubbling gaseous hydrogen through aqueous solutions of copper(II)sulphate or silver nitrate does not reduce the copper or silver ions to the metal, even though hydrogen is higher in the electrochemical series.

Experiment 5.1
Displacement reactions

(*i*) Observe what happens when the metals indicated are added to the following solutions: (a) a piece of granulated zinc to a few cm^3 of aqueous copper sulphate(VI) in a test-tube, (b) pieces of iron wire to a solution of lead nitrate, (c) a small coil of copper wire to a solution of silver nitrate. In each case write an equation for the reaction which occurs.

(*ii*) Add a few drops of chlorine water to 3–4 cm^3 of aqueous potassium chloride, potassium bromide and potassium iodide solutions in test-tubes. In each case note any colour changes which are produced and then add 1–2 cm^3 of trichloromethane (chloroform) or tetrachloromethane. Shake gently and then compare the colour of the lower (non-aqueous) layers. Repeat the experiment using a few drops of bromine water instead of chlorine water.

(*c*) *Corrosion protection*

Magnesium is higher than iron in the electrochemical series and is therefore more easily oxidised. This difference in reactivity is used to prevent expensive iron objects from rusting. The iron is attached to a piece of magnesium by a wire to ensure that the metals are in good electrical contact. The magnesium is attacked preferentially and is slowly corroded or oxidised leaving the iron unattacked.

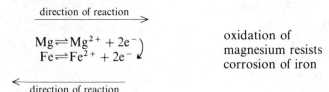

direction of reaction

$$Mg \rightleftharpoons Mg^{2+} + 2e^-$$
$$Fe \rightleftharpoons Fe^{2+} + 2e^-$$

oxidation of magnesium resists corrosion of iron

direction of reaction

This method is known as 'sacrificial protection', as the magnesium is corroded in place of the iron. Aluminium or zinc-based corrosion-resistant paints work on a similar principle.

(*d*) *The extraction of metals*

The relative ease of reducing a metal cation to the metal:

$$M^{n+} + ne^- \rightleftharpoons M$$

is represented by the standard electrode potential. This is the reaction which must be accomplished to extract a metal from its ore. Although the electrode (reduction) potentials in Table 5.1 refer to standard conditions, i.e. a temperature of 298 K at atmospheric pressure with solutions of unit activity or concentration, and metal extraction is usually carried out at high temperatures in a furnace or electrolytic cell, the electrochemical series does provide an indication of the extraction method required. The metals at the top of the series are the most powerful reducing agents and are therefore the most difficult to obtain from their ores. Electrolytic reduction of the fused chloride (or oxide in the case of aluminium) is therefore employed to extract these metals. Zinc, tin, lead and iron are easier to extract and the ores are first converted to the oxide, where necessary, and are then reduced with carbon or carbon monoxide:

$$MO + C \longrightarrow M + CO$$

$$MO + CO \longrightarrow M + CO_2$$

Silver, mercury and copper are the easiest metals to extract and metallic gold is so stable that it is usually found in the uncombined state. The extraction methods are summarised for reference in Table 5.5.

5.6
Electrochemical cells

Specific objectives: *The expected learning outcome of this section is that the student: (i) calculates the e.m.f. of a simple cell using $E°$ values only; (ii) defines the cathode as the electrode associated with reduction; (iii) defines the anode as the electrode associated with oxidation; (iv) states that the cathode of a galvanic cell is positive, and the anode is negative.*

Electrochemical (or galvanic) cells convert the chemical energy of a reaction into electrical energy (see Section 1.1). They are formed by the combination of two half-cells or electrodes which may be linked *via* a salt-bridge or by a porous partition. The standard e.m.f. of a simple cell is calculated by subtracting the standard electrode potentials of the appropriate electrodes or half-cells. For example, the Daniell cell consists essentially of a zinc electrode and copper electrode separated by a porous pot or joined by a salt-bridge (see Fig. 1.1). The cell may be written as:

$$Zn \,|\, Zn_{(aq)}^{2+} \,(c = 1 \text{ M}) \,\|\, Cu_{(aq)}^{2+} \,(c = 1 \text{ M}) \,|\, Cu$$

The standard electrode potentials of the two half-cells are:

(i) $Cu^{2+} + 2e^- \rightleftharpoons Cu$ $E_H° = +0.34$ V
(ii) $Zn^{2+} + 2e^- \rightleftharpoons Zn$ $E_H° = -0.76$ V

and the net cell reaction is the displacement of copper ions from solution by metallic zinc:

$$Cu_{(aq)}^{2+} + Zn_{(s)} \longrightarrow Cu_{(s)} + Zn_{(aq)}^{2+}$$

i.e. Equation (i) − Equation (ii). This is equivalent to the *addition* of the separate reduction and oxidation reactions:

$$(Cu^{2+} + 2e^- \longrightarrow Cu - (Zn^{2+} + 2e^- \longrightarrow Zn) =$$

$Cu^{2+} + 2e^- \longrightarrow Cu$	reduction step
$Zn \longrightarrow Zn^{2+} + 2e^-$	oxidation step
$Cu^{2+} + Zn \longrightarrow Cu + Zn^{2+}$	net redox reaction

Table 5.5 Extraction of metals

Metal	Occurrence	Principal source
K	Highly reactive (electropositive) metals – not found free in nature	$KCl.MgCl_2.6H_2O$ carnallite
Ca	As chlorides, carbonates, nitrates, sulphates	$CaCO_3$ limestone
Na		NaCl rock salt, brine and sea water (*ca* 3% NaCl)
Mg		$MgCO_3$ magnesite, $MgCO_3CaCO_3$ dolomite, carnallite Sea water (*ca* 0.13% Mg^{2+})
Al	As simple and complex oxides and silicates	$Al_2O_3.xH_2O$ bauxite
Ti		TiO_2 rutile $FeTiO_3$ ilmenite
Mn		MnO_2 pyrolusite
Zn		ZnS zinc blende
Cr		$FeO.Cr_2O_3$ chromite
Fe		Fe_2O_3 haematite, $Fe_2O_3.3H_2O$ limonite, Fe_3O_4 magnetite, $FeCO_3$ siderite
Ni		NiS (with FeS) pentlandite
Sn	As sulphides and oxides	SnO_2 tinstone (or cassiterite)
Pb		PbS galena
Cu		$CuFeS_2$ pyrites
Hg	Occasionally native	HgS cinnabar
Ag	Unreactive (noble) metals	Native and as Ag_2S argentite and AgCl horn silver
Au	Native	Native and small amounts in other ores, e.g. pyrites

Reactivity of metal decreases

	Ease of reduction	Extraction method
K		
Ca		Electrolytic reduction of fused chloride $M^{n+} + ne^- \longrightarrow M$ (at cathode) $2Cl^- \longrightarrow Cl_2 + 2e^-$ (at carbon anode)
Na		
Mg		
Al		Electrolysis of purified oxide dissolved in molten cryolite (Na_3AlF_6) at 1200 K: $Al^{3+} + 3e^- \longrightarrow Al$ (at cathode) $2O^{2-} \longrightarrow O_2 + 4e^-$ (at carbon anode)
Ti		Reduction of chloride with Mg or Na $TiCl_4 + 2Mg \longrightarrow Ti + 2MgCl_2$
Mn		Reduction of oxide with C or Al
Zn		Reduction of oxide with C/CO or electrolysis
Cr		Reduction of oxide with C or electrolysis (for chromium plating)
Fe		
Ni		
Sn		Sulphide roasted to oxide and oxides reduced by C/CO
Pb		
Cu		
Hg		Sulphide roasted in air $HgS + O_2 \xrightarrow{\; >800\ K\;} Hg + SO_2$
Ag		Displaced from cyanide solution by zinc e.g. $2[Ag(CN)_2]^- + Zn + 4OH^- \rightarrow 2Ag + [Zn(OH)_4]^{2-} + 4CN^-$
Au		

Ease of reduction $M^{n+} + ne^- \longrightarrow M$ increases

Ease of reduction to metal $M^{n+} + ne^-$

The e.m.f. of the cell under standard conditions, $E°$ is given by:

$(E_H°$ for Cu^{2+}/Cu electrode$) - (E_H°$ for Zn^{2+}/Zn electrode$)$
$= +0.34 - (-0.76) = +1.10$ V

Sign convention
If the cell e.m.f. is calculated as described above, i.e. $E° = E_H°$ for the right-hand electrode in the cell diagram minus $E_H°$ for the left-hand electrode, the sign of the cell e.m.f. gives the polarity of the right-hand electrode. The cathode of a galvanic cell is positive and the anode is negative. A positive e.m.f. indicates that the cell reaction is thermodynamically favourable and can occur spontaneously as it takes place with the liberation of energy. As the electrode reactions of the cell indicate, the *cathode* is the electrode which is associated with *reduction*, while the *anode* is associated with *oxidation*. The electrons travel from the anode to the cathode in the wires of the external circuit:

electrons in external circuit

$(-)$ $\qquad\qquad\qquad\qquad\qquad\qquad (+)$

$Zn|Zn^{2+}_{(aq)}$ $\qquad\qquad\qquad\qquad\qquad Cu^{2+}_{(aq)}|Cu$

anode $\qquad\qquad ||\qquad\qquad\qquad$ cathode

$Zn \xrightarrow{\text{oxidation}} Zn^{2+} + (2e^-) \qquad Cu^{2+} + (2e^-) \xrightarrow{\text{reduction}} Cu$

A negative cell e.m.f. indicates that the cell reaction, as written directly from the cell diagram, is not thermodynamically favourable and would require energy from an external source to occur. However, by reversing the cell diagram (and the equation for the cell reaction) a thermodynamically favourable reaction would be obtained (see Example 5.1). The cathode of an electrochemical cell is always the terminal with the more positive electrode potential, i.e. the metal or non-metal which is the stronger oxidising agent and is thus more easily reduced. The cell e.m.f. is the difference between the two electrode potentials as indicated in the chart in fig. 5.8.

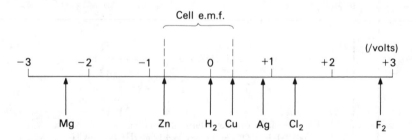

Fig. 5.8 Chart for the determination of cell e.m.f.

Example 5.1

Calculate the standard e.m.f. of the following cell:

$$\text{Sn} \,|\, \text{Sn}^{2+}_{(aq)} \,(c = 1 \text{ M}) \,\|\, \text{Mg}^{2+}_{(aq)} \,(c = 1 \text{ M}) \,|\, \text{Mg}$$

Write an equation for the spontaneous cell reaction which occurs and state which electrode is the cathode.

Solution

From the values of the standard electrode potentials in Table 5.1,

$$
\begin{aligned}
\text{cell e.m.f.} &= E^\circ_H \text{ (for the right-hand electrode)} \\
&\quad - E^\circ_H \text{ (for the left-hand electrode)} \\
&= E^\circ_H (\text{Mg}^{2+} \,|\, \text{Mg}) - E^\circ_H (\text{Sn}^{2+} \,|\, \text{Sn}) \\
&= -2.21 - (-0.14) = -2.07 \text{ V}
\end{aligned}
$$

The right-hand electrode (the magnesium electrode) thus has a negative charge and is the anode, for which the electrode reaction is

$$\text{Mg} \longrightarrow \text{Mg}^{2+} + 2e^- \text{ (oxidation).}$$

The left-hand electrode (the tin electrode) is the cathode, for which the electrode reaction involves reduction:

$$\text{Sn}^{2+} + 2e^- \longrightarrow \text{Sn (reduction).}$$

The overall, spontaneous (thermodynamically favourable) reaction is thus:

$$\text{Mg} + \text{Sn}^{2+}_{(aq)} \longrightarrow \text{Mg}^{2+}_{(aq)} + \text{Sn}_{(s)}$$

Summary

1. An equilibrium is set up when a metal is placed in a solution of its ions: $\text{M}_{(s)} \rightleftharpoons \text{M}^{n+}_{(aq)} + ne^-$. This equilibrium results in a potential difference between the solution and the metal and the system is known as an *electrode* or *half-cell*.

2. The standard hydrogen electrode is used as the reference for the measurement of electrode potentials:

$$\underbrace{\text{Pt, H}_2 \,(1 \text{ atm}) \,|\, \text{H}^+_{(aq)} \,(a = 1)}_{\text{standard hydrogen electrode}} \,\|\, \text{M}^{n+}_{(aq)} \,(1 \text{ M}) \,|\, \text{M}_{(s)}$$

Cell e.m.f. at 298 K = standard electrode potential of M^{n+}/M electrode. By convention, the standard electrode potential, E°_H, of the standard hydrogen electrode at 298 K is zero.

3. A metal which has a greater tendency to form cations than has hydrogen (i.e. is a more powerful reducing agent than hydrogen) has a negative standard electrode potential.

4. Standard electrode potentials apply for solutions of unit activity (or concentration) at a pressure of one atmosphere ($101\,325$ Nm^{-2}) and a temperature of 298 K ($25°C$).

5. The electrochemical series is obtained by arranging the elements in order of increasing standard electrode potential.

6. The reactivity of metals decreases down the electrochemical series.

7. Any metal above hydrogen in the electrochemical series will displace hydrogen from a solution of its ions.

8. Any metal will displace one lower in the series from a solution of its ions.

9. Displacement reactions are examples of redox processes. Electrons are transferred from the reducing agent (electron donor) to the oxidising agent (electron acceptor).

10. Predictions based on the electrochemical series refer to the feasibility of reactions at 298 K. They indicate only whether the reaction is thermodynamically favourable, and not that it will proceed at a measurable rate at the conditions of the standard state.

11. An electrochemical (or galvanic) cell converts chemical energy of a reaction into electrical energy.

12. The standard e.m.f. of a galvanic cell is calculated by subtracting the less positive E_H° (standard electrode potential) from the more positive value.

13. In a galvanic cell, the cathode (or positive electrode) is associated with reduction and the anode (or negative electrode) is associated with reduction.

Questions

1. Explain, with a suitable example in each case, what is meant by (a) a half-cell, (b) a metal electrode and (c) a gas electrode.

2. Explain why there is a potential difference between a metal and the

solution of its ions in contact with it. How is this potential difference measured?

3. What is a 'salt-bridge'? What is it used for?

4. Define (a) electrode potential and (b) standard electrode potential.

5. What is the standard hydrogen electrode?

6. State the temperature, pressure and solution concentration which are employed for measurements of standard electrode potentials.

7. Why does an increase in the concentration of the cations in contact with a metal affect the electrode potential?

8. What is the electrochemical series? Give three examples of its use.

9. Discuss (with reference to suitable examples) the relationship between a metal's position in the electrochemical series and the method used to extract the metal from its ore.

10. Explain the displacement reactions of (a) the halogens and (b) $Zn_{(s)}/Cu^{2+}_{(aq)}$ and $Cu_{(s)}/Ag^{+}_{(aq)}$ in terms of electron transfer using the standard electrode potentials listed in Table 5.1.

11. Discuss (with reference to suitable examples) the relationship between the position of an element in the electrochemical series and (a) its reactivity and (b) the chemical properties of its compounds.

12. Hydrogen is evolved when iron and zinc (but not copper) is treated with an aqueous solution of an acid. How do you account for this observation?

13. Describe (and explain) the tests you would use to distinguish a chloride from a bromide and an iodide.

14. Explain how magnesium or zinc may be used to protect iron from corrosion (rusting).

15. What is an electrochemical cell? Describe with reference to suitable examples the general reactions which occur at the anode and cathode of such a cell.

16. Use the data in Table 5.1 to calculate the standard cell e.m.f. and give the chemical equations for the spontaneous reactions which occur in the following cells:

(a) $H_2(p = 1 \text{ atm})|H^+_{(aq)} (a = 1)\|Zn^{2+}_{(aq)}|Zn;$

(b) $Fe|Fe^{2+}_{(aq)}\|Pb^{2+}_{(aq)}|Pb;$

(c) $Cu|Cu^{2+}_{(aq)}\|Pb^{2+}_{(aq)}|Pb;$

(d) $Ag|Ag^+_{(aq)}\|Fe^{2+}_{(aq)}|Fe;$

(e) $Mg|Mg^{2+}_{(aq)}\|Cu^{2+}_{(aq)}|Cu.$

Solutions are of unit activity.

D The colloidal state

6 Properties of colloidal systems

General objective: *The expected learning outcome of this chapter is that the student is able to describe some aspects of the colloidal state.*

6.1
Introduction

Specific objective: *The expected learning outcome of this section is that the student recognises the difference between true solution, colloidal solutions and suspensions in terms of particle size.*

(*a*) *Distinctions between colloidal systems, suspensions and true solutions*
Depending on its solubility and on the size and nature of the particles produced, a solid may be dispersed in a liquid in three different ways. The two extremes are the *true solution* and the *suspension*. In a true solution the substance (which is known as the *solute*) dissolves completely in the liquid (or *solvent*) to form a uniform or homogeneous solution, i.e. it consists of a single phase only, thus:

solute + solvent = solution.

A true solution may be defined as *a homogeneous mixture of two or more components.*

The solute is present in solution as neutral, covalent molecules or, as in the case of strong electrolytes (see Section 4.1), the substance is dispersed in the liquid phase in the form of charged ions. Once a solution has been prepared and mixed well it will remain as a single uniform phase and will not separate out under gravity on standing. The individual molecules or ions of the solute cannot be removed by filtration, nor can the particles be seen under a microscope.

The solid particles in a *suspension* are considerably larger, and will settle to the bottom or top of the container and separate out on standing or on centrifugation. Examples of suspensions include iron filings, powdered carbon or iron oxide and water. The system consists of two phases: the solid particles of the suspended substance and the liquid, and is therefore *heterogeneous*. The particles of a suspension can be seen under a simple light microscope and may be separated from the liquid by filtration.

The *colloidal state* is intermediate between the true solution and the suspension. The solid (or *disperse phase*) is distributed in the liquid, or *dispersion medium*, either as very large individual molecules (e.g. proteins, polymers or other macromolecules) or is present as aggregates of molecules, known as *micelles*. The particles are larger than the individual molecules or ions in a true solution, but are smaller than the particles of a suspension (see Table 6.1).

Table 6.1   Particle size in solution

Type of dispersion	Particle size (/metre)
True solution (free ions or molecules)	$< 10^{-9}$
Colloidal particles	10^{-9}–10^{-7}
Suspension	$> 10^{-7}$

An *emulsion*, e.g. of oil in water, is a colloidal dispersion of one liquid in another, while an *aerosol* is a colloidal suspension of a liquid in air. Other classes of colloidal dispersion are listed in Table 6.2. All gases are completely miscible, so it is not possible to have a two phase gas–gas dispersion.

The resolution limit of the light microscope is about 500 nm so the particles of a substance in the colloidal state are too small to be seen

Table 6.2   Classification of colloidal systems

Disperse phase	Dispersion medium	Class	Examples
Gas	Liquid	Foam	Whipped cream
Gas	Solid	Solid foam	Pumice, polyurethane foam
Liquid	Gas	Aerosol	Fog, mist, clouds
Liquid	Liquid	Emulsion	Milk, cream
Liquid	Solid	Solid emulsion	Butter
Solid	Gas	Smoke	Smoke
Solid	Liquid	Sol	Paint
Solid	Solid	Solid sol	Some alloys, opals and many other gemstones, coloured glass

using an optical microscope, although they are visible under the enormous magnification of the electron microscope. The particles will pass through a filter paper and will not separate out under gravity on standing; however, some separation is obtained on spinning the colloidal suspension extremely fast in an ultracentrifuge. Centrifugation in an ultracentrifuge is one of the techniques used to fractionate proteins and other mixtures of substances whose large molecular size brings them into the range covered by the colloidal state. The soluble proteins in blood plasma, for example, may be divided by centrifugation into a number of fractions according to their relative molecular masses.

This classification into true solutions, colloidal solutions and suspensions is somewhat arbitrary and it is possible for a substance to be dispersed in a liquid in all three states. A substance distributed in a liquid to form the colloidal state is known as a *sol*. As a result of the small particle size, a substance distributed in a liquid in colloidal form has an enormous surface area. This is reflected in their catalytic ability (see Section 3.1(*a*) and (*e*)) and in the ready adsorption of dyes or other substances from solution. The distinction between *adsorption* and *absorption* is an important one. A solid may take up material by both methods, but adsorption refers to that adhering to the surface while absorbed material is taken into the entire volume of the solid in the same way that a sponge soaks up water.

(*b*) Preparation of colloids
The methods of preparing a substance in the colloidal state may be classified as either *condensation* or *dispersion* methods, depending (respectively) on whether the particles of colloidal size are formed by combining smaller particles together, or by breaking larger masses into fragments.

Condensation methods
(*i*) Precipitation by chemical reaction
This method is probably the most widely used and has been employed for the preparation of sols of metals (e.g. gold and silver), non-metallic elements (such as sulphur or phosphorus) and a wide range of inorganic substances. For example, a colloidal solution of hydrated iron(III)-oxide (ferric 'hydroxide') may be prepared by stirring a few cm^3 of concentrated iron(III)chloride solution into a large volume of warm water. The iron(III)chloride is hydrolysed:

$$FeCl_{3(aq)} + 3H_2O \xrightarrow[\text{water at 70–80}°]{\text{large volume of}} \text{`Fe(OH)}_{3(s)}\text{'} + 3HCl_{(aq)}$$
$$\text{brown-red}$$

but owing to the dispersion of the reactant in such a large volume, precipitation and particle growth do not proceed beyond colloidal size.

Hydrated aluminium(III)oxide is formed as a gelatinous, partly colloidal precipitate by the addition of aqueous ammonia to an aqueous solution of an aluminium salt:

$$Al^{3+}_{(aq)} + 3OH^-_{(aq)} \longrightarrow \text{`}Al(OH_3)_{(s)}\text{'}$$

Gold or silver sols may be prepared by reducing aqueous solutions of the corresponding metal salts with phosphine, methanal (formaldehyde), tannic acid or other non-ionic reducing agents:

$$Ag^+_{(aq)} \qquad + e^- \longrightarrow \qquad Ag_{(s)}$$

e.g. as $AgNO_{3(aq)}$ a brown sol

Sulphur is frequently obtained in a non-filterable, colloidal form by passing hydrogen sulphide into an acidified solution of an oxidising agent, such as sodium dichromate(VI).

(ii) Change of dispersion medium

Some substances may be converted into the colloidal state by simply adding a second solvent to a solution of the material. For example, the addition of water to a solution of phosphorus in ethanol causes phosphorus to separate in colloidal form. Similarly, a silver iodide sol is obtained if a solution of silver iodide in aqueous potassium iodide is diluted with a large volume of water:

$$\underset{\text{soluble in aqueous KI}}{K^+[AgI_2]^-_{(aq)}} \xrightarrow{\text{excess of water}} \underset{\text{colloidal}}{AgI_{(s)}} + KI_{(aq)}$$

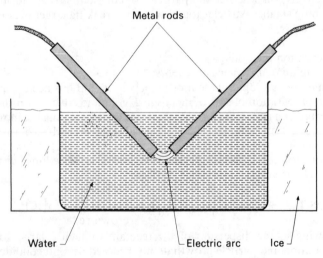

Fig. 6.1 Bredig's arc

(*iii*) *Bredig's arc* (*1898*)
This method may be used to prepare sols of gold, silver, copper, platinum and other metals. An electric arc is struck between two electrodes of the metal which are submerged in water in a vessel cooled in ice (see fig. 6.1). Immense heat is produced which melts and vaporises some of the metal. The metal is formed in the colloidal state by the sudden cooling of its vapour by the water. The method is therefore a condensation rather than a dispersion process. Larger particles of metal are removed from the sol by filtration.

Dispersion methods
(*i*) *Direct solution*
Gum, glue, egg albumen, gelatin and other substances of high molecular mass (i.e. *macromolecules*) yield a colloidal solution on warming with the solvent.

(*ii*) *Colloid mill*
As its name implies, the colloid mill acts by grinding the material into fine particles between metal plates or concentric cones revolving in opposite directions. The coarser granules are removed by filtration and the colloidal solution is collected as the filtrate.

Experiment 6.1
Preparation of colloidal solutions

(*a*) *Hydrated iron(III)oxide* Pour 5 cm^3 of aqueous 30% iron(III)-chloride solution with stirring into 250 cm^3 of boiling distilled water. Note the formation of the red, stable hydrated iron(III)oxide sol.
(*b*) *Starch* Stir about 0.2 g of starch into about 250 cm^3 of hot water and note the formation of a pale, opalescent sol which passes through a filter paper.
(*c*) *Gelatin* This sol is prepared by stirring about 2 g of powdered gelatin into 250 cm^3 of water at 90°.
(*d*) *Silver sol* Add 1 cm^3 of a 1% solution of hydrazine, or tannin, drop by drop to about 100 cm^3 of 0.01 M aqueous silver nitrate solution containing 1–2 cm^3 of 2 M aqueous ammonia. Note the formation of a silver sol.
(*e*) *Sulphur* Method (i) Add dilute hydrochloric acid drop by drop to a 0.2 M aqueous solution of sodium thiosulphate. Note the slow formation of a milky suspension of colloidal sulphur:

$$S_2O_{3(aq)}^{2-} + 2H_{(aq)}^+ \longrightarrow S_{(s)} + SO_{2(g)} + H_2O$$

Method (ii) Pass hydrogen sulphide (*Care*: this gas is highly toxic so the preparation must be carried out in a fume-cupboard) into a 3% aqueous solution of sodium dichromate(VI) acidified with dilute sulphuric acid. Note the colour changes and the gradual formation of colloidal sulphur.

These sols may be used to demonstrate the properties of colloidal solutions (see **Experiment 6.2**).

6.2
Classification of colloids

Specific objective: *The expected learning outcome of this section is that the student states the characteristics of lyophobic and lyophilic colloids.*

Colloids are classified according to their stability as *lyophobic* (from two Greek words meaning 'solvent hating', i.e. low stability) and *lyophilic* (Greek: 'solvent loving', i.e. very stable). The corresponding terms when the dispersion medium is water are *hydrophobic* and *hydrophilic* respectively. Examples of lyophilic (hydrophilic) colloids include gelatin, gum and egg albumen. Lyophilic colloids are often readily prepared by direct solution. The process is reversible and the material reverts to the *gel form* on dehydration:

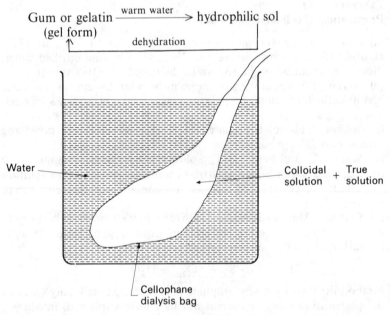

Fig. 6.2 Dialysis: Separation of colloidal particles from a true solution

Lyophobic (or hydrophobic) colloids, such as hydrated iron(III)oxide, gold, silver and other metal sols, are much less stable and are easily precipitated by the addition of electrolytes or boiling. They do not revert to the colloidal state after dehydration. Small amounts of gelatin or other highly stable lyophilic colloids are often added to metal sols to protect or stabilise them. These substances are known as *stabilising agents* or *protective colloids*. This stabilisation also applies to liquid–liquid colloidal systems. For example, mayonnaise (an emulsion of corn oil or other edible oil in water) is stabilised by egg yolk. The egg protein forms a protective layer around the oil droplets and stabilises them. The protein *casein* acts as a stabiliser in milk where it stabilises the emulsion of butterfat in the aqueous solution.

Most lyophilic colloids are macromolecules and are best prepared by dispersion methods. Lyophobic colloids are usually aggregates of molecules or atoms of a substance which is normally insoluble. Hydrophilic sols are best prepared by chemical methods.

**6.3
Dialysis**

Specific objective: *The expected learning outcome of this section is that the student describes the effect of dialysis on colloidal sols.*

Because of their smaller size, the ions or molecules in a true solution diffuse faster than the micelles or macromolecules of the colloidal suspension. This property may be used to separate a sol from a true solution. The mixture is divided from the pure solvent by a membrane made of cellophane, parchment or other suitable material. Gradually, the faster solute particles of the true solution diffuse through the membrane leaving most of the larger particles of the colloidal suspension behind (see fig. 6.2). This process was discovered by Graham in 1861 and is known as *dialysis*. The technique is frequently used to separate and purify sols, including proteins, hormones and other naturally occurring macromolecules.

The dialysis membrane allows *both* types of particle to pass through it, but because the ions and other small molecules in a true solution diffuse hundreds of times faster than gelatin, starch or large protein molecules, a satisfactory separation may be obtained. Dialysis is therefore distinct from osmosis, where only the solvent (and not the solute) is able to pass through the semi-permeable membrane. Kidney machines depend on dialysis to separate urea and other small toxic molecules from the blood.

6.4
Electrophoresis

Specific objective: *The expected learning outcome of this section is that the student describes electrophoresis in terms of migration of charged colloidal particles in an electrical field.*

The particles of a colloidal suspension usually carry an electrical charge. This charge is gained by the adsorption of ions (usually $H^+_{(aq)}$ or $OH^-_{(aq)}$) from the dispersion medium or by the transference of electrons. The colloidal particles (disperse phase) and the dispersion medium thus have an equal and opposite charge and will tend to move in opposite directions in an electrical field. This migration of particles in an electrical field is known as *electrophoresis*. Examples of positively and negatively charged colloids are listed in Table 6.3.

Table 6.3   Electrical charges of common sols

Positive colloids	Negative colloids
Hydrated aluminium(III)oxide	Sulphur
Hydrated iron(III)oxide	Arsenic(III)sulphide
	Silicic acid
	Gold, silver, platinum
	Gum, gelatin

The movement of the strongly coloured gold or hydrated iron(III)-oxide sols in an electrical field may be demonstrated using the apparatus shown in fig. 6.3. The U-tube is filled with the sol and a potential difference of about 200 V is applied between the two platinum electrodes. The movement of the negative gold sol towards the anode, or of the positively charged hydrated iron(III)oxide towards the cathode, is shown by the concentration of the colour around the relevant electrode. Electrophoresis may also be demonstrated by the micro-method of observing the movement of individual 'particles' for short periods under the influence of an electric field under the ultramicroscope (see Section 6.6(*b*)).

Electrophoresis may be used to separate proteins in solution. The charge on different protein molecules is strongly dependent on pH and by controlling the pH of the solution with a buffer (see Section 4.5) a separation of the different protein molecules may be obtained. Electrophoresis is used in industry to 'plate' latex from a colloidal solution

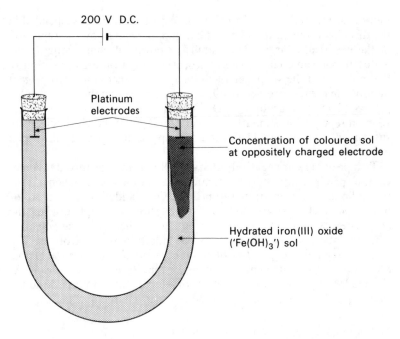

Fig. 6.3 Electrophoresis

of rubber onto metals and to paint or rustproof car bodies. The charged particles of latex, paint etc. are attracted to the metal by giving it an opposite charge.

6.5
Precipitation of colloids: effect of electrolytes

Specific objective: *The expected learning outcome of this section is that the student describes qualitatively the effect of the addition of electrolytes to colloidal solutions (Hardy–Schultze rule).*

Two factors prevent the particles of the disperse phase in a colloidal solution from coming together to form larger masses which separate out as a suspension under the influence of gravity. These are: (a) the repulsion of the electrical charges on the particles and (b) the kinetic energy (thermal motion) of the molecules of the dispersion medium. The molecules of the dispersion medium are moving about rapidly at random and colliding with the particles of the colloidal sol. This thermal motion of the molecules of the liquid keeps the particles suspended in the dispersion medium and coagulation is prevented by the repulsion of the electrical charges. The stabilising power of emulsifying agents is due to the same effect. The hydrocarbon (hydrophobic) portion of the molecule of the soap, detergent, protein or other emulsifying agent dissolves in the fine droplets of oil, fat or grease leaving the water soluble (hydrophilic) ionic group ($-CO_2^-$, $-NH_3^+$ or $-SO_3^-$) on the surface where it repels other similarly charged droplets and thereby keeps them suspended in the water. The action of soaps or detergents is illustrated in fig. 6.4.

Two positively or negatively charged colloids may be mixed together without precipitation, but immediate precipitation occurs when a positive colloid, such as hydrated iron(III)oxide, is added to a silver sol or other negatively charged colloid. Precipitation is complete when the charges exactly cancel one another out, i.e. at the *isoelectric point*.

Coagulation is also induced by the addition of electrolytes. *The precipitating effect of an electrolyte on a colloid depends on the charge of the ion.* This statement is known as the *Hardy–Schultze rule.* As expected, the precipitating effect of ions for equal amounts of added electrolyte depends on the magnitude of their charge and increases in the order:

Precipitation of negatively charged colloids

Na^+	Mg^{2+}	Al^{3+}
K^+ $<$	Ca^{2+} $<$	
NH_4^+	Zn^{2+}	Fe^{3+}
	Cu^{2+}	
	Fe^{2+}	

Precipitation of positively charged colloids

Cl^-	SO_4^{2-}	
Br^- $<$		$<$ PO_4^{3-}
I^-	CO_3^{2-}	
NO_3^-		

$$\xrightarrow{\hspace{4cm}}$$
precipitating effect increases

The relative magnitude of the increasing precipitating effect of univalent, divalent and trivalent ions is approximately 1:50–100:1000 respectively. Lyophilic colloids are much more resistant to precipitation by added electrolytes than lyophobic colloids. The particles of a lyophilic colloid are highly solvated, while the stability of lyophobic colloids is dependent mainly on adsorbed ions.

Examples of the precipitating effect of electrolytes on substances in the colloidal state include the purification of water by adding aluminium sulphate to separate out suspensions of bacteria and fine particles of clay and the use of alum, $K_2SO_4.Al_2(SO_4)_3.24H_2O$, to coagulate blood.

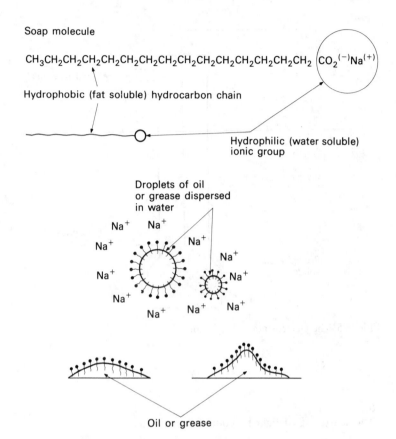

Fig. 6.4 Action of a soap or detergent

The formation of the huge triangular mudflats (known as 'deltas') at the mouth of the Nile, Mississippi and other rivers is explained by the precipitation of the colloidal clay particles in river water as it meets the salts dissolved in the sea. Large amounts of electrolytes are also used to 'salt out' proteins and other colloidal macromolecules from solution.

Electrostatic precipitation
The electrical charge on fine particles of smoke, blast furnace dust and other solid pollutants in flue gases etc. is used to separate them in the electrostatic precipitator (see fig. 6.5). The gases are passed between plates maintained at a high potential. The particles of dust are attracted to the oppositely charged plate where they separate out.

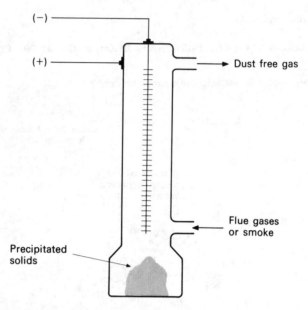

Fig. 6.5 The electrostatic precipitator

6.6
The scattering of light by colloidal particles

Specific objective: *The expected learning outcome of this section is that the student recognises the Tyndall beam effect and gives a reason for it.*

(a) *The Tyndall beam effect*
The path of a beam of light is visible when it is passing through a colloidal solution (see fig. 6.6), but not when it is passing through a true solution. This was first discovered by Tyndall in 1869 and is known as the *Tyndall beam effect*. The visibility of the path of the beam is due to the scattering of light by the colloidal particles. A similar effect is seen when beams of sunlight pass through a smokey, misty or dust-laden atmosphere. Light scattering also accounts for the colour (see Section 6.6(c)) and opalescent appearance of many colloidal solutions compared with the transparency of true solutions and the opaqueness of a suspension. The Tyndall effect following filtration is the easiest method of characterising a colloid.

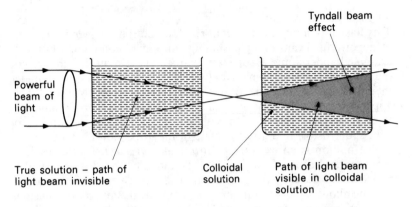

Fig. 6.6 The Tyndall beam effect

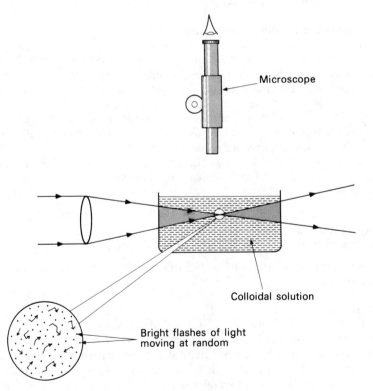

Fig. 6.7 The ultramicroscope

(*b*) *Brownian movement*
Tiny flashes of light in continuous random motion are seen if the focus of a powerful beam of light shining through a colloidal solution is examined under a microscope (see fig. 6.7). These spots of light are not the colloidal particles themselves (which are too small to be seen under the microscope), but the flashes of light scattered by them. This apparatus is known as the *ultramicroscope* and was used by Zsigmondy to estimate the diameter of the colloidal particles from the number of light spots visible in a given volume of the dispersion medium.

The motion is an example of *Brownian movement*. It is a result of the bombardment of the small colloidal particles by the smaller molecules of the dispersion medium. The molecules of the liquid are moving about rapidly at random and, if, in any instant, more collisions occur on one side of the particle than the other the particle is displaced first in one direction and then in another. This phenomenon was discovered by the botanist Robert Brown, in 1827, who noticed that pollen grains suspended in water appeared to be in continuous motion when observed under the microscope.

(*c*) *The colour of colloidal solutions*
Colloidal solutions are sometimes coloured, for example gold sols are usually red or blue. The different colours are determined by the size and shape of the particles and are produced by the scattering of light. For example, the particles in blue gold sols are larger and less symmetrical than those in the red sol. The size of the particles is of a similar order of magnitude as the wavelength of visible light (*cf.* approximate wavelength of blue and red light = 450–500 and 620–750 nm respectively; approximate diameter of colloidal particles = 1–100 nm). The colour of a sunset is also caused by light scattering, in this case by particles of dust, smoke or droplets of moisture in the atmosphere.

Experiment 6.2
To demonstrate the properties of colloidal solutions

The preparation of the sols used in this demonstration was described in Experiment 6.1.

(*a*) *Dialysis*
Fill a dialysis bag with the hydrated iron(III)oxide sol/dilute hydrochloric acid mixture obtained by the hydrolysis of iron(III)chloride (see Experiment 6.1(*a*)), but do not tie it at the top. Suspend the bag in a beaker of distilled water and allow it to stand overnight. Test the water in the beaker with (a) universal indicator paper and (b) 1–2 cm^3 of aqueous silver nitrate solution. Compare the colours of the solutions

in the bag and in the beaker. How do you account for the results obtained?

This experiment may also be carried out with the dialysis bag filled with a starch sol (see Experiment 6.1(*b*)) containing a few cm^3 of 10% sodium chloride solution. After 6–8 hours test samples of the water in the beaker with aqueous silver nitrate and with 1 cm^3 of a 1% aqueous solution of iodine. Repeat the iodine test with 1–2 cm^3 of the solution from the dialysis bag.

(*b*) *Precipitation of colloids*
(i) Add a few cm^3 of the hydrated iron(III)oxide sol drop by drop to test-tubes containing 4–5 cm^3 of sols of hydrated aluminium(III)-oxide, sulphur, silver and starch and note which solutions become turbid (see Table 6.3).
(ii) Investigate the effect of adding 0.1 M solutions of potassium nitrate, calcium nitrate and aluminium nitrate drop by drop to 3–4 cm^3 of (a) the hydrated iron(III)oxide sol and (b) a sulphur or silver sol. Compare the volumes of the electrolyte solution required to produce turbidity by coagulation of the sol. How do you interpret your observations?
(iii) Add 0.1 M solutions of sodium chloride, sodium sulphate and sodium citrate drop by drop to tubes containing 7–8 cm^3 of hydrated iron(III)oxide sol.
How do you account for the difference in the volumes of electrolyte required to produce coagulation?

(*c*) *Tyndall beam effect*
Use a convex lens and slide projector (see fig. 6.6) to pass a strong beam of light through a hydrated iron(III)oxide or sulphur sol contained in a glass or Perspex vessel with plane, parallel sides. Filter or centrifuge the sol and return it to the container and again pass a beam of light through it. Compare the effect of passing the light beam through an aqueous solution of sodium chloride.

Empty the glass container and wash it out with distilled water before refilling it with a 0.1 M solution of sodium thiosulphate. Project a beam of light through the solution at a white screen and note what happens when a few cm^3 of dilute hydrochloric acid are added to the thiosulphate solution.

(*d*) *Brownian movement and light scattering*
Focus a microscope onto the point at which the beam of light in Experiment 6.2(*c*) converges in a hydrated iron(III)oxide sol. Attempt to draw the path followed by an individual point of light over a period of about 20 seconds.

Summary

1. The principal differences in the properties of true solutions, colloidal solutions and suspensions are summarised in Table 6.4.

2. Substances may be obtained in the colloidal state by: (a) precipitation, (b) Bredig's arc, (c) direct solution, (d) grinding particles to colloidal size (see Section 6.1(b)).

3. Lyophilic (or, when the dispersion medium is water, hydrophilic) colloids are more stable than lyophobic (hydrophobic) colloids.

4. Ions and small molecules present as a true solution may be separated from substances dispersed in the colloidal state by dialysis (see Section 6.3).

5. Metal sols are stabilised (protected) by the addition of small amounts of gelatin or other lyophilic colloids.

6. Colloidal particles are usually electrically charged owing to the adsorption of $H_{(aq)}^+$, $OH_{(aq)}^-$ or other ions from the dispersion medium. These charged colloidal particles migrate to the oppositely charged electrode in an electrical field. This process is known as *electrophoresis*.

7. The coagulation of colloidal particles is normally prevented by the thermal motion of the molecules of the dispersion medium and by the repulsion of the electrical charges adsorbed on the colloidal particles.

8. The precipitating effect of an electrolyte on a colloidal solution depends on the magnitude of the charge on the oppositely charged ion (*Hardy-Schultze rule*).

9. The path of a beam of light through a colloidal solution is made visible by the scattering of light by the colloidal particles (*Tyndall beam effect*).

10. The colour of colloidal solutions is largely a result of light scattering. A red sol consists of smaller particles than a blue sol.

Table 6.4 Comparison of true solutions, colloidal solutions and suspensions

Property	True solution	Colloidal solution	Suspension
Particle size (/m)	$< 10^{-9}$	10^{-9}–10^{-7}	$> 10^{-7}$
Visibility of particles under light microscope	Invisible	Invisible	Visible
Nature of dispersed particles	Ions or molecules	Macromolecules or aggregates of molecules (micelles)	Grains of insoluble solid
Number of phases	1	2	2
Homogeneity	Homogeneous	Intermediate	Heterogeneous
Filterability of particles	Passes through filter paper	Passes through filter paper	Can be filtered
Effect of light	Transparent	Generally translucent. Shows Tyndall beam effect.	Opaque or translucent

Questions

1. What is (a) a true solution and (b) a suspension? Give three examples of each and describe three tests which could be used to distinguish between the two classes.

2. What is a colloidal solution? Describe two methods of preparing substances in this state.

3. What are the principal differences between a true solution, a colloidal solution and a suspension?

4. What is (a) an emulsion and (b) an aerosol? Give two examples of each.

5. Explain what is meant by the following terms: (a) disperse phase, (b) dispersion medium, (c) micelle, (d) a sol, (e) dialysis, (f) protective colloid (or stabilising agent).

6. What is the difference between absorption and adsorption? Explain why a sol, such as hydrated aluminium(III)oxide, is able to adsorb a large amount of a water-soluble dye.

7. Describe the action of soap or detergent in dispersing droplets of oil or grease.

8. Distinguish between the terms: 'lyophobic' and 'lyophilic' when they are applied to a substance in the colloidal state.

9. What is meant by the term 'electrophoresis'? Describe how you would demonstrate the process using a suitable colloidal solution.

10. Why do colloidal particles usually carry an electrical charge?

11. What is 'dialysis'? Describe how you would separate a sol of hydrated iron(III)oxide from an aqueous solution of sodium chloride.

12. Why is it important to control the pH of a solution containing a mixture of proteins when they are being separated by electrophoresis? Give two other applications of electrophoresis in industry.

13. Why don't colloidal particles settle to the bottom of the container on standing?

14. Discuss the relationship between the charge on an ion and its precipitating effect on a colloid of opposite charge.

15. Describe and explain three examples of the precipitating effect of electrolytes on substances in the colloidal state.

16. What is the Tyndall beam effect and how do you account for it?

17. What is Brownian movement? Describe how you would demonstrate this motion of particles in the colloidal state.

E The periodic table and the properties of the elements

7 The Periodic Table

General objective: *The expected learning outcome of this chapter is that the student describes the periodic table in terms of periodic functions.*

7.1
Definitions

The *relative atomic mass* (RAM or A_r) of an element =

$$\frac{\text{Mean mass of 1 atom of element}}{\frac{1}{12} \text{ of mass of 1 atom of carbon–12}}$$

The *relative molecular mass* (RMM or M_r) of a substance =

$$\frac{\text{Mean mass of 1 molecule of the substance}}{\frac{1}{12} \text{ of mass of 1 atom of carbon–12}}$$

The *atomic number* of an element is equal to the number of protons (or the number of electrons) in a neutral atom of the element. It is also equal to the order of the element in the Periodic Table (see Section 7.2) and, with few exceptions – such as the placing of potassium (RAM = 39.10) and argon (RAM = 39.95) – it is the same as the position of the element in a list of increasing relative atomic mass. Atomic number is usually given the symbol, Z.

The *mass number* (A) of an atom is equal to the sum of the number of protons and neutrons in its nucleus. From these definitions it follows that:

Number of neutrons in an atom = Mass number − Atomic number = $A - Z$. By convention, the mass number and atomic number of an atom are written as a superscript and subscript, respectively, to the symbol of the element to distinguish between the various nuclides.

For example, naturally occurring chlorine (RAM 35.45) consists of a mixture of the isotopes:

Mass number —
$^{35}_{17}Cl$ and $^{37}_{17}Cl$
Atomic number —

Number of protons	17	17
Number of electrons	17	17
Number of neutrons	18	20

in such a proportion (approx. 75% $^{35}_{17}Cl$:25% $^{37}_{17}Cl$) to give a mean relative atomic mass of 35.5.

The isotopes of any element have the same atomic number (i.e. they have the same number of protons or electrons) but a different mass number, and therefore differ in the number of neutrons in the nucleus. They have the same electronic configuration and, hence, the same chemical properties (see Section 7.2(*a*)(ii)). For example, there are three hydrogen isotopes:

	^1_1H	^2_1H (or deuterium, symbol D)	^3_1H (or tritium, symbol T)
Number of protons	1	1	1
Number of electrons	1	1	1
Number of neutrons	0	1	2

The first two isotopes are stable, while tritium is unstable or radioactive. The chemical properties of the three isotopes and their compounds are identical, but there are small differences in such physical properties as density, boiling-point and melting-point because of the differences in mass. The physical properties of water (H_2O) and 'heavy water' (deuterium oxide, D_2O) are listed in Table 7.1.

Table 7.1   The physical properties of H_2O and D_2O

Property	H_2O	D_2O
RMM	18.02	20.03
Melting-point (/°C)	0	3.8
Boiling-point (/°C)	100	101.4
Density (/g cm^{-3}) at 4°C	1.00	1.105

7.2
Classification of the elements: the Periodic Table

Specific objectives: *The expected learning outcome of this section is that the student: (i) recognises that a sequence of elements in order of increasing atomic number shows periodic variations in physical and chemical properties; (ii) describes general characteristics of the periodic table across periods and down groups (e.g. metallic and non-metallic nature, basicity/ acidity of oxides, ionic/covalent nature of chloride).*

Over one hundred different elements are now known, including some, such as promethium and lawrencium, which do not occur in nature, but were produced artificially in the laboratory as a result of nuclear transformations. The task of studying the chemistry of each of these elements and its compounds would be enormous and extremely tedious if there were no similarities, common trends or relationships between them. Early attempts at classification were based on physical state and other immediately obvious properties, thus elements were classified as gases, liquids and solids:

Gas	Liquid	Solid
hydrogen, chlorine nitrogen, oxygen	bromine mercury	carbon, silicon, sulphur, iron, lead, phosphorus, sodium

or as metals and non-metals:

Metals	Non-metals
sodium, magnesium, iron silver and copper	carbon, sulphur, nitrogen oxygen and hydrogen

The first successful attempts at a systematic classification were those of Newlands (1864), Lothar Meyer (1869) and the Russian chemist, Mendeleef (1869–71). Meyer plotted the atomic volume of the elements, i.e.

$$\text{Atomic volume} = \frac{\text{Relative atomic mass}}{\text{density}}$$

against atomic number (see fig. 7.1), while Newlands and Mendeleef arranged the elements which were then known in order of increasing atomic mass and found that there was a regular pattern or *periodic variation* in both chemical and physical properties. *The periodic law* was proposed as a consequence of such observations. This law states that *the properties of the elements are a periodic function of their atomic number.*

Newlands found that this repetition of the similarity in properties occurred with every eighth element (the noble gases were unknown at that time) and suggested a similarity to octaves in music. Mendeleef arranged the elements in a table to emphasise their similarities. This table made it possible to predict the existence and properties of as-yet undiscovered elements. A modern simplified form of Mendeleef's Periodic Table is shown in fig. 7.2. A fuller version is shown in fig. 7.12. The table consists of a number of vertical *groups* (e.g. Group O and Groups I, II, III, IV etc.) and a series of horizontal *periods*. The table provides a useful summary of the trends and similarities in the properties of the elements.

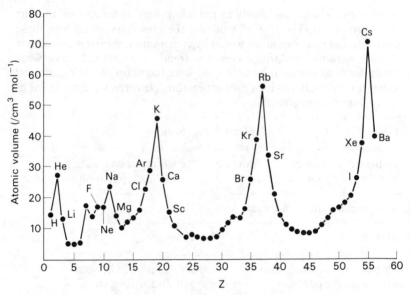

Fig. 7.1 Graph of atomic volume against atomic number

Period	I	II	III	IV	V	VI	VII	O
					Group			
First (n=1)	(H) 1							He 2
Second (n=2)	Li 2,1	Be 2,2	B 2,3	C 2,4	N 2,5	O 2,6	F 2,7	Ne 2,8
Third (n=3)	Na 2,8,1	Mg 2,8,2	Al 2,8,3	Si 2,8,4	P 2,8,5	S 2,8,6	Cl 2,8,7	Ar 2,8,8
Fourth (n=4)	K 2,8,8,1	Ca 2,8,8,2	Ga	Ge	As	Se	Br 2,8,18,7	Kr 2,8,18,8
Fifth (n=5)	Rb 2,8,18,8,1	Sr 2,8,18,8,2	In	Sn	Sb	Te	I 2,8,18,18,7	Xe 2,8,18,18,8
Sixth (n=6)	Cs 2,8,18,18,8,1	Ba 2,8,18,18,8,2	Tl	Pb	Bi	Po	At	Rn
	Metals						Non metals	

Fig. 7.2 The Periodic Table

(*a*) *Trends within a group*

(i) Elements in the same vertical group have similar chemical and physical properties. This similarity within a group is illustrated by the highly active alkali metals (lithium, sodium, potassium, rubidium and caesium) in Group IA, or by the chemically unreactive gases (helium, neon, argon, krypton, xenon and radon) in Group O. All the elements in Group IA, for example, are univalent and the general formulae of their compounds are M_2O, MH, MOH, MCl, M_2SO_4, M_2CO_3, MNO_3 etc., where M represents the alkali metal.

(ii) Elements in the same vertical group have similar electronic configurations. This statement, taken in conjunction with the fact that elements in the same group have similar chemical properties, suggests that the chemical properties of an element are determined by its electronic configuration and particularly by the number and arrangement of the electrons in the outermost 'shell' or energy level. This is not unexpected as it is this part of the atom which interacts first when the atoms of elements approach one another prior to reaction. The simple electronic configurations of a number of elements in terms of the principal energy shells are shown in fig. 7.2.

(iii) The electropositivity of an element, i.e. the ease with which an atom will lose an electron or electrons to form a positively charged ion:

$$M \longrightarrow M^{n+} + ne^-$$
$$\text{atom} \qquad \text{cation}$$

increases down the group. This is a result of the increasing size of the atom:

Atom:	Li	Na	K	Rb	Cs
Atomic radius (/nm)	0.152	0.186	0.231	0.244	0.262

The outer (or valency) electrons become more distant from the positively charged nucleus and are shielded by filled electron shells, thus making electron loss and cation formation much easier. This explains the increase in reactivity of the alkali and alkaline earth metals in Groups IA and IIA:

		Group IA	Group IIA
		Li	Be
Atomic		Na	Mg
radius	electropositivity	K	Ca
increases	increases	Rb	Sr
		Cs	Ba

For example, calcium, strontium and barium are more reactive than magnesium and liberate hydrogen from cold water:

$$M \quad + 2H_2O \longrightarrow M(OH)_2 + H_{2(g)}$$
(Ca, Sr or Ba)

while magnesium will only react with steam or hot water:

$$Mg + H_2O \longrightarrow MgO + H_{2(g)}$$

(iv) The electronegativity of the elements, i.e. the ease with which an atom will attract an electron or electrons, decreases down the group (see Section 8.3). This again is partly a result of the increase in atomic radius. Fluorine is the most electronegative of the halogens (Group VIIB of the Periodic Table):

		Group VIIB Atom	Covalent radius (/nm)
Atomic radius increases	electronegativity increases	F	0.072
		Cl	0.099
		Br	0.114
		I	0.133

Fluorine is the smallest atom in the group, thus the electron which is added to yield the fluoride anion:

$$F + e^- \longrightarrow F^-$$

is closer to the positively charged nucleus than it is in the corresponding reaction of the other halogens.

(b) *Trends across the periods*
The main changes in the general characteristics of the elements across the Periodic Table are:
(i) A decrease in metallic character across the period from Groups I and II (the alkali and alkaline earth metals) to the non-metals in the groups towards the right-hand side of the Periodic Table (see fig. 7.2). Metallic character also increases down a group, for example in Group IV:

C	Si	Ge	Sn	Pb
non-metals		a metalloid, i.e. a non-metal with some metallic properties	metals	

metallic character increases →

(ii) The electronegativity of the elements *increases* (and the electropositivity *decreases*) across the periods with increasing atomic number.

This is largely a result of the greater force of attraction between the electrons and the nucleus, as the number of protons in the atom and hence the positive charge of the nucleus (see Section 7.5) increases.

(iii) There is a uniform change in the principal valency exerted by the element. In the first four groups and Group O, the group valency is the same as the group number (i.e. 1, 2, 3, 4 and O), whereas in Groups V–VII the main valency is (8 – the group number) = 3, 2 and 1 respectively. In addition, many of the elements in Groups V–VII exert a higher valency towards oxygen (and occasionally halogen) which is equal to the group number. These changes are illustrated in Table 7.2 by the formulae of the hydrides and oxides of the elements of the third period of the Periodic Table. The elements in the second period follow the same pattern, except that oxygen and fluorine do not show the higher valencies of 6 and 7.

(iv) There is a change from basicity to acidity in the nature of the oxides across a period. The oxides of the elements in Groups IA and IIA are strongly basic, and sodium oxide, for example, dissolves in water with the evolution of heat to yield a strongly alkaline solution of sodium hydroxide:

$$Na_2O_{(s)} \xrightarrow{H_2O} 2NaOH_{(aq)}$$

The reaction with an aqueous solution of a strong acid such as sulphuric(VI)acid or hydrochloric acid to yield the corresponding salt and water:

$$Na_2O + H_2SO_4 \longrightarrow Na_2SO_4 + H_2O$$

could be explosively violent.

The basicity of the oxides decreases across the Periodic Table, thus aluminium oxide is *amphoteric*, i.e. the compound can act as a *base*:

$$Al_2O_3 + HCl_{(aq)} \longrightarrow 2AlCl_{3(aq)} + 3H_2O$$
a base   an acid   a salt   water

or as an *acid*:

$$Al_2O_3 + 2NaOH \longrightarrow 2NaAlO_2{}^1 + H_2O$$
acting as an   a base   sodium aluminate   water
acid   (a salt)

while the oxides of carbon are neutral (carbon monoxide, CO) or weakly acidic (carbon dioxide, CO_2):

$$H_2O + CO_2 \rightleftharpoons H_2CO_3 \rightleftharpoons H^+_{(aq)} + HCO^-_{3(aq)}$$

[1] The aluminate anion is usually written in its hydrated form as $[Al(OH)_4]^-$.

Table 7.2 Principal valencies of the elements in the second period of the Periodic Table

Group:	IA	IIA	IIIB	IVB	VB	VIB	VIIB	O
Formula of hydride	NaH	MgH_2	$(AlH_3)_n$	SiH_4	PH_3	H_2S	HCl	none
Valency of the element	1	2	3	4	3	2	1	0
Formula of the oxides	Na_2O	MgO	Al_2O_3	SiO_2	P_2O_3 P_2O_5	SO_2 SO_3	Cl_2O Cl_2O_7	none
Valency of the element towards oxygen	1	2	3	4	5 or 3	6 or 4	7 or 1	0

The oxides of the elements towards the right-hand side of the periods are mostly strongly acidic. If an element forms more than one oxide, the compound becomes more acidic as the proportion of oxygen in the molecule increases:

Group V

$\left.\begin{array}{l} N_2O \\ NO \end{array}\right\}$ neutral

N_2O_3 weakly acidic: $N_2O_3 + H_2O \longrightarrow 2HNO_2$ (a weak acid)

N_2O_4 acidic: $N_2O_4 + H_2O \longrightarrow HNO_2 + HNO_3$

N_2O_5 strongly acidic: $N_2O_5 + 2H_2O \longrightarrow 2HNO_3$

$P_4O_6(P_2O_3)$ acidic: $P_4O_6 + 6H_2O \longrightarrow 4H_3PO_3$

$P_4O_{10}(P_2O_5)$ strongly acidic: $P_4O_{10} + 2H_2O \longrightarrow 4HPO_3$
$$\downarrow H_2O$$
$$H_3PO_4 \text{ or } H_4P_2O_7$$

Group VI

SO_2 acidic: $SO_2 + H_2O \rightleftharpoons H_2SO_3 \rightleftharpoons 2H^+_{(aq)} + SO_3^{2-}_{(aq)}$

SO_3 strongly acidic: $SO_3 + H_2O \longrightarrow H_2SO_4$

(v) There is a change in the ionic and covalent nature of the halides across the period from the purely ionic chlorides of the elements of Groups IA and IIA to the covalent chlorides of the elements at the

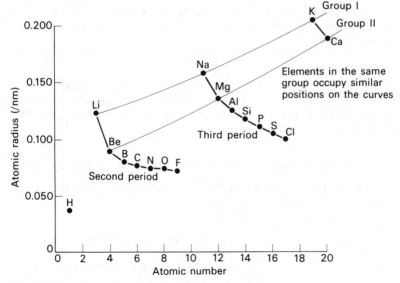

Fig. 7.3 Plot of atomic radius against atomic number

right-hand side of the Periodic Table (see also Section 8.3). For example,

I	II	III		IV	V	VI	VII
Li^+Cl^-				CCl_4	NCl_3	Cl_2O	ClF
Na^+Cl^-	$Mg^{2+}Cl_2^-$	$Al^{3+}F_3^-$		$SiCl_4$	PCl_3	S_2Cl_2	ClF_3
		ionic			PCl_5	SCl_4	Cl_2
K^+Cl^-	$Ca^{2+}Cl_2^-$	Al_2Cl_6					

aluminium chloride
is dimeric $(AlCl_3)_2$
and covalent

ionic ⎵ covalent

(vii) The atomic radius of the elements decreases across a period with increasing atomic number (see fig. 7.3). This is mainly a result of the increasing attractive force between the electrons and the positively charged nucleus as the number of protons in the atom increases. The variation in the melting-points of the elements across the second and third periods is shown in fig. 7.4. The melting-points increase to a maximum in Group IV.

7.3
Ionisation energy

Specific objectives: *The expected learning outcome of this section is that the student: (i) defines ionisation energy; (ii) recognises periodicity in a graph of first ionisation energies for the first 20 elements plotted against atomic number.*

The ionisation energy of an element is defined as *the energy required to remove an electron from the atoms of that element against the attraction of the nucleus.* The *first ionisation energy* applies to the removal of one electron from the neutral atom:

$$M \longrightarrow M^+ + e^-$$

Enthalpy change, ΔH_1 = first ionisation energy (units = kJ mol^{-1})

while *successive ionisation energies* apply to the progressive removal of electrons from the charged ion:

$$M^+ \longrightarrow M^{2+} + e^-$$

ΔH_2 = second ionisation energy

$$M^{2+} \longrightarrow M^{3+} + e^-$$

ΔH_3 = third ionisation energy

The total energy (or, more strictly, enthalpy) change for the process:

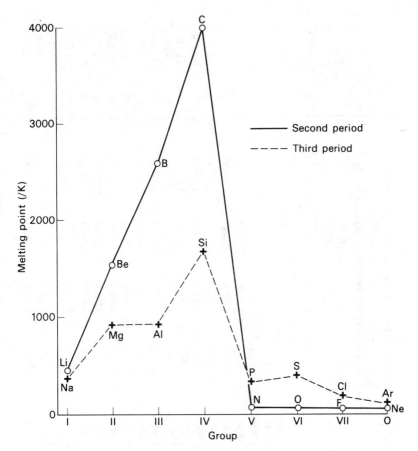

Fig. 7.4 Melting points of the elements of the second and third periods of the Periodic Table

$$M \longrightarrow = M^{n+} + ne^-$$

is equal to the sum of the successive ionisation energies:

$$\Delta H_{overall} = \Delta H_{(first\ ionisation)} + \Delta H_{(second\ ionisation)} \cdots + \Delta H_{(nth\ ionisation)}$$

As we shall see in the next two sections, the relative magnitudes of the ionisation energies provide useful information about the electronic configuration of the elements. The ionisation energies of the first twenty elements in the Periodic Table are listed in Table 7.3. The graph of the first ionisation energy of the elements plotted against atomic number (see fig. 7.5) shows periodic variation with the alkali metals placed at the minima in the curve and the noble gases at the maxima.

Table 7.3 Successive ionisation energies of the first twenty elements in the Periodic Table

Element	Atomic number	Successive ionisation energies (/kJ mol^{-1})							
		1st	2nd	3rd	4th	5th	6th	7th	8th
H	1	1310							
He	2	2370	5250						
Li	3	519	7300	11 800					
Be	4	900	1760	14 800	21 000				
B	5	799	2420	3660	25 000	32 800			
C	6	1090	2350	4610	6220	37 800	47 000		
N	7	1400	2860	4590	7480	9440	53 200	64 300	
O	8	1310	3390	5320	7450	11 000	13 300	71 000	84 100
F	9	1680	3370	6040	8410	11 000	15 100	17 900	91 600
Ne	10	2080	3950	6150	9290	12 100	15 200	20 000	23 000
Na	11	495	4560	6950	9540	13 400	16 600	20 100	25 500
Mg	12	735	1450	7740	10 500	13 600	18 000	21 700	25 600
Al	13	577	1820	2740	11 600	14 800	18 400	23 400	27 500
Si	14	786	1580	3230	4360	16 000	20 000	23 600	29 100
P	15	1060	1900	2920	4960	6280	21 200	25 900	30 500
S	16	1000	2260	3390	4540	6990	8490	27 100	31 700
Cl	17	1260	2300	3850	5150	6540	9330	11 000	33 600
Ar	18	1520	2660	3950	5770	7250	8790	12 000	13 800
K	19	420	3070	4600	5850	7990	9620	11 400	14 900
Ca	20	590	1150	4940	6480	8120	10 700	12 300	14 600

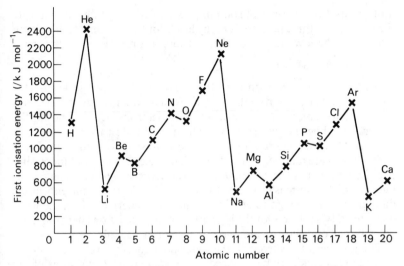

Fig. 7.5 Graph of the first ionisation energy of the elements plotted against atomic number

Assignment

Use the data in Table 7.3 to plot a graph of the first ionisation energy of the first twenty elements in the Periodic Table against atomic number. Compare the positions of the elements on the graph with (a) their position in the Periodic Table and (b) their position on the graph of atomic volume against atomic number (see fig. 7.1). Plot a graph of the first ionisation energy of lithium, sodium, potassium, rubidium and caesium (metallic radii = 0.152, 0.186, 0.231, 0.244 and 0.262 nm respectively) against atomic (metallic) radius. How do you interpret the relationship between these two quantities?

7.4
Energy levels

Specific objective: *The expected learning outcome of this section is that the student interprets the graphs of successive ionisation energies against the number of electrons removed in terms of energy levels.*

Graphs of the successive ionisation energies of the various elements plotted against the number of electrons removed provide the evidence for the existence of different energy levels within which the electrons are arranged in the atom. For example, the large gaps after the first and ninth ionisation energies of sodium (see Table 7.3 and fig. 7.6) indicate the presence of three principal energy levels for the sodium atom's eleven electrons. The low energy for the first ionisation:

$$Na \longrightarrow Na^+ + e^-$$

indicates that this electron is in the atom's highest energy level. This energy level is farthest from the nucleus, which explains why this electron is so easy to remove. The following eight electrons occupy and fill the next shell, while the two electrons which are hardest to remove are in the atom's lowest energy level and are closest to the nucleus. These energy levels are numbered $n = 1, n = 2, n = 3$ etc. in order of increasing energy, where n is the *principal quantum number*. The electronic configuration of sodium is thus 2, 8, 1 (see fig. 7.7). Because of the enormous difference in the magnitude of the ionisation energies of an element, it is often advisable to plot the logarithm of the ionisation energy against the number of electrons removed as shown in fig. 7.6.

The number of electrons in the outermost energy level of the atoms of other elements may be deduced in the same way. The graphs of the successive ionisation energies of carbon, aluminium and fluorine, for example (see fig. 7.8), indicate that the atoms of these elements have four, three and seven electrons respectively in their outermost energy level and confirm that their electronic configurations are:

C 2, 4   Al 2, 8, 3   and   F 2,7.

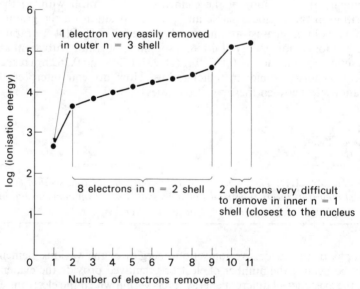

Fig. 7.6 Plot of successive ionisation energies of sodium

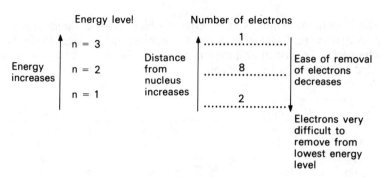

Fig. 7.7 Energy level diagram to show the electronic configuration of the sodium atom

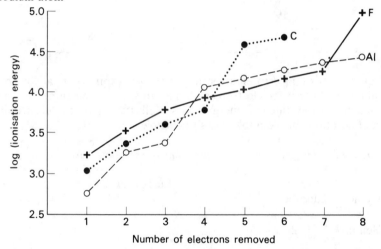

Fig. 7.8 Plot of successive ionisation energies of carbon, aluminium and fluorine

Table 7.4 *Maximum numbers of electrons in the principal energy levels*

Energy levels	Maximum number of electrons = $2n^2$
$n = 1$	$2 \times 1^2 = 2$
$n = 2$	$2 \times 2^2 = 8$
$n = 3$	$2 \times 3^3 = 18$
$n = 4$	$2 \times 4^2 = 32$

The maximum numbers of electrons which can be fitted into the principal energy level is given by the expression $2n^2$ (see Table 7.4), where n is the principal quantum number. The n = 3 energy level is filled at first with eight electrons:

Atom	Atomic number Z	Electronic configuration			
		n = 1	n = 2	n = 3	n = 4
Cl	17	2	8	7	
Ar	18	2	8	8	
K	19	2	8	8	1
Ca	20	2	8	8	2

but this is extended to eighteen in the elements following calcium by filling in a further ten electrons within a sub-shell (see Section 7.5). The capacity of the different energy levels is illustrated by the electronic configurations of the noble gases (see Table 7.5).

Table 7.5 The electronic configurations of the noble gases

Element	Atomic number n = 1	Energy levels				
		2	3	4	5	6
Helium	2	2				
Neon	10	2	8			
Argon	18	2	8	8		
Krypton	36	2	8	18	8	
Xenon	54	2	8	18	18	8
Radon	86	2	8	18	32	18	8

Assignment

Plot and interpret graphs of the successive ionisation energies of nitrogen, lithium, magnesium and calcium against the number of electrons removed.

7.5
Subsidiary energy levels

Specific objectives: *The expected learning outcome of this section is that the student: (i) recognises the existence of subsidiary energy levels from graphs of the first ionisation energy of the first twenty elements plotted against atomic number, (ii) writes down the electron configuration (in terms of $1s^2$, $2s^2$ etc.) for the first twenty elements of the Periodic Table, (iii) relates electronic configuration to the position of an element in the Periodic Table.*

(a) *Types of sub-shell*
The variation in the first ionisation energy of the elements with atomic number (see fig. 7.5 and Table 7.3) may be interpreted in terms of the progressive filling of electron *sub-shells* which consist of a number of *orbitals*, each capable of holding a maximum of two electrons. The two electrons in a filled orbital have opposite spins and are represented thus: ⇅ .

The different type of sub-shell are indicated by the letters s, p, d and f. The capacity of these sub-shells and the number of orbitals they contain are listed in Table 7.6; and the types of sub-shell in each of the energy levels are listed in Table 7.7. The different sub-shells are prefixed by the principal quantum number (1s, 2s, 2p etc.) to indicate the energy level or 'shell' to which they belong.

Table 7.6   Capacity of sub-shells

Type of sub-shell	Number of orbitals	Maximum number of electrons in sub-shell
s	1	$1 \times 2 = 2$
p	3	$3 \times 2 = 6$
d	5	$5 \times 2 = 10$
(f	7	$7 \times 2 = 14)$[1]

The 'solar system' model in which the electrons are moving about in shells or orbits about the positively charged nucleus, like planets moving round the sun (see fig. 7.9), can only provide a simple representation of the arrangement of the electrons in an atom. This difficulty stems partly from the impossibility of defining both the exact position

[1] A discussion of f-orbitals is not required for the T.E.C. Level 2 Chemistry unit.

Table 7.7   Types of sub-shell within the main electrons energy levels

Principal quantum number, n	Type of sub-shell	Maximum number of electrons in energy level
1	1s	2
2	2s 2p	$2 + 6 = 8$
3	3s 3p 3d	$2 + 6 + 10 = 18$
(4	4s 4p 4d 4f	$2 + 6 + 10 + 14 = 32$)

and energy (or momentum) of an electron at any instant. A better description is provided by *orbitals* which are defined as the space within which there is a maximum probability of finding an electron at any instant. The shapes of the 1s orbital and the three 2p orbitals are shown in figs. 7.10 and 7.11. The 2p orbitals are labelled $2p_x$, $2p_y$ and $2p_z$ as

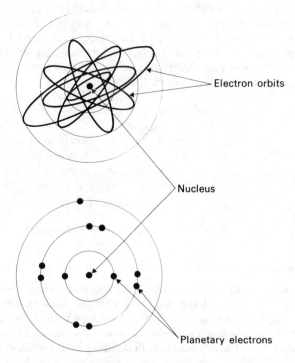

Fig. 7.9 Solar system model of the sodium atom

the lobes of these orbitals are directed along the x, y and z axes respectively.

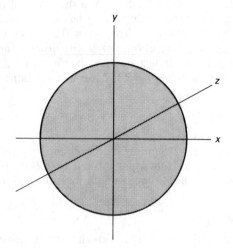

Fig. 7.10 The 1s-orbital

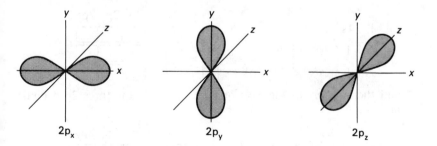

Fig. 7.11 The 2p-orbitals

(b) Interpretation of the relationship between first ionisation energy and atomic number

The increase in the first ionisation energy from 1310 kJ mol^{-1} for hydrogen to 2370 kJ mol^{-1} for helium in the graph of the first ionisation energy against atomic number (see fig. 7.5 and Table 7.3) is due to the increased attraction resulting from the higher nuclear charge. The sudden decrease in ionisation energy with lithium, the third element in the Periodic Table, indicates that the first (n = 1) energy level (consisting of the 1s orbital) is filled once it contains two electrons (*cf.* fig. 7.7):

$$\text{H} \quad 1s^1 \quad \overset{\text{1s orbital}}{\boxed{\uparrow}} \qquad \text{He} \quad 1s^2 \quad \overset{\text{1s orbital}}{\boxed{\uparrow\downarrow}}$$

The third electron is beginning a second energy level (the 2s) more distant from the nucleus from which it is partly shielded by the electrons in the 1s orbital. The electronic configuration of lithium is:

$$\text{Li} \quad 1s^2\, 2s^1 \quad \overset{\text{1s}}{\boxed{\uparrow\downarrow}} \quad \overset{\text{2s}}{\boxed{\uparrow}}$$

The increase in ionisation energy with the fourth element, beryllium, is consistent with the greater attraction with the higher positive charge of the nucleus and the 2s orbital is filled:

$$\text{Be} \quad 1s^2\, 2s^2 \quad \overset{\text{1s}}{\boxed{\uparrow\downarrow}} \quad \overset{\text{2s}}{\boxed{\uparrow\downarrow}}$$

The decrease in ionisation energy with the fifth element, boron, is consistent with the beginning of a new sub-shell (the 2p), the three p orbitals of which are first occupied singly:

		1s	2s	2p$_x$ 2p$_y$ 2p$_z$
B	$1s^2\, 2s^2\, 2p_x^1$	$\boxed{\uparrow\downarrow}$	$\boxed{\uparrow\downarrow}$	$\boxed{\uparrow\ \ |\ \ |\ \ }$
C	$1s^2\, 2s^2\, 2p_x^1\, 2p_y^1$	$\boxed{\uparrow\downarrow}$	$\boxed{\uparrow\downarrow}$	$\boxed{\uparrow\ |\ \uparrow\ |\ \ }$
N	$1s^2\, 2s^2\, 2p_x^1\, 2p_y^1\, 2p_z^1$	$\boxed{\uparrow\downarrow}$	$\boxed{\uparrow\downarrow}$	$\boxed{\uparrow\ |\ \uparrow\ |\ \uparrow}$

and then doubly as the electrons are paired in the three 2p orbitals in turn:

		1s	2s	2p$_x$ 2p$_y$ 2p$_z$
O	$1s^2\, 2s^2\, 2p_x^2\, 2p_y^1\, 2p_z^1$	$\boxed{\uparrow\downarrow}$	$\boxed{\uparrow\downarrow}$	$\boxed{\uparrow\downarrow\ |\ \uparrow\ |\ \uparrow}$
F	$1s^2\, 2s^2\, 2p_x^2\, 2p_y^2\, 2p_z^1$	$\boxed{\uparrow\downarrow}$	$\boxed{\uparrow\downarrow}$	$\boxed{\uparrow\downarrow\ |\ \uparrow\downarrow\ |\ \uparrow}$
Ne	$1s^2\, 2s^2\, 2p_x^2\, 2p_y^2\, 2p_z^2$	$\boxed{\uparrow\downarrow}$	$\boxed{\uparrow\downarrow}$	$\boxed{\uparrow\downarrow\ |\ \uparrow\downarrow\ |\ \uparrow\downarrow}$

The drop in the magnitude of the first ionisation energy between nitrogen and oxygen reflects the repulsion of the electrons in the three partly filled 2p orbitals to pairing with the fourth electron. The n = 2 energy level is filled with the noble gas configuration of neon ($1s^2$ $2s^2$ $2p^6$) and the eleventh electron enters the 3s orbital:

Na ($1s^2$ $2s^2$ $2p^6$) $3s^1$

where ($1s^2$ $2s^2$ $2p^6$) is the neon core of filled orbitals.

Sodium has a lower ionisation energy reflecting the ease of removal of this single 3s electron. The ionisation energies of the elements in the third period (i.e. sodium–argon) follow the same pattern as was described for the second period (lithium–neon) (see fig. 7.5) and the 3s and 3p orbitals are filled in turn:

Na ($1s^2$ $2s^2$ $2p^6$) $3s^1$

Mg ($1s^2$ $2s^2$ $2p^6$) $3s^2$

Al ($1s^2$ $2s^2$ $2p^6$) $3s^2$ $3p_x^1$

Si ($1s^2$ $2s^2$ $2p^6$) $3s^2$ $3p_x^1$ $3p_y^1$

P ($1s^2$ $2s^2$ $2p^6$) $3s^2$ $3p_x^1$ $3p_y^1$ $3p_z^1$

S ($1s^2$ $2s^2$ $2p^6$) $3s^2$ $3p_x^2$ $3p_y^1$ $3p_z^1$

Cl ($1s^2$ $2s^2$ $2p^6$) $3s^2$ $3p_x^2$ $3p_y^2$ $3p_z^1$

Ar ($1s^2$ $2s^2$ $2p^6$) $3s^2$ $3p_x^2$ $3p_y^2$ $3p_z^2$

With the completion of the 3p orbitals with argon (electronic configuration: $1s^2$ $2s^2$ $2p^6$ $3s^2$ $3p^6$), the next electron enters a higher energy level, the 4s:

K ($1s^2$ $2s^2$ $2p^6$ $3s^2$ $3p^6$) $4s^1$

Argon core

from which it is easily removed as the lower ionisation energy indicates.

(c) Electronic configuration of the elements

The electronic configurations of the first twenty elements in the Periodic Table are listed in Table 7.8. After calcium (electronic configuration: $1s^2$ $2s^2$ $2p^6$ $3s^2$ $3p^6$ $4s^2$) there is a change in the sequence of filling the subsidiary energy level and the inner 3d shell (which can contain a maximum of ten electrons) is filled before beginning the 4p shell. The difference in energy between the 4s and 3d orbitals is small, and electrons are readily transferred from one orbital to the other. This fact explains many of the properties of the '*3d-block*' or *transition elements* (see Section 8.7). The electronic configurations of these elements are given in Table 7.9. All these elements have the argon core $1s^2$ $2s^2$ $2p^6$ $3s^2$ $3p^6$.

A modern form of the Periodic Table with the electronic configurations of the elements represented in terms of the s, p and d subsidiary energy levels is shown in fig. 7.12. The elements are separated into s, p and d-blocks according to the subsidiary energy levels, or orbitals, of the electrons which determine the element's chemical properties. Hydrogen and helium are placed separately from the main blocks of elements owing to their small size and the many unique properties of the hydrogen atom. The relationship between an element's electronic configuration and its position in the Periodic Table is apparent in fig. 7.12.

Table 7.8   Electronic configuration of the first twenty elements

Name	Symbol	Atomic number	Electronic configuration
Hydrogen	H	1	$1s^1$
Helium	He	2	$1s^2$
Lithium	Li	3	$1s^2\ 2s^1$
Beryllium	Be	4	$1s^2\ 2s^2$
Boron	B	5	$1s^2\ 2s^2\ 2p^1$
Carbon	C	6	$1s^2\ 2s^2\ 2p^2$
Nitrogen	N	7	$1s^2\ 2s^2\ 2p^3$
Oxygen	O	8	$1s^2\ 2s^2\ 2p^4$
Fluorine	F	9	$1s^2\ 2s^2\ 2p^5$
Neon	Ne	10	$1s^2\ 2s^2\ 2p^6$
Sodium	Na	11	$1s^2\ 2s^2\ 2p^6\ 3s^1$
Magnesium	Mg	12	$1s^2\ 2s^2\ 2p^6\ 3s^2$
Aluminium	Al	13	$1s^2\ 2s^2\ 2p^6\ 3s^2\ 3p^1$
Silicon	Si	14	$1s^2\ 2s^2\ 2p^6\ 3s^2\ 3p^2$
Phosphorus	P	15	$1s^2\ 2s^2\ 2p^6\ 3s^2\ 3p^3$
Sulphur	S	16	$1s^2\ 2s^2\ 2p^6\ 3s^2\ 3p^4$
Chlorine	Cl	17	$1s^2\ 2s^2\ 2p^6\ 3s^2\ 3p^5$
Argon	Ar	18	$1s^2\ 2s^2\ 2p^6\ 3s^2\ 3p^6$
Potassium	K	19	$1s^2\ 2s^2\ 2p^6\ 3s^2\ 3p^6\ 4s^1$
Calcium	Ca	20	$1s^2\ 2s^2\ 2p^6\ 3s^2\ 3p^6\ 4s^2$

Fig. 7.12 The Periodic Table

Period ($n=$)	Core	I	II	d-block elements	III	IV	V	VI	VII	O
		s-block								p-block
1		H $1s^1$								He $1s^2$
2	$1s^2$ = Helium	Li $2s^1$	Be $2s^2$		B $2s^2\,2p^1$	C $2s^2\,2p^2$	N $2s^2\,2p^3$	O $2s^2\,2p^4$	F $2s^2\,2p^5$	Ne $2s^2\,2p^6$
3	$1s^2\,2s^2\,2p^6$ = Neon	Na $3s^1$	Mg $3s^2$		Al $3s^2\,3p^1$	Si $3s^2\,3p^2$	P $3s^2\,3p^3$	S $3s^2\,3p^4$	Cl $3s^2\,3p^5$	Ar $3s^2\,3p^6$
4	Argon	K $4s^1$	Ca $4s^2$	Sc ------ Zn $3d^1$ ------ $3d^{10}$	Ga $4s^2\,4p^1$	Ge $4s^2\,4p^2$	As $4s^2\,4p^3$	Se $4s^2\,4p^4$	Br $4s^2\,4p^5$	Kr $4s^2\,4p^6$
5	Krypton	Rb $5s^1$	Sr $5s^2$	Y ------ Cd $4d^1$ ------ $4d^{10}$	In $5s^2\,5p^1$	Sn $5s^2\,5p^2$	Sb $5s^2\,5p^3$	Te $5s^2\,5p^4$	I $5s^2\,5p^5$	Xe $5s^2\,5p^6$
6	Xenon	Cs $6s^1$	Ba $6s^2$	La $5d^1$ | Ce-Lu $4f^{1-14}$ | Hf ------ Hg $5d$–$5d^{10}$	Tl $6s^2\,6p^1$	Pb $6s^2\,6p^2$	Bi $6s^2\,6p^3$	Po $6s^2\,6p^4$	At $6s^2\,6p^5$	Rn $6s^2\,6p^6$

Table 7.9   Electronic configuration of the 3d elements

Name	Symbol	Atomic number	Electronic configuration
Scandium	Sc	21	(Argon-core) $3d^1$ $4s^2$
Titanium	Ti	22	(Argon-core) $3d^2$ $4s^2$
Vanadium	V	23	(Argon-core) $3d^3$ $4s^2$
Chromium	Cr	24	(Argon-core) $3d^5$ $4s^1$
Manganese	Mn	25	(Argon-core) $3d^5$ $4s^2$
Iron	Fe	26	(Argon-core) $3d^6$ $4s^2$
Cobalt	Co	27	(Argon-core) $3d^7$ $4s^2$
Nickel	Ni	28	(Argon-core) $3d^8$ $4s^2$
Copper	Cu	29	(Argon-core) $3d^{10}$ $4s^1$
Zinc	Zn	30	(Argon-core) $3d^{10}$ $4s^2$

Summary

1. The periodic law states that the properties of the elements are a periodic function of their atomic number.

2. The atomic number of an element is equal to the number of protons in the nucleus of its atoms. It is also equal to the order of the element in the Periodic Table (see figs. 7.2 and 7.12).

3. The principal trends in the Periodic Table are discussed in Section 7.2.

4. The first ionisation energy of an element is defined as the energy required to remove an electron from an atom of that element against the attraction of the nucleus. The units are kJ mol^{-1}.

5. Electronic configurations and the existence of subsidiary energy levels may be deduced from graphs of the first and subsequent ionisation energies (see Sections 7.4 and 7.5).

6. The s, p and d sub-shells can contain a maximum of 2, 6 and 10 electrons respectively. The number of orbitals in these subsidiary energy levels is 1 (for the s sub-shell), 3 (for the p sub-shell) and 5 (for the d sub-shell). An atomic orbital can contain a maximum of two electrons.

7. The electronic configurations of the first twenty elements in the Periodic Table are listed in Table 7.8. Elements are described as s-block, p-block and d-block elements according to the subsidiary energy-levels of the electrons which determine their chemical properties.

Questions

1. Define the following terms: (a) relative atomic mass, (b) atomic number and (c) mass number.

2. What is an isotope? Give three examples.

3. Calculate the number of protons, neutrons and electrons in the following atoms:

$$^{19}_{9}F, \ ^{40}_{20}Ca, \ ^{39}_{19}K, \ ^{238}_{92}U \text{ and } ^{208}_{82}Pb.$$

4. How do you account for the fact that the relative atomic mass of naturally occurring chlorine is 35.45?

5. State the periodic law. Discuss three examples of properties which illustrate this law.

6. What is the Periodic Table? What are its uses? Give three examples of (a) trends within a group and (b) trends across a period.

7. Why does argon (RAM 39.95) come before potassium (RAM 39.1) in the Periodic Table?

8. Discuss the changes in (a) the metallic character of the elements, (b) the basicity of the oxides, (c) the valencies of the elements and (d) the ionic or covalent nature of the chlorides across the second or third periods of the Periodic Table.

9. Define ionisation energy. Use the data in Table 7.3 to calculate the total enthalpy changes for the following processes:

(a) $Mg \longrightarrow Mg^{2+} + 2e^-$
(b) $Li \longrightarrow Li^{3+} + 3e^-$
(c) $Al \longrightarrow Al^{3+} + 3e^-$

10. Deduce the electronic configurations of the elements X and Y in fig. 7.13(a) and (b) from the graphs of their successive ionisation energies against the number of electrons removed.

11. How do you account for the relative magnitudes of the first

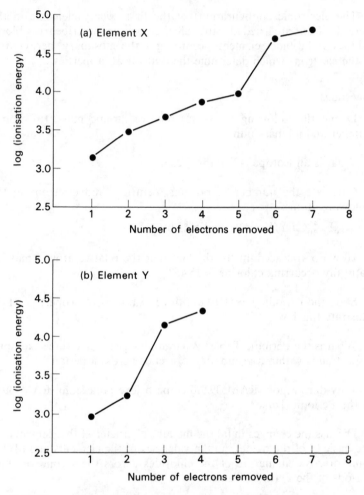

Fig. 7.13 Plots of log (ionisation energy) against number of electrons removed from elements X and Y

ionisation energies of lithium, sodium and potassium and of hydrogen, helium, lithium, beryllium and boron?

12. Write down the electronic configuration (in terms of $1s^2$, $2s^2$ etc.) of the first twenty elements of the Periodic Table.

13. What is the relationship between the electronic configuration of an element and its position in the Periodic Table?

14. What is meant by the terms: (a) an s-block element and (b) a p-block element? Give at least two examples of each.

15. Why is hydrogen (and occasionally helium) placed separate from the main blocks of elements in the Periodic Table?

8 The properties of the elements

General objective: *The expected learning outcome of this chapter is that the student describes and explains the properties of some elements in relationship to their electronic configurations, position in the Periodic Table, and the bonding in their compounds.*

8.1
Bonding between atoms

Specific objectives: *The expected learning outcome of this section is that the student: (i) draws 'dot and cross' diagrams for both ionic and covalent compounds (ii) explains how an orderly arrangement of particles forms a lattice structure (iii) draws 'dot and cross' diagrams for compounds with lone (non-bonding) pairs of electrons (iv) describes the formation of dative covalent bonds in NH_3BF_3 and NH_4^+ (v) describes metallic bonding in terms of a lattice of ions in a 'sea' of electrons.*

The principal types of bond between atoms are:
(a) Ionic (or electrovalent),
(b) Covalent,
(c) Dative covalent (this is also known as a co-ionic or co-ordinate bond),
(d) Metallic bonding.

The elements in Group O of the Periodic Table are the highly unreactive *noble gases*: helium, neon, argon, krypton, xenon and radon (see fig. 7.2). Except for the formation of a few unstable compounds, such as XeF_4, KrF_4, XeO_3 and XeO_2F_2, these elements do not undergo chemical reaction. As we saw in Section 7.2(a), the chemical properties of an element are determined by the number and arrangement of the electrons in the outer 'shells'. The lack of reactivity of the noble gases is attributed to the great stability of their electronic configurations with completely filled s and p–orbitals, i.e. an outer energy level of eight electrons (s^2p^6), or two electrons ($1s^2$) in the case of helium.

Atoms react to attain the electronic configuration of the noble gases wherever possible. This structure in which each of the atoms forming the bond has completely filled s and p-orbitals may be obtained by two distinct methods: either the atoms *transfer* electrons to one another or they *share* them. The bonds produced by these two methods are known as *ionic* (or *electrovalent*) and *covalent* respectively.

(a) The ionic bond

An ionic bond is formed when atoms gain or lose electrons to form a more stable electronic configuration. Charged particles (or *ions*) are obtained as a result of this electron transfer. Positively charged ions (or *cations*) are formed when an atom (usually a metal) loses electrons:

$$M \longrightarrow M^{n+} + ne^-$$

while negatively charged ions (or *anions*) are obtained when an atom (usually a non-metal) gains electrons:

$$X + ne^- \longrightarrow X^{n-}$$

The formation of sodium chloride, for example, involves the transference of an electron from the sodium atom to an atom of chlorine:

$$Na \xrightarrow{\text{loss of an electron}} Na^+ + e^-$$

a sodium atom   a sodium ion

Electronic configuration:
$1s^2 2s^2 2p^6 3s^1$ $1s^2 2s^2 2p^6$

$$Cl + e^- \xrightarrow{\text{gain of an electron}} Cl^-$$

a chlorine atom   a chloride ion

Electronic configuration:
$1s^2 2s^2 2p^6 3s^2 3p^5$ $1s^2 2s^2 2p^6 3s^2 3p^6$

Both the ions obtained have the electronic configuration of a noble gas: the sodium ion has the same number of electrons and electronic configuration as neon and is said to be *isoelectronic* with it, while the chloride ion is isoelectronic with argon. As a result of their noble gas configurations, the sodium and chloride ions are considerably more stable than the highly reactive atoms from which they are derived. This electron transfer from the outer 'shell' of the sodium atom to that of the chlorine atom may be expressed in terms of simple dot and cross diagrams:

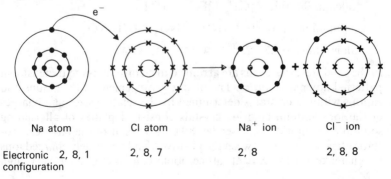

| Na atom | Cl atom | Na$^+$ ion | Cl$^-$ ion |

Electronic configuration   2, 8, 1   2, 8, 7   2, 8   2, 8, 8

The formation of magnesium oxide involves the transfer of two electrons from the magnesium atom to the oxygen atom.

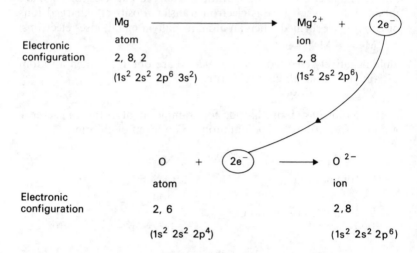

The magnesium ions and oxide ions which are obtained have the same electronic configuration and are isoelectronic with the noble gas, neon. A number of isoelectronic anions and cations are listed in Table 8.1 with their ionic radii. The greater attractive force exerted on the electrons by the nucleus explains the decrease in ionic radius as the positive charge on the ion increases.

General properties of ionic compounds

Ionic compounds are composed of cations and anions which are present in such proportions as to balance out their charges. For example,

sodium oxide $2Na^+ : 1O^{2-}$ $Na_2^+ O^{2-}$

calcium fluoride $1Ca^{2+} : 2F^-$ $Ca^{2+} F_2^-$

ammonium nitrate(v) $1NH_4^+ : 1NO_3^-$ $NH_4^+ NO_3^-$

aluminium oxide $2Al^{3+} : 3O^{2-}$ $Al_2^{3+} O_3^{2-}$

In the solid state these ions are arranged in an orderly three-dimensional pattern, known as a *lattice*. The precise arrangement of the anions and cations within a crystal is determined by the relative sizes and charges of the ion. Sodium chloride crystals consist of planes of alternating sodium and chloride ions (see fig. 8.1). As a result of the large electrostatic attractive force between the positively and negatively charged ions which make up the crystal lattice, ionic compounds have very high

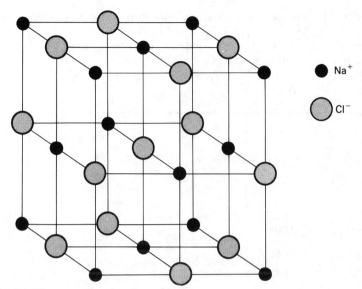

Fig. 8.1 The structure of sodium chloride

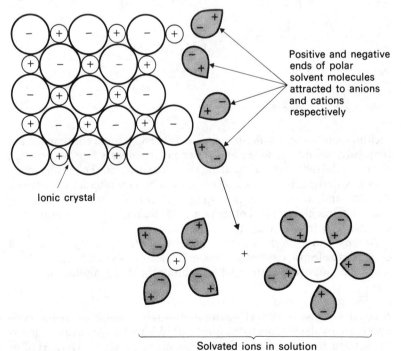

Positive and negative ends of polar solvent molecules attracted to anions and cations respectively

Ionic crystal

Solvated ions in solution

Fig. 8.2 Solution of an ionic solid in a polar solvent

Table 8.1   The radii and electronic configurations of isoelectronic ions

Ion or atom	Ionic radius (/nm)	Electronic configuration
H^-	0.208	
He	—	$1s^2$
Li^+	0.060	
O^{2-}	0.140	
F^-	0.136	
Ne	—	$1s^2 2s^2 2p^6$
Na^+	0.095	
Mg^{2+}	0.065	
Al^{3+}	0.050	
S^{2-}	0.184	
Cl^-	0.181	
Ar	—	$1s^2 2s^2 2p^6 3s^2 3p^6$
K^+	0.133	
Ca^{2+}	0.099	

melting-points and boiling-points (see Table 8.2). Ionic compounds are frequently soluble in water and other polar solvents (see Section 8.3) owing to the reduction of the attractive force between the ions by inter-action with the solvent molecules (see fig. 8.2). This interaction between the ions and solvent does not occur with petrol, tetrachloromethane (carbon tetrachloride) and other non-polar liquids, so ionic compounds are generally insoluble in these solvents.

Anions and cations are attracted by electrical charges and will conduct an electric current and undergo electrolysis (see Section 4.1(*a*)) when the ions are free to move in solution or in the molten state.

(b) The covalent bond

A covalent bond is formed when atoms attain a stable electronic con-figuration by sharing electrons. Single, double and triple covalent bonds are formed by sharing two, four or six electrons respectively. Half of these electrons are donated by each of the two atoms forming the bond

Table 8.2   Melting point and boiling point of ionic compounds

Compound	Formula	Melting point (/°C)	Boiling point (/°C)
Sodium fluoride	NaF	988	1697
Sodium chloride	NaCl	801	1467
Sodium bromide	NaBr	747	1380
Sodium iodide	NaI	647	1320
Magnesium chloride	$MgCl_2$	714	1530
Magnesium oxide	MgO	2900	3600
Aluminium oxide (corundum)	Al_2O_3	2040	2980

Table 8.3   Formation of covalent bonds

Type of covalent bond	Number of shared electrons		Bond represented as
Single	2	$\overset{x}{\cdot}$	—
Double	4	$\begin{matrix} x \\ x \\ \cdot \\ \cdot \end{matrix}$	=
Triple	6	$\begin{matrix} x \\ x \\ x \\ \cdot \\ \cdot \\ \cdot \end{matrix}$	≡

and are usually distinguished by representing them as dots and crosses as shown in Table 8.3. For example, both hydrogen atoms in the hydrogen molecule obtain the helium configuration when they share their single 1s electron to form a single covalent bond:

H·   +   x H   ⟶   (H (ẋ) H)

‿‿‿‿‿‿‿‿‿‿‿‿‿‿‿‿‿‿

Hydrogen atoms   A hydrogen molecule, H_2

A molecular orbital in which the electrons are concentrated in the space between the nuclei of the hydrogen atoms is formed by overlap of the two atomic orbitals (see fig. 8.3).

Similarly, a molecule of hydrogen chloride containing a single covalent bond is formed by the sharing of the 1s electron of hydrogen with the 3p electron of chlorine:

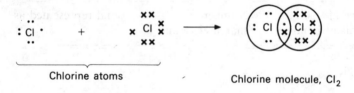

Hydrogen atom   Chlorine atom   Hydrogen chloride
                                                molecule, H—Cl

By sharing a pair of electrons with hydrogen the chlorine atom in the hydrogen chloride molecule has formed the electronic configuration of argon. This stable configuration is obtained in the chlorine molecule by the formation of a single covalent bond consisting of two shared electrons between the two chlorine atoms:

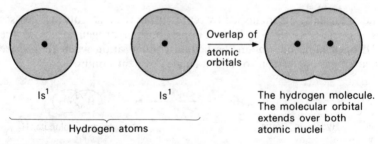

Chlorine atoms   Chlorine molecule, Cl_2

Other examples of single, double and triple covalent bonds are shown in fig. 8.4. The ammonia and water molecules are examples of compounds containing pairs of electrons which are not involved in bonding. These *lone* (or *non-bonding*) *pairs* of electrons play an important role in determining the shape (see Section 8.2) and reactivity (see Section 8.3) of the molecules which contain them.

$1s^1$ $1s^1$ Overlap of
                                              atomic
                                              orbitals

                                              The hydrogen molecule.
                                              The molecular orbital
                                              extends over both
Hydrogen atoms   atomic nuclei

Fig. 8.3 Formation of the hydrogen molecule

Table 8.4 Comparison of melting point and boiling point of simple
covalent and ionic compounds

| Covalent compounds | | | | Ionic compounds | | | |
Formula	RMM	m.p. (/°C)	b.p. (/°C)	Formula	RMM	m.p. (/°C)	b.p. (/°C)
C_4H_{10}	58	-138	-0.5	NaCl	58.5	801	1467
PCl_3	137	-112	76	AgF	127	435	1160
CCl_4	154	-23	77	$BaCl_2$	208	957	1560
Paraffin wax	—	50–55	—	—			

General properties of covalent compounds

There is little attraction between the uncharged molecules of a covalent
compound so these substances usually have low melting points and
boiling points compared with ionic compounds of similar relative
molecular mass (see Table 8.4). Giant molecules – such as diamond and
silica, where, in effect, a single crystal is one large molecule of the substance – have very high melting points and boiling points. The structure
of diamond is shown in fig. 8.5. Each carbon atom is linked to four
other carbon atoms at the corner of a tetrahedron by single covalent
bonds to form an immensely hard, covalent network crystal. Covalent
compounds do not conduct electricity and are usually insoluble in water
or other polar solvents unless they react with it, e.g.

$$HCl \ + H_2O \longrightarrow H_3O^+ + Cl^-$$
covalent

$$SO_2 \ + H_2O \longrightarrow \ H_2SO_3$$
sulphur   sulphuric(IV) acid
dioxide   (sulphurous acid)
(covalent)

or contain hydroxy (—OH) groups or amino (—NH$_2$) groups. Compounds containing these groups dissolve in water by interacting with
the solvent. For example, CH_4, C_2H_6, CCl_4 and $CHCl_3$ are insoluble
in water, while methanol (CH_3OH) and ethanol (C_2H_5OH) are miscible[1]
with water in all proportions.

---

[1] The terms *miscible* and *immiscible* are frequently used to describe the mutual solubility
of liquids and indicate respectively whether or not the two substances will mix to form
a single homogeneous solution.

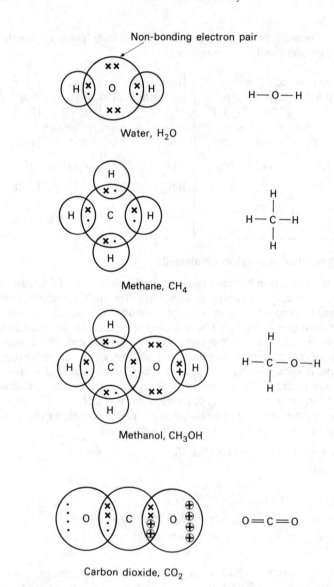

Fig. 8.4 Covalent molecules

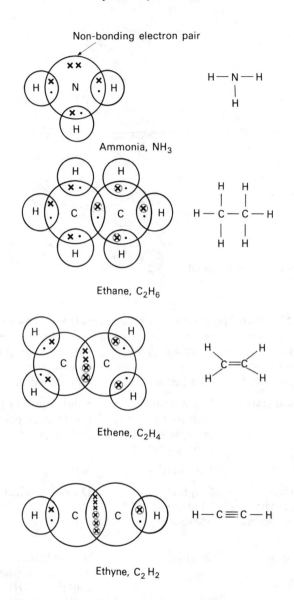

Ammonia, NH$_3$

Ethane, C$_2$H$_6$

Ethene, C$_2$H$_4$

Ethyne, C$_2$H$_2$

This effect, which is known as *hydrogen bonding*, is discussed in greater detail in Section 8.4(*c*). Covalent compounds are usually soluble in petrol, propanone (acetone), tetrachloromethane and other organic solvents.

Covalent molecules have a definite shape as – unlike the simple electrostatic attraction between the oppositely charged ions of an ionic

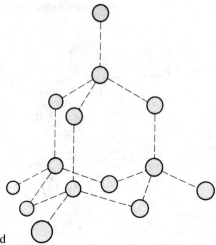

Fig. 8.5 Structure of diamond

Table 8.5 *General properties of ionic and covalent compounds*

Property	Ionic compounds	Covalent compounds
1. Composition	Charged ions	Uncharged molecules
2. Physical state	Solids with very high melting point and boiling point	Solid, liquid or gas – low melting point and boiling point
3. Hardness	Very hard	Soft
4. Electrical conductivity in solution or fused state	Conduct Electrolysis occurs	Do not conduct
5. Solubility in water	Soluble	Insoluble unless reaction occurs or compound contains —OH or —NH$_2$ groups
6. Solubility in organic solvents	Insoluble	Soluble
7. Shape of molecules	Indefinite	Definite

compound, such as sodium chloride or magnesium fluoride – the covalent bond is directional, with definite bond angles and bond lengths (see Section 8.2). The principal general differences between ionic and covalent compounds are summarised in Table 8.5.

(c) *The dative covalent bond*

The dative covalent bond is also known as the *co-ordinate* or *co-ionic bond*. It may be regarded as a special type of covalency in which *both* the shared electrons forming the bond are donated by a single atom. The bond is represented by an arrow in which the base of the arrow indicates the electron donor and the head of the arrow denotes the electron acceptor:

A : B   (*cf* a covalent bond

or   A $\times$ B or A $-$ B)

A$\longrightarrow$B
donor   acceptor

Alternatively, the bond may be regarded as being formed by the transference of an electron from atom A to atom B to give an ionic link ($A \cdot^+ \cdot B^-$). The electrons are then shared to form a covalent bond and the net result is a covalent-ionic link (or *co-ionic bond*):

$A^+ - B^-$

The formation of the ammonium ion by the reaction between a proton and the unbonded pair of electrons on the nitrogen atom of the ammonia molecule (see fig. 8.4) is an example of the dative covalent bond:

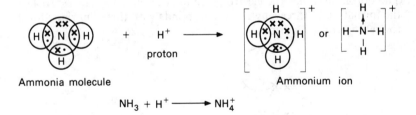

Ammonia molecule   Ammonium ion

$$NH_3 + H^+ \longrightarrow NH_4^+$$

By sharing the pair of electrons on the nitrogen atom the proton (or hydrogen ion, H^+) obtains the electronic configuration of the noble gas, helium.

The hydrogen ion (or free proton) is too small to exist in aqueous solution in the uncombined state. The ion does not have a noble gas configuration and the charge density on such a small particle would be enormous, see Table 8.6.

Table 8.6   Comparative sizes of particles

Particle	Diameter (/m)
Proton	10^{-15}
Other ions	approx. 10^{-10}
Atoms	approx. 10^{-10}

The proton achieves stability in aqueous solution by forming a dative covalent bond with the lone pair of electrons on the oxygen atom in the water molecule to form the *hydroxonium ion* (see pp. 58–60):

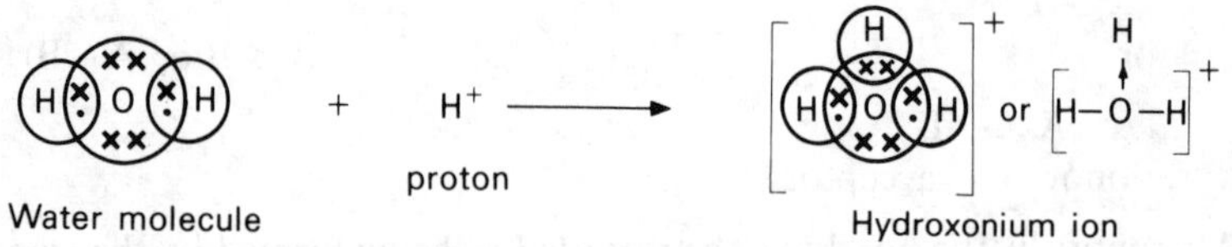

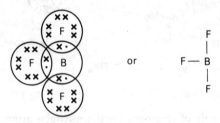

$$H_2O + H^+ \longrightarrow H_3O^+$$

The oxygen atom in the hydroxonium ion still possesses a non-bonding pair of electrons, but the atom does not form a second dative covalent bond to yield H_4O^{2+} owing to the repulsion of the positively charged ion to the approach of the second proton.

The boron trifluoride–ammonia adduct
The boron atom has the electronic configuration 2,3 (or $1s^2 2s^2 2p^1$) so the formation of three single covalent bonds with three fluorine atoms to yield boron trifluoride:

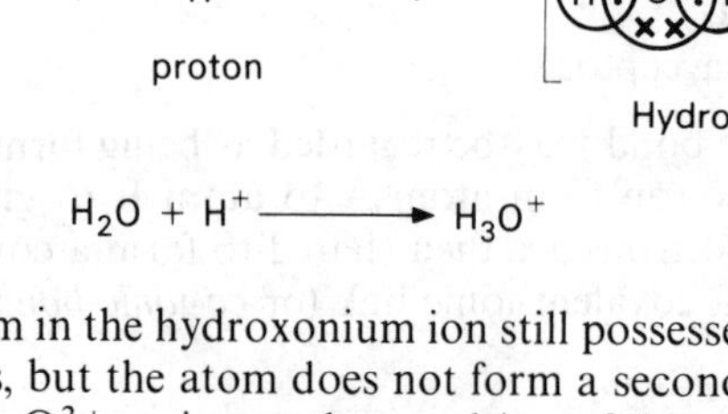

produces an electron deficient compound. The boron atom in this molecule has a share in only six electrons and does not have a noble gas configuration. The boron atom achieves stability in the boron trifluoride–ammonia adduct by forming a dative covalent bond with the lone pair of electrons on the nitrogen atom of ammonia:

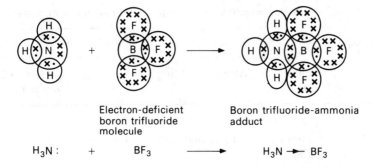

| Electron-deficient boron trifluoride molecule | Boron trifluoride-ammonia adduct |

$$H_3N : \quad + \quad BF_3 \quad \longrightarrow \quad H_3N \rightarrow BF_3$$

(d) The metallic bond

The atoms in a solid metal are arranged in a lattice structure as cations. For example, metallic silver in the solid state consists of a regular array of Ag^+ ions:

$$
\begin{array}{ccccccc}
Ag^+ & Ag^+ & Ag^+ & Ag^+ & Ag^+ & Ag^+ & Ag^+ \\
 & Ag^+ & Ag^+ & Ag^+ & Ag^+ & Ag^+ & Ag^+ & Ag^+ \\
Ag^+ & Ag^+ & Ag^+ & Ag^+ & Ag^+ & Ag^+ & Ag^+
\end{array}
$$

which are held in place by the valency electrons. These electrons are not associated with a single atom or ion but are spread over the entire metal structure, which thus consists of a lattice of positively charged ions in a 'sea' of electrons. The attraction between the cations and the negatively charged electron cloud forms the metallic bond. These electrons move very readily as soon as a potential difference is applied across the ends of the material (see fig. 8.6). This explains the high electrical conductivity of metals.

This structure also explains other typical metallic properties such as *malleability* and *ductility*. A solid is said to be malleable if it can be hammered into shape, and ductile if it can be drawn into wire. Continual hammering of a metallic structure would force the metal ions into fewer layers, but – as the electrons would still be free to move throughout the entire structure – the bonding between the metal ions would not be affected (see fig. 8.7). The principal general differences between metals and non-metals are summarised in Table 8.7.

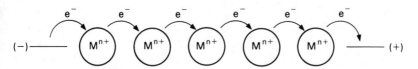

Fig. 8.6 The metallic bond: conductivity of metals

Table 8.7　General properties of metallic and non-metallic elements

Property	Metals	Non-metals
1. Bonding in solid state	Metallic bonding	Covalent molecules held together by van der Waals' forces (see Section 8.4(*a*))
2. Melting point and boiling point	Usually high	Usually low
3. Density	Usually high	Usually low
4. Lustrous appearance	Lustrous, can be polished. Opaque	Not lustrous
5. Electrical conductivity	Good conductors	Do not conduct
6. Thermal conductivity	Good conductors	Poor conductors of heat
7. Malleability and ductility	Malleable and ductile	Brittle
8. Reactivity of element	Electropositive. Loses electrons to form cations	Electronegative. Usually gains electrons to form anions or shares electrons to form covalent bonds
9. Nature of chloride	Ionic solids	Covalent volatile liquids or gases
10. Nature of oxide	Basic or amphoteric	Acidic or neutral

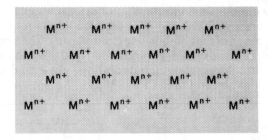

(a) Lattice of metal cations in a 'sea' of electrons

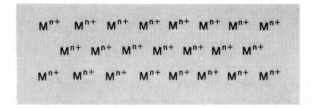

(b) Metal cations hammered or drawn into fewer layers,
but electrons still free to move

Fig. 8.7 The metallic bond: malleability and ductility of metals

8.2
Shapes of covalent molecules

Specific objective: *The expected learning outcome of this section is that the student is able to explain the shapes of simple gaseous molecules using the electron-pair repulsion approach for $BeCl_2$, BF_3, CH_4, NH_3 and H_2O.*

The shapes of simple covalent molecules are determined mainly by the mutual repulsion of the pairs of electrons about the central atom. This repulsion applies to both the bonding and the non-bonding electron pairs and the groups attached to the central atom will get as far apart as possible within the confines of the molecule in order to reduce this repulsion energy to a minimum. For example, the four hydrogen atoms in the methane molecule are arranged tetrahedrally about the carbon atom (see fig. 8.8(a)) as this configuration gives the maximum separation of the groups, while the ammonia (see fig. 8.8(b)) and water molecules (see fig. 8.8(c)) are pyramidal and bent (i.e. non-linear) respectively, owing to the repulsion of the non-bonding electron pairs. The formation of dative covalent bonds with a proton to yield the ammonium and hydroxonium ions produces tetrahedral and pyramidal cations respectively:

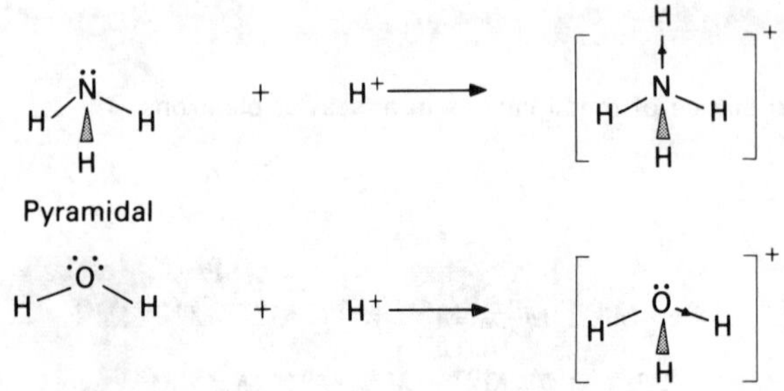

Pyramidal

Gaseous diatomic molecules, such as hydrogen chloride, must be linear, but the gaseous beryllium dichloride and carbon dioxide molecules (see fig. 8.9) are linear because this arrangement gives the greatest separation of the bonding electron pairs. The repulsion of the three bonding pairs of electrons about the boron atom in gaseous boron trifluoride produces a flat or planar molecule:

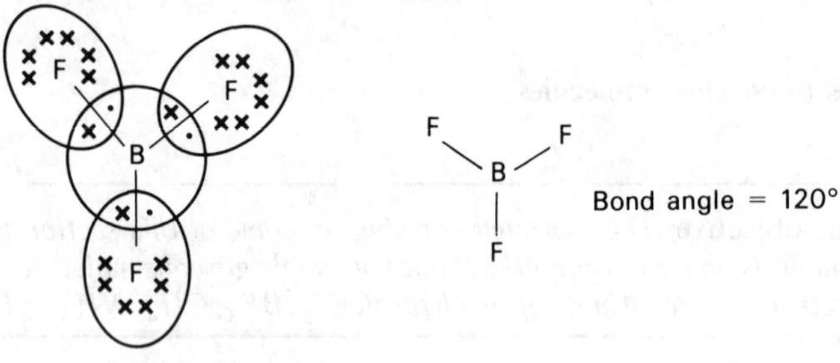

Bond angle = 120°

The shapes of simple molecules, such as those of water, ammonia and methane, may be used to predict the shapes of more complex structures. The shapes of the methanol, ethane, ethanol and methylamine molecules, for example, are shown in fig. 8.10.

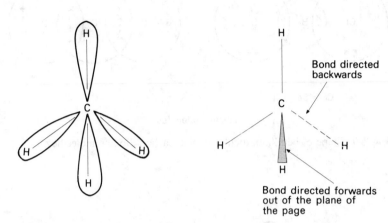

Bond angle = 109°28′

Bond directed
backwards

Bond directed forwards
out of the plane of
the page

Fig. 8.8(a) The methane molecule

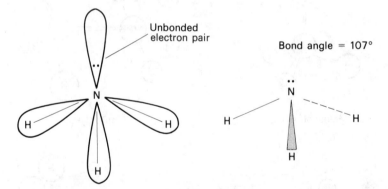

Unbonded
electron pair

Bond angle = 107°

Fig. 8.8(b) The ammonia molecule

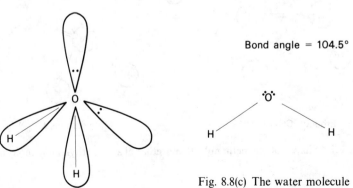

Bond angle = 104.5°

Fig. 8.8(c) The water molecule

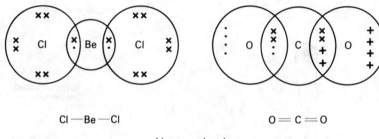

Cl —Be —Cl

O = C = O

Linear molecules

Fig. 8.9 Shape of beryllium dichloride and carbon dioxide molecules

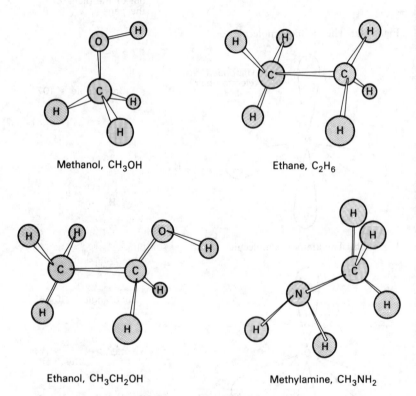

Methanol, CH_3OH

Ethane, C_2H_6

Ethanol, CH_3CH_2OH

Methylamine, CH_3NH_2

Fig. 8.10 Shapes of the methanol, ethane, ethanol and methylamine molecules

Experiment 8.1
To demonstrate the shape of simple covalent molecules

Equipment required
A ball and stick atomic model kit. Plasticine or polystyrene balls and cocktail sticks may be used if a molecular model kit is not available.
Procedure
Build models to demonstrate the shapes of the following molecules: HCl, $BeCl_2$, CH_4, NH_3, H_2O, C_2H_6 and CH_3OH. Demonstrate the changes which occur when the ammonium and hydroxonium ions are formed from the ammonia and water molecules respectively.

8.3
Polarisation of covalent bonds

Specific objectives: *The expected learning outcome of this section is that the student: (i) states that unequal sharing of electrons in bonds is due to the differing extent to which different atoms attract electrons (ii) states that this unequal sharing of electrons gives rise to bond polarisation (iii) recognises that ionic and covalent bonds are extreme forms and that intermediate forms can occur (iv) describes the hydrolysis of the halides of the p-block elements as evidence of (i) and (ii).*

Covalent bonds are formed by the sharing of electrons between two atoms. This sharing will be equal in the absence of an electrical field if the two atoms or groups forming the bond are the same. Hydrogen, chlorine and ethane are examples of molecules of this type, thus

$$H \times H \quad Cl \times Cl \quad CH_3 \times CH_3$$

However, sharing between the two atoms will not be equal if the atoms or groups joined by the bond differ in the extent to which they will attract electrons. For example, the chlorine atom in the gaseous hydrogen chloride molecule is more electronegative than hydrogen and thus exerts a greater force of attraction on the electrons in the bond. The electrons are displaced towards the chlorine atom and there is therefore a slightly higher electron density on this end of the molecule than on the hydrogen atom. This effect is known as the *inductive effect* and is represented by the arrow $\longrightarrow$:

$$\overset{\delta +}{H} \longrightarrow \overset{\delta -}{Cl} \qquad \overset{\delta +}{H} \overset{\bullet}{\underset{\times}{\quad}} \overset{\delta -}{Cl} \quad \text{higher electron density}$$

electron
deficiency
electrons in
bond attracted
towards the
chlorine atom

The points of relative electron deficiency and of relatively higher electron density are indicated by the symbols $\delta+$ and $\delta-$ respectively, where δ is the Greek letter, *delta*. This symbol is frequently used to indicate partial quantities or small differences. The overall charge on the hydrogen chloride molecule is zero, but the molecule as a whole is now a *dipole* as it has separated regions or points of opposite electrical charge. This displacement of electrons within a bond is known as *polarisation* and molecules in which there is an *overall* charge separation, i.e. where the molecule as a whole is a dipole, are said to be *polar*.

Water is an example of a polar solvent owing to the different electronegativities of the hydrogen and oxygen atoms in the non-linear molecule:

$$
\begin{array}{c}
\overset{\delta+}{H} \\
\searrow\;\;\overset{\delta-}{O} \\
\overset{\delta+}{H}\nearrow
\end{array}
$$

Tetrachloromethane is a non-polar molecule as the dipoles from the four carbon–chlorine bonds cancel one another out in the symmetrical molecule (fig. 8.11). This difference may be demonstrated using the apparatus shown in fig. 8.12. An ebonite rod is given a negative charge by rubbing it with *dry* fur. The charged rod deflects the stream of water, trichloromethane (chloroform), propanone (acetone) or other polar liquids emerging from the burette, but has no effect on tetrachloromethane or cyclohexane. The polar liquid is attracted towards a positive or a negative charge, e.g.

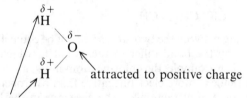

attracted to positive charge

attracted to negative charge

Demonstration 8.1
To demonstrate the attraction of a polar solvent by a charged ebonite rod

Apparatus and materials
An ebonite rod. A piece of fur. A burette and burette stand. 100 cm³ beaker. Water, trichloromethane and tetrachloromethane.

Method
Set up the apparatus as shown in fig. 8.12. Dry the fur thoroughly by

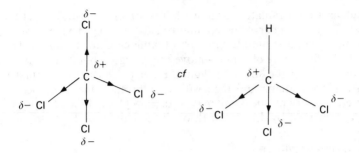

Effect cancels out —
CCl$_4$ molecule not polar

Fig. 8.11 Structure of tetrachloromethane

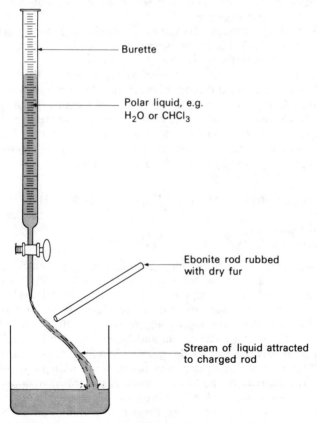

Fig. 8.12 Deflection of a polar liquid by a charged ebonite rod

placing it on a radiator for a few hours, or in a warm oven at about 100°, and then charge the ebonite rod by rubbing it vigorously with the fur. Open the burette tap and – taking care not to splash the rod with the fine spray of water – move the charged ebonite rod to within about 1 cm of the stream of liquid. Repeat this experiment first with tetrachloromethane and then with trichloromethane from clean, dry burettes. A dry plastic comb may be used in place of the ebonite rod. It is first charged by drawing it through the hair several times.

(a) Electronegativity

The electronegativity of an atom in a molecule is a measure of its power to attract electrons. Naturally this attraction – and hence the degree of polarity within the bond – will depend on the electronegativity of the other atoms to which the atom is attached in the molecule. Various attempts have been made to give numerical values to the electro-negativities of the atoms. The most widely used scale was devised by Pauling from bond strengths.

The Pauling electronegativity values of a number of common elements are listed in fig. 8.13. The electronegativities of hydrogen and chlorine are 2.1 and 3.0 respectively. The higher value of chlorine indicates that it is negatively charged relative to the hydrogen atom in the hydrogen chloride molecule. The difference between the electronegativities of the two atoms forming a bond is a measure of the bond's polarity. The decreasing electronegativity of the halogens in terms of Pauling electro-negativity values with increasing atomic radius (see Section 7.2(a)(iv)) is shown in fig. 8.14 and is reflected in the decreasing polarisation (or ionic character) of the hydrogen–halogen bond in:

Pauling electronegativity value:	H$\rightarrow$F	H$\rightarrow$Cl	H$\rightarrow$Br	H$\rightarrow$I
	2.1 4.0	2.1 3.0	2.1 2.8	2.1 2.5
Difference in electronegativity:	1.9	0.9	0.7	0.4

Covalent and ionic bonds may be regarded as extreme forms of polarisation of a covalent bond. This charge separation is virtually complete in purely ionic compounds, such as potassium fluoride, where the difference in electronegativity of the two atoms is as high as three units. However, there are many compounds, e.g. $FeCl_2$, LiI and FeS, in which the electron distribution, and hence the type of bonding, is intermediate between that of the pure ionic and pure covalent bond. The change from predominantly ionic to covalent bonding with decreas-ing electronegativity of the halogen atom is illustrated by aluminium fluoride and aluminium chloride or bromide. Aluminium fluoride, AlF_3, is an ionic compound with the expected high melting point, while the corresponding chloride and bromide are *dimeric* covalent compounds,

			H				
			2.1				

Li	Be			B	C	N	O	F
1.0	1.5			2.0	2.5	3.0	3.5	4.0

Na	Mg			Al	Si	P	S	Cl
0.9	1.2	d-block elements:		1.5	1.8	2.1	2.5	3.0
K	Ca	electronegativity		Ga	Ge	As	Se	Br
0.8	1.0	varies between		1.6	1.8	2.0	2.4	2.8
Rb	Sr	1.3 and 1.9						I
0.8	1.0							2.5
Cs	Ba							
0.7	0.9							

Fig. 8.13 Pauling electronegativity values of the elements

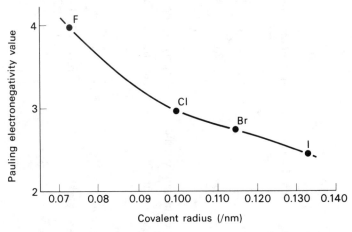

Fig. 8.14 Relationship between Pauling electronegativity value of the halogens and atomic (covalent) radius

$(AlCl_3)_2$ or $(AlBr_3)_2$, which either sublime readily on heating or have low melting points (see Table 8.8). The two $AlCl_3$ or $AlBr_3$ *monomer* units in the dimeric aluminium chloride or aluminium bromide molecules are joined together by dative covalent bonds.

(b) Hydrolysis of the chlorides of the p-block elements
The action of water on the halides of the s- and p-block elements provides evidence for the polarisation of the bonds. The chlorides of the highly electropositive metals of the s-block (except beryllium) are

Table 8.8 Comparison of the aluminium halides

	Aluminium fluoride	Aluminium chloride	Aluminium bromide
Structure	$Al^{3+}F_3^-$	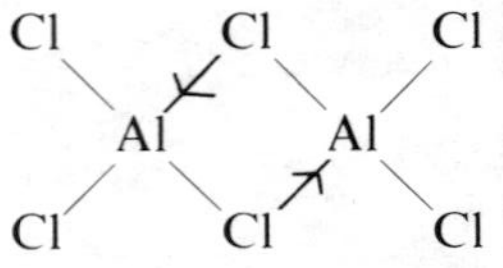	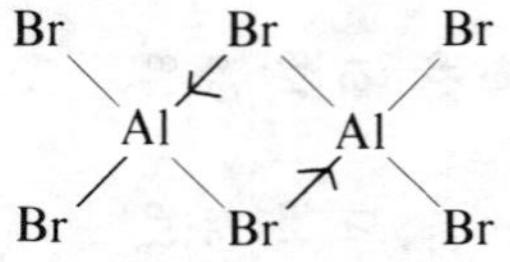
Bonding	predominantly ionic	largely covalent	covalent
Melting point (/°C)	sublimes at 1291	sublimes at 178	97.5
Boiling point (/°C)	—	—	263 at 747 mmHg
Solubility in organic solvents	Insoluble	Soluble	Soluble
Action of water	Insoluble	Violently hydrolysed (see Section 8.3(b))	Violently hydrolysed

ionic. They are not hydrolysed by water, but dissolve to give an aqueous solution of metal cations and chloride anions from which the anhydrous salt may be recovered by evaporation to dryness. The halides of the elements of the p-block are predominantly covalent and many are intermediate in both bonding and behaviour. As we saw in the last section, aluminium fluoride is not affected by water (a characteristic property of an ionic halide), but aluminium chloride and aluminium bromide fume in moist air owing to the formation of the strongly acid hydrogen chloride or hydrogen bromide vapour. This chemical breakdown by the action of water (i.e. hydrolysis) is typical of the covalent chlorides. Additional evidence is provided by their physical properties; thus most of the chlorides of the non-metals of the p-block are volatile liquids or gases (see Table 8.9). The chemical equations for the hydrolysis of the chlorides of a number of p-block elements of the second and third periods are given in Table 8.10.

The boron atom in boron trichloride has only six electrons in the valency shell (see Section 8.1(*c*)) and thus readily forms a dative covalent bond with the unbonded pair of electrons on the oxygen atom of a water molecule. Progressive replacement of chlorine atoms by hydroxyl groups follows as hydrogen chloride is eliminated:

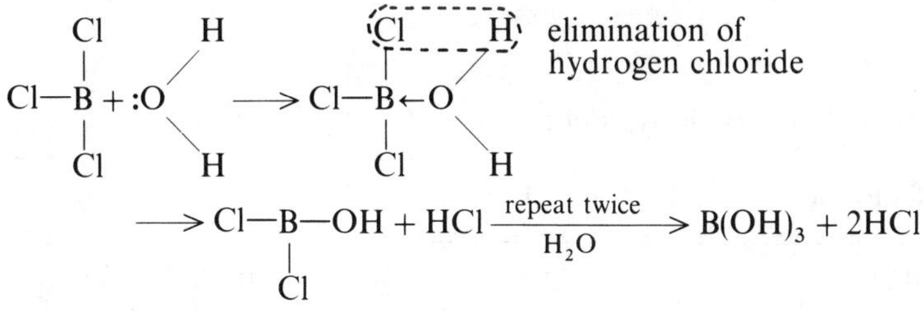

The carbon atom in tetrachloromethane has a filled valency shell of four bonding pairs of electrons and is inert to water. The central atom of the other chlorides in this period have at least one non-bonding electron pair which interacts with the hydrogen atom of water, e.g.

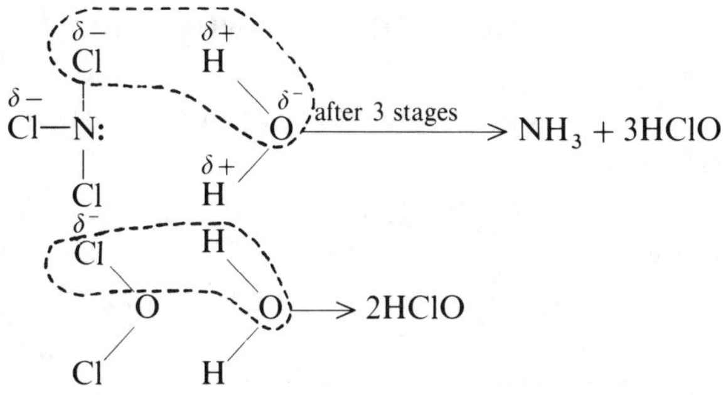

Table 8.9   Melting points and boiling points of the chlorides of the p-block elements

	BCl_3	CCl_4	NCl_3	Cl_2O	ClF
m.p. (/°C)	-107	-23	-40 (approx.)	-20	-155 (approx.)
b.p. (/°C)	12.5	76.5	71 (approx.)	explodes at 3°	-100

	Al_2Cl_6	$SiCl_4$	PCl_3	SCl_2	(Cl_2)
m.p.	sublimes at 178	-70	-112	-78	-101
b.p.	—	58	77	59 (decomposes)	-34.6

Table 8.10   Hydrolysis of the chlorides of p-block elements

Chloride	Equation
BCl_3 boron trichloride	$BCl_3 + 3H_2O \longrightarrow B(OH)_3 + 3HCl$ boric acid
CCl_4 tetrachloromethane	does not react with water
$SiCl_4$ silicon tetrachloride	$SiCl_4 + 4H_2O \longrightarrow SiO_2 2H_2O + 4HCl$ hydrated silica
NCl_3 nitrogen trichloride	$NCl_3 + 3H_2O \longrightarrow NH_3 + 3HClO$
PCl_3 phosphorus trichloride	$PCl_3 + 3H_2O \longrightarrow H_3PO_3 + 3HCl$
Cl_2O chlorine monoxide	$Cl_2O + H_2O \longrightarrow 2HClO$
Cl_2 chlorine	$Cl_2 + H_2O \longrightarrow HCl + HClO$

Experiment 8.2
To investigate the effect of water on the chlorides of s-block and p-block elements

Materials and apparatus
Sodium or potassium chloride. Phosphorus trichloride. Sulphur dichloride or sulphur monochloride (SCl_2 or S_2Cl_2). Anhydrous aluminium chloride (Al_2Cl_6). Hydrated aluminium chloride [$Al(H_2O)_6]Cl_3$. Tetrachloromethane (carbon tetrachloride). Aqueous silver nitrate solution. Sodium carbonate solution. Distilled water. Test-tubes. Universal indicator paper or litmus.

Note: the covalent chlorides should be *treated with care* as these materials and their fumes are harmful to the eyes, skin and lungs.

Method
(a) Dissolve a small amount of sodium (or potassium) chloride in distilled water in a test-tube and determine its approximate pH with indicator paper. Divide the solution into three portions, A, B and C. Evaporate A to dryness. Test B and C with aqueous silver nitrate and sodium carbonate solution respectively.

(ii) Shake 1–2 cm^3 of pure tetrachloromethane with 2–3 cm^3 of aqueous silver nitrate solution. Note whether any reaction occurs.

(iii) Heat a sample of hydrated aluminium chloride in a test-tube. Smell the gas evolved and test it with litmus or indicator paper. Allow the residue to cool and then add a little distilled water. Determine the approximate pH of the mixture. Separate the liquid into two portions and test the first with silver nitrate solution and the second with aqueous sodium carbonate. Compare the results with those of similar tests (i.e. the pH and the action of silver nitrate or sodium carbonate) on samples of an aqueous solution of hydrated aluminium chloride.

(iv) Note the effect of water on *small* amounts of phosphorus trichloride, sulphur dichloride and anhydrous aluminium chloride.

Record all results and observations in your practical book. How do you interpret these observations?

8.4
The forces between molecules

Specific objectives: *The expected learning outcome of this section is that the student: (i) states that van der Waals' forces exist between atoms and covalent molecules (ii) states that weak electrostatic forces exist between polar covalent molecules (iii) describes hydrogen-bonding as a special case of these dipole-dipole attractive forces, using water as an example (iv) explains the anomalous boiling point of water and ammonia on this basis,* *given graphs of boiling points of hydrides against atomic number (v) places the following forces in order of increasing magnitude: ion/ion, dipole/ dipole, van der Waals' (vi) relates this order to the physical characteristics of $NaCl_{(s)}$, $H_2O_{(l)}$ and $O_{2(g)}$.*

The weak attractive forces between the uncharged molecules of covalent substances, such as paraffin wax, iodine and carbon dioxide, in the solid state explains the low melting point and the softness of many *molecular crystals* compared with the hard, high melting point *ionic crystals* (e.g. sodium chloride, see fig. 8.1) and *covalent network crystals* (such as diamond, see fig. 8.5). These forces are considerably weaker than covalent bonds (e.g. bond dissociation energy of H–H and C–H bonds = 436 and 412 kJ mol^{-1} respectively) and the powerful electrostatic attraction between oppositely charged ions. Nevertheless, their existence plays an important and even vital role in determining the shape and properties of many covalent molecules, including those of such biologically important substances as proteins and carbohydrates. The principal types of intermolecular forces are:
(a) van der Waals' forces,
(b) dipole–dipole interactions,
(c) hydrogen bonding.
The strong electrostatic forces between the oppositely charged ions of an ionic compound were discussed in Section 8.1(*a*).

(a) van der Waals' forces
Van der Waals' forces are present in all matter and even exist between such non-polar molecules as hydrogen, nitrogen, chlorine and the noble gases. The existence of these forces explains why such substances can be liquefied and why iodine exists as a solid at room temperature. The forces are produced by the *temporary* distortion or polarisation of the electron cloud around the atom or molecule. As an average over a period of time, this electron distribution within a chlorine or a hydrogen molecule, for example, or an atom of neon or argon is symmetrical. However, at a given instant the electron distribution at one end of the molecule may be larger momentarily than at the other, thus forming a temporary dipole (see fig. 8.15). This dipole will induce a dipole in any molecule or atom which approaches it *either* by attracting the electrons towards its positive end *or* repelling them from its negative end (see fig. 8.16).

This temporary polarisation of the molecule may be reversed in the next instant by the redistribution of the electron cloud and will therefore reverse the polarisation of the molecules in the immediate vicinity. This fluctuating polarisation produces weak attractive forces between the molecules which are known as *van der Waals' forces* after their discoverer. The effect is negligible at low pressures as the molecules are

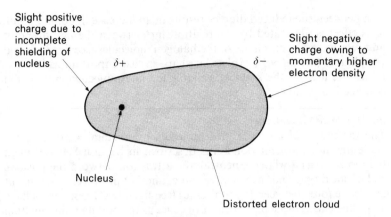

Fig. 8.15 Formation of a temporary dipole

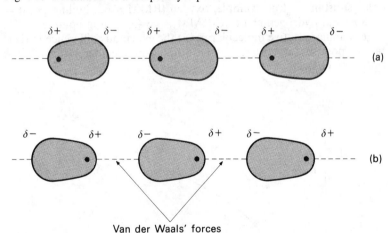

Fig. 8.16 Van der Waals' forces

too far apart, but it becomes increasingly important as the gas is compressed and the molecules are forced closer together. If the gas is cooled under pressure, the van der Waals' forces are sufficient for it to liquefy or even form a solid. Van der Waals' forces are very weak and are usually between a tenth and a hundredth of the strength of a covalent bond. Because the electron cloud is more easily polarised, the strength of the van der Waals' forces increases as the number of electrons in the molecule increases. The number of electrons in a molecule increases with relative molecular mass, so the greater attraction between the induced dipoles results in an increase in boiling point. This effect is illustrated by the relationship between the boiling point and relative molecular mass of the halogen molecules (see fig. 8.17) and the alkanes (see fig. 9.1). Molecular shape is also important as it determines the area of the surface available for intermolecular interaction (see Section 9.5(a)).

(b) Dipole–dipole interactions

The formation of a dipole in a molecule by unequal sharing of the electrons in a covalent bond was described in Section 8.3. Although the molecule as a whole is neutral, the attraction between the positive end of one dipole and the negative end of another produces a significant attractive force between the molecules (see fig. 8.18). These forces have a marked effect on such physical properties as the boiling point, melting point, vapour pressure and hardness of polar as compared with non-polar substances. For example, oxygen (RMM = 32, boiling point = $-183°$) and hydrogen chloride (RMM = 36.45, boiling point = $-85°$) have a similar relative molecular mass; the enormous difference in their boiling points is largely a result of the dipole–dipole interaction in liquid hydrogen chloride.

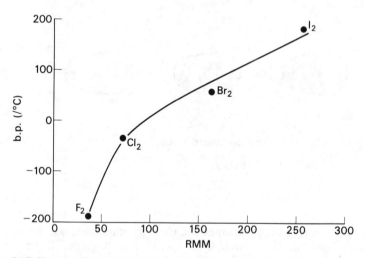

Fig. 8.17 Van der Waals' forces: Relationship between the boiling point and RMM of the halogens

Fig. 8.18 Dipole–dipole attraction in hydrogen chloride

(c) Hydrogen bonding

Certain compounds exhibit considerably stronger intermolecular attractive forces. These forces are apparent in molecules in which a hydrogen atom is linked to a fluorine, oxygen or nitrogen atom and are called *hydrogen bonds* to distinguish them from other dipole–dipole interactions. Intermolecular hydrogen bonding results in far higher melting points and boiling points than would be expected from the compound's relative molecular mass (see fig. 8.19). In general, the boiling point of compounds of similar structure increase with increasing relative molecular mass as the hydrides of the Group IV elements indicate. However, the boiling points of water, ammonia and hydrogen fluoride are unusually high because of the partial association (or joining together) of the molecules by hydrogen-bonding (see fig. 8.19(b)), e.g.

Hydrogen bonds

More energy is needed to separate these molecules from the attraction of their neighbours before the substance can pass from the liquid phase into the vapour state and the liquid will therefore have a lower vapour pressure and a higher boiling point.

Hydrogen bonding is a special type of dipole–dipole interaction. Fluorine, oxygen and nitrogen are the three most electronegative elements of small radius (see fig. 8.13) and strongly attract the pair of electrons in a covalent bond with the hydrogen atom. As hydrogen has no inner electron shell, the displacement of these electrons leaves the hydrogen nucleus exposed and readily available to attract other dipoles (see fig. 8.20). Hydrogen chloride does not form hydrogen bonds, even though the electronegativity of the chlorine atom is the same as nitrogen, because of the repulsion of the non-bonding electron pairs on the larger halogen atom (see fig. 8.21).

Hydrogen bonding is responsible for the solubility of compounds with hydroxyl groups (such as alcohols and sugars) or amino groups (e.g. ammonia) in water (see Section 8.1(*b*)), e.g.

The open structure of the ice crystal (see fig. 8.22) which gives it a lower density than that of water at 0° is held together by hydrogen bonding between the water molecules. Similarly, the stability of the spiral (α-helix) structure of the polypeptide chain in naturally occurring protein molecules is a result of hydrogen bonding (see fig. 8.23).

Hydrogen bonds are slightly stronger than van der Waals' forces, but are considerably weaker than covalent bonds or the enormously strong electrostatic attraction between the oppositely charged ions of an ionic compound. The relative bond strengths are summarised in Table 8.11 and the order of increasing magnitude is thus: van der Waals' forces, dipole–dipole interaction/hydrogen bonding, ion–ion attraction. This is reflected in the differences in physical properties of oxygen, hydrogen chloride, water and sodium chloride:

Property	O_2	HCl	H_2O	NaCl
Melting point (/°C)	−218	−115	0	801
Boiling point (/°C)	−183	−85	100	1467
Type of attraction between particles	van der Waals'	dipole–dipole interaction	H–bonding	ion–ion electrostatic attraction

However it should be remembered that it is not possible to consider these different forces in isolation as van der Waals' forces are also present between the molecules of hydrogen chloride or water.

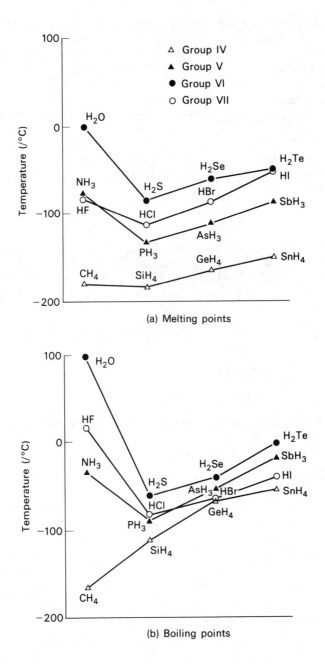

Fig. 8.19 Hydrogen bonding: melting points and boiling points of hydrides

Table 8.11 Relative strengths of intermolecular forces and chemical bonds

Bond or force	Strength (/kJ mol^{-1})
van der Waals'	3 approx.
Dipole–dipole interaction/ hydrogen bonding	5–40
Covalent bonds ionic bonds	100–800

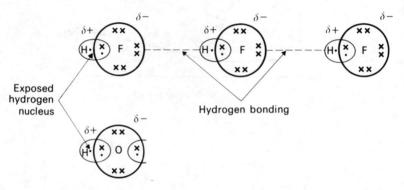

Fig. 8.20 Hydrogen bonding in hydrogen fluoride and the hydroxyl group

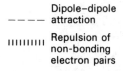

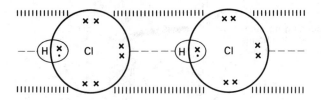

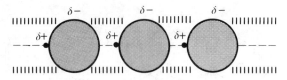

Fig. 8.21 Intermolecular forces in hydrogen chloride

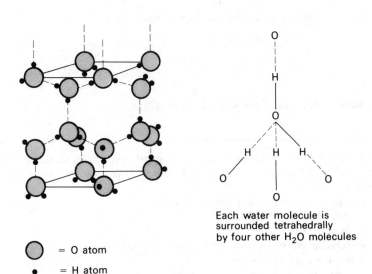

Each water molecule is
surrounded tetrahedrally
by four other H_2O molecules

⬡ = O atom

● = H atom

- - - - Hydrogen bonding

Fig. 8.22 The structure of ice

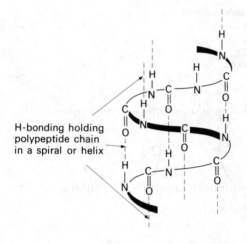

Fig. 8.23 Hydrogen bonds and the shape of the polypeptide chain

8.5
General properties of the s-block elements

Specific objectives: *The expected learning outcome of this section is that the student:* (i) *describes the general properties associated with s-block elements, e.g.*
1. *cation forming ability (reducing ability)*
2. *invariable ionic valency*
3. *basicity of oxides*
4. *relative thermal stability of carbonates and nitrates*
5. *ionic nature of chlorides*
6. *very limited gradation of properties within the block*

(ii) *describes examples of at least two s-block elements which illustrate these properties.*

The s-block elements consist of the alkali and alkaline earth metals of Groups IA and IIA respectively. These two groups are characterised by electronic configurations containing one or two electrons respectively in the s-orbital of the next highest energy level from a stable noble gas configuration:

Alkali metals (Group IA)

Li	Na	K	Rb	Cs
(He) $2s^1$	(Ne) $3s^1$	(Ar) $4s^1$	(Kr) $5s^1$	(Xe) $6s^1$

Alkaline earth metals (Group IIA)

Be	Mg	Ca	Sr	Ba
(He) $2s^2$	(Ne) $3s^2$	(Ar) $4s^2$	(Kr) $5s^2$	(Xe) $6s^2$

This similarity in electronic configuration is paralleled by a considerable uniformity in the chemical and physical properties of the s-block elements and of their compounds. Any differences result mainly from differences in the size and charge of the atoms or ions of the elements concerned (see fig. 8.24) and is apparent in the stability and solubility of some of the compounds of the Group IA and Group IIA elements. Beryllium is largely omitted from the following discussion. It has the smallest atom and forms the smallest ion in the two groups and is therefore slightly different in many of its properties from the other s-block elements. The main similarities within these groups are in the following properties:

(a) Metallic character and cation forming ability
All the s-block elements are metals (*cf* Table 8.6). They conduct electricity and are malleable and ductile (particularly the alkali metals). They have a shiny surface when freshly cut, but this rapidly becomes tarnished by the formation of a surface film of oxide and carbonate on exposure to air, e.g.

$$4Na + O_2 \longrightarrow 2Na_2O$$
$$2Ca + O_2 \longrightarrow 2CaO$$

This attack is particularly fast with the alkali metals which are usually stored under liquid paraffin for this reason. These metals also react with water. For example, if a small piece of sodium is dropped into a beaker of water the metal melts and moves about rapidly on the surface of the liquid as it dissolves to give a strongly alkaline solution of sodium hydroxide:

$$Na_{(s)} + 2H_2O_{(l)} \longrightarrow 2NaOH_{(aq)} + H_{2(g)}$$

Potassium is even more reactive in this respect and the heat liberated is sufficient to ignite the metal and the hydrogen which is evolved. The reaction of large pieces of sodium, potassium or the other alkali metals with water can be explosive. The alkaline earth metals are less reactive,

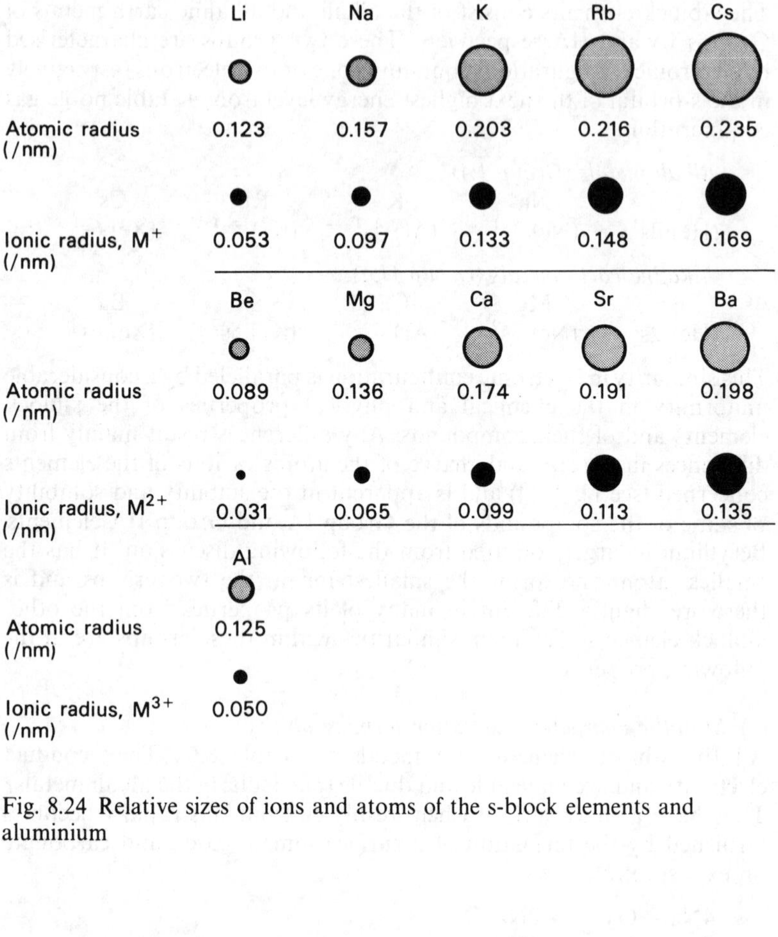

	Li	Na	K	Rb	Cs
Atomic radius (/nm)	0.123	0.157	0.203	0.216	0.235
Ionic radius, M^+ (/nm)	0.053	0.097	0.133	0.148	0.169

	Be	Mg	Ca	Sr	Ba
Atomic radius (/nm)	0.089	0.136	0.174	0.191	0.198
Ionic radius, M^{2+} (/nm)	0.031	0.065	0.099	0.113	0.135

	Al
Atomic radius (/nm)	0.125
Ionic radius, M^{3+} (/nm)	0.050

Fig. 8.24 Relative sizes of ions and atoms of the s-block elements and aluminium

thus calcium reacts slowly with cold water:

$$Ca + 2H_2O \longrightarrow Ca(OH)_2 + H_2$$

while magnesium will react only with hot water or steam. Magnesium ribbon burns brilliantly in steam to yield the oxide and hydrogen:

$$Mg_{(s)} + H_2O_{(g)} \longrightarrow MgO_{(s)} + H_{2(g)}$$
$$\text{steam}$$

The alkali metals have low melting points and densities, and are softer than the alkaline earth metals (see Table 8.12). Sodium and potassium, for example, can be cut with a knife, while calcium is a hard, brittle metal. All the s-block elements are powerful reducing agents owing to the ease with which they will form cations:

$$M \longrightarrow M^{n+} + ne^-$$
$$\text{metal} \qquad \text{cation}$$

This cation forming ability is reflected in their standard electrode potential (see Section 5.4) and as the most electropositive of the metals they are found at the head of the electrochemical series (see Section 5.5). The metals are isolated by the electrolysis of their fused chloride (see Section 5.5(d). The powerful reducing ability of magnesium or sodium is employed to isolate the useful metal titanium from its chloride:

$$TiCl_4 + 2Mg \xrightarrow{\;850\;} Ti + 2MgCl_2$$

(b) Invariable ionic valency
The alkali and alkaline earth metals attain a stable, noble gas configuration by the loss of one or two electrons respectively from the outermost s-orbital, e.g.

$$K \longrightarrow K^+ + e^-$$
$$(Ar)\ 4s^1 \qquad (Ar)$$

$$Mg \longrightarrow Mg^{2+} + 2e^-$$
$$(Ne)\ 3s^2 \qquad (Ne)$$

Thus the elements have an invariable valency of $+1$ and $+2$ respectively and virtually all their compounds are ionic. The s-block cations are colourless and the only coloured salts of the Group IA and Group IIA elements are those containing a coloured anion, such as chromate(VI),

Table 8.12   Physical properties of the s-block elements

	Group IA			Group IIA	
Element	m.p. ($/^\circ$C)	Density ($/g\ cm^{-3}$)	Element	m.p. ($/^\circ$C)	Density ($/g\ cm^{-3}$)
Li	180	0.53	Be	1280	1.86
Na	98	0.97	Mg	650	1.75
K	63.5	0.86	Ca	850	1.55
Rb	39	1.53	Sr	770	2.60
Cs	28.5	1.90	Ba	720	3.60

dichromate(VI) or manganate(VII) (permanganate), e.g.

$$\left.\begin{array}{l} \text{NaCl, KCl, NaI, KBr, Na}_2\text{CO}_3, \\ \text{NaHCO}_3, \text{Na}_3\text{PO}_4, \text{KNO}_3, \text{MgCl}_2, \\ \text{CaCl}_2, \text{MgCO}_3, \text{CaCO}_3, \text{Mg(NO}_3)_2 \end{array}\right\}$$ white or colourless

$\text{Na}_2\text{CrO}_4, \text{K}_2\text{CrO}_4, \text{BaCrO}_4$ yellow

$$\left.\begin{array}{l} \text{Na}_2\text{Cr}_2\text{O}_7 \\ \text{K}_2\text{Cr}_2\text{O}_7 \end{array}\right\}$$ orange

KMnO_4 purple

(c) Basic strength of the oxides and hydroxides

The oxides and hydroxides of the s-block elements are both basic and those of the alkali metals are significantly stronger than the corresponding compounds of the alkaline earths (see Section 7.2(b)(iv)). In each case the basic strength increases with increasing radius of the metal cation because of the greater difference in electronegativity (see fig. 8.13). The oxides of the alkali metals dissolve violently in water to yield an aqueous solution of the corresponding metal hydroxide, e.g.

$$\text{K}_2\text{O}_{(s)} + \text{H}_2\text{O}_{(l)} \longrightarrow 2\text{KOH}_{(aq)}$$

Unlike the corresponding compounds of the alkali metals, the hydroxides of the alkaline earth metals are only slightly soluble in water, increasing from 2×10^{-4} g l^{-1} for magnesium hydroxide to approximately 40 g l^{-1} for barium hydroxide. Magnesium oxide reacts only slowly with water and is sparingly soluble. Calcium, strontium and barium oxides are hydrolysed more violently:

$$\text{O}^{2-} + \text{H}_2\text{O} \longrightarrow 2\text{OH}^-$$

and considerable amounts of heat are evolved, often sufficient to cause any excess of water to boil.

Sodium oxide and potassium oxide are usually prepared by reducing the nitrate(V) with the corresponding alkali metal, e.g.

$$2\text{KNO}_{3(s)} + 10\text{K}_{(s)} \xrightarrow{\text{heat}} 6\text{K}_2\text{O}_{(s)} + \text{N}_{2(g)}$$

although sodium oxide may be obtained by the direct reaction of sodium with air:

$$4\text{Na}_{(s)} + \text{O}_{2(g)} \xrightarrow{\text{heat}} 2\text{Na}_2\text{O}_{(s)}$$

The oxides of the alkaline earth metals are formed by heating the carbonate in an open vessel:

$$\text{MCO}_3 \underset{\xrightarrow{\text{heat}}}{\rightleftharpoons} \text{MO} + \text{CO}_2$$

(*d*) *Relative thermal stability of carbonates and nitrates*

In general, the compounds of the Group IIA metals decompose at a lower temperature than the corresponding compound of the Group IA element in the same period. Thermal stability is particularly low in compounds consisting of a small cation (e.g. Li^+, Be^{2+} and Mg^{2+}) and large anion (e.g. CO_3^{2-} or NO_3^-) owing to polarisation and distortion of the anion by the high charge density of the metal ion. Thus, lithium carbonate decomposes on heating to yield lithium oxide and carbon dioxide:

$$Li_2CO_{3(s)} \xrightarrow{\text{heat}} Li_2O_{(s)} + CO_{2(g)}$$

while the carbonates of the other alkali metals are stable to heat. The carbonates of all the alkaline earth metals decompose on heating, e.g.

$$CaCO_3 \xrightarrow{\text{heat}} CaO + CO_2$$

and the decrease in stability with decreasing size of the cation is illustrated by the decomposition temperatures at atmospheric pressure (see Table 8.13).

Table 8.13   Decomposition temperatures of the carbonates of the Group IIA metals

Compound:	$BeCO_3$	$MgCO_3$	$CaCO_3$	$SrCO_3$	$BaCO_3$
Decomposition temperature ($/^\circ C$)	25	540	900	1290	1360

The nitrates of the s-block elements show a similar trend in their thermal stability. Lithium nitrate yields lithium oxide, nitrogen dioxide and oxygen on heating:

$$2LiNO_{3(s)} \xrightarrow{\text{heat}} Li_2O_{(s)} + 2NO_{2(g)} + \tfrac{1}{2}O_{2(g)}$$

while sodium nitrate and potassium nitrate melt at 316° and 336° respectively and then decompose on stronger heating to form the nitrite and oxygen:

$$2NaNO_{3(s)} \xrightarrow{\text{heat}} 2NaNO_{2(s)} + O_{2(g)}$$

$$2KNO_{3(s)} \xrightarrow{\text{heat}} 2KNO_{2(s)} + O_{2(g)}$$

The lower stability of sodium nitrite compared with the corresponding potassium compound is confirmed by the formation of brown fumes of nitrogen dioxide on stronger heating.

Of the Group IIA metals only calcium, strontium and barium form anhydrous nitrates. Their thermal stability increases down the group with increasing size of the cation, thus barium nitrate decomposes only on strong heating:

$$2Ba(NO_3)_{2(s)} \xrightarrow{\text{heat}} 2BaO_{(s)} + 4NO_{2(g)} + O_{2(g)}$$

The hydrated nitrates of the alkaline earth metals, e.g. $Be(NO_3)_2 \cdot 4H_2O$, $Mg(NO_3)_2 \cdot 6H_2O$, $Ca(NO_3)_2 \cdot 4H_2O$ and $Sr(NO_3)_2$, also decompose on heating. Hydrated calcium and strontium nitrate first lose their water of crystallisation to yield the anhydrous salt. Beryllium and magnesium nitrate are hydrolysed on heating to about 200° and 400° respectively and decompose completely to form the oxide without first yielding the anhydrous salt, e.g.

$$2Mg(NO_3)_2 \cdot 6H_2O \xrightarrow{\text{heat}} 2MgO + 4NO_2 + O_2 + 12H_2O$$

Experiment 8.3
To compare the thermal stability of the carbonates and nitrates of the s-block elements

Apparatus and materials
Test-tubes. Delivery tubes. Wooden splints to test for oxygen. Lime water. Lithium carbonate. Sodium or potassium carbonate. Calcium carbonate. Zinc carbonate or basic copper carbonate. Lithium nitrate. Potassium nitrate. Magnesium nitrate.

Method
Heat small amounts of the carbonates in turn in test-tubes fitted with a delivery-tube to pass any gases evolved into lime water. Compare the rates at which the lime water becomes turbid and from your results list the carbonates in order of increasing thermal stability.

Heat small amounts of the nitrates in dry test-tubes. Test for the evolution of oxygen with a glowing splint and note whether brown fumes of nitrogen dioxide are evolved.

(e) Ionic nature of the chlorides
The chlorides of the alkali metals have high melting points (see Table 8.14) and are strongly ionic. They dissolve in water to give a neutral solution of the simple hydrated ions which reforms the anhydrous salt on evaporation, i.e. hydrolysis does not occur. The chlorides of the alkaline earth metals, except beryllium and to some extent magnesium, are also ionic. Anhydrous beryllium chloride is a covalent white solid which

Table 8.14   Melting points of the chlorides of the s-block elements

| Group IA metals | | Group IIA metals | |
Formula	Melting point (/°C)	Formula	Melting point (/°C)
LiCl	605	$BeCl_2$	405
NaCl	801	$MgCl_2$	714
KCl	770	$CaCl_2$	782
RbCl	718	$SrCl_2$	875
CsCl	645	$BaCl_2$	957

fumes in air (*cf.* Section 8.3(*b*)). Anhydrous magnesium chloride shows some covalent character. Hydrated magnesium chloride, $MgCl_2 2H_2O$ or $MgCl_2 6H_2O$, or an aqueous solution of the salt is partly hydrolysed on heating to yield basic chlorides, such as Mg(OH)Cl, and hydrogen chloride. The anhydrous salt is therefore prepared by heating the hydrate in gaseous hydrogen chloride or by the action of chlorine on the hot oxide in the presence of carbon:

$$MgO + C + Cl_2 \xrightarrow{\text{heat}} MgCl_2 + CO$$

(*f*) *Limited gradation of properties in the group*
As we have seen, the chemical and physical properties of the elements and compounds of the Group IA and IIA metals are similar in nature but different in degree. Thus,
(i)   the element of the s-block are all reactive metals;
(ii)   they have a single oxidation state in all their compounds;
(iii) they are powerful reducing agents and are difficult to isolate from their ores (i.e. considerable amounts of energy are required to reduce their compounds);
(iv) their densities and melting points are considerably lower than those of other metals in the Periodic Table. For example, virtually all the d-block metals have a density greater than 7 g cm^{-3}. The densities of the s-block elements are in the range 0.5–3.6 g cm^{-3};
(v)   virtually all their compounds are ionic. This includes the hydrides (see Section 8.6);
(vi) the thermal stability of their compounds is higher than the corresponding salts of other metals;
(vii) except for magnesium, they all give characteristic colours when small amounts of their compounds (usually the chloride) are introduced into a Bunsen burner flame. This test is usually carried out by dipping a platinum or nichrome wire moistened with concen-

trated hydrochloric acid into the powdered salt and then placing it in the Bunsen burner flame (see fig. 8.25). The different flame colours are listed in Table 8.15.

Table 8.15   Flame colours of the s-block elements

Metal	Flame colour
Lithium	Intense pink
Sodium	Persistent golden yellow Invisible through blue glass
Potassium	Lilac or violet. Appears red through blue glass
Calcium	Red
Strontium	Scarlet
Barium	Apple-green

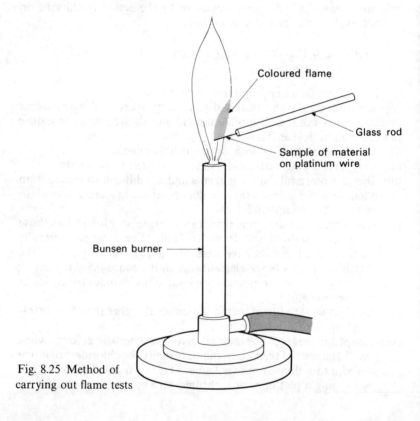

Fig. 8.25 Method of carrying out flame tests

The chemical properties of sodium and magnesium as examples of Group IA and Group IIA elements are summarised in fig. 8.26 and fig. 8.27 respectively.

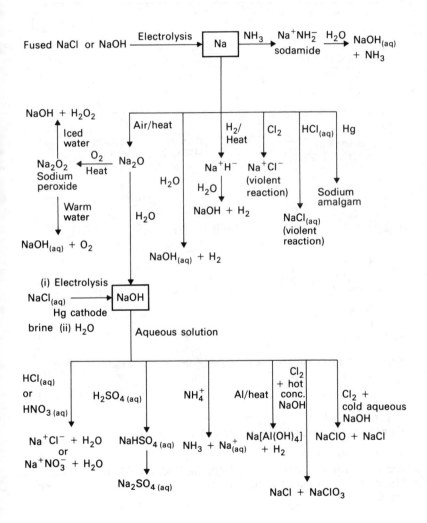

Fig. 8.26 Preparation and chemical properties of sodium

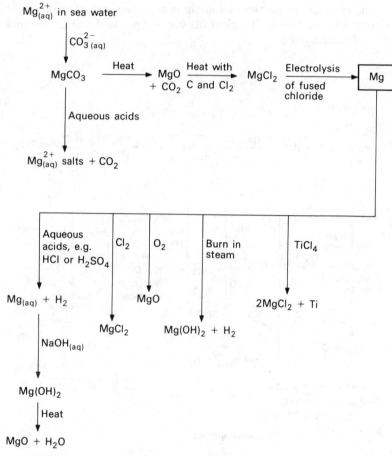

Fig. 8.27 Preparation and chemical properties of magnesium

Experiment 8.4
To compare the reactivities of the s-block elements

Apparatus and materials
100 cm³ beakers. A pen-knife. Lithium. Sodium. Magnesium ribbon. Magnesium powder. Calcium turnings. Litmus paper or Universal indicator paper.

Method
Taking care not to touch the metal with the fingers, cut pieces of lithium and sodium into *small* (approx. 3 mm) cubes. Wipe them with a filter paper to remove any oil and note the shiny surface of the freshly

cut metal. Place a piece of the metal in a beaker containing about 50 cm³ of cold water. Test the solution with litmus or with Universal indicator paper after the reaction. Compare with the effect of magnesium ribbon and calcium on cold water. Add some magnesium powder to hot water and note what happens.

Experiment 8.5
Compare the solubility of lithium chloride and sodium chloride in ethanol or anhydrous methanol. How do you interpret your results.

Demonstration 8.2
To compare the ionic volumes of sodium and potassium
Apparatus and materials
Sodium chloride. Potassium chloride. Propanone (acetone). 2 dry 10 cm³ measuring cylinders.
Method
Add 0.1 mole (5.84 g) of sodium chloride to 5 cm³ of propanone in a measuring cylinder and note the total volume of the mixture. Calculate the volume occupied by one mole of sodium chloride. Repeat the determination using 0.1 mole (7.46 g) of potassium chloride. What information about the relative ionic volumes of sodium and potassium may be deduced from your results? Sodium chloride and potassium chloride have the same crystal structure.

8.6
The p-block elements

Specific objectives: *The expected learning outcome of this section is that the student: (i) states, with examples, that the chemical and physical properties of the p-block elements are less easily characterised than those of the s-block elements (ii) states, with examples, that the p-block element can form covalent compounds as well as cations and anions (iii) describes (a) the anion-forming ability and (b) the covalent bonding ability of chlorine (iv) describes variations in oxidising ability within Group VII by reference to displacement reactions involving chlorine, bromine and iodine (v) describes the properties and reactions of aluminium and sulphur and of their oxides and chlorides to illustrate the diversity of p-block behaviour.*

The decrease in atomic radius across a period and the change in character of the elements from the metals of the s-block to the non-metals of the groups at the right-hand side of the Periodic Table was described in Section 7.2. This change to non-metals is reflected in the higher electronegativity of the p-block (see fig. 8.13). The change is not a sharp one, thus aluminium, tin and lead, for example, are all metals, while silicon and germanium have some metallic character. The non-metallic elements exist as covalent molecules with low melting points and boiling points. For example, the halogens, nitrogen and oxygen exist as diatomic molecules (e.g. Cl_2, I_2, N_2 and O_2), while the molecules of phosphorus and sulphur are P_4 and S_8 respectively (see fig. 8.28). Carbon and silicon exist as giant molecules with very high melting points. There are two forms of carbon: diamond (see fig. 8.5) and graphite. Graphite consists of layers of hexagonally arranged carbon atoms separated from one another by van der Waals' forces (see fig. 8.29). These forces are weak enough to allow the layers to slide over each other, which explains the softness of graphite and its use as a solid lubricant, while the free electrons account for its electrical conductivity.

The chlorides of the p-block elements are mostly covalent compounds and, with the exception of CCl_4, are hydrolysed by water (see Section 8.3). Their oxides (except Al_2O_3 and SiO_2) are generally volatile and acidic (e.g. CO_2, SO_2 and SO_3) or neutral (e.g. CO and N_2O) (see Section 7.2(*b*)). Aluminium oxide is amphoteric and dissolves in and reacts with aqueous sodium hydroxide:

$$Al_2O_{3(s)} + 2NaOH_{(aq)} + 3H_2O \longrightarrow 2NaAl(OH)_4$$

or dilute aqueous acids:

$$Al_2O_{3(s)} + 6HCl_{(aq)} \longrightarrow 2Al^{3+}_{(aq)} + Cl^-_{(aq)} + 3H_2O_{(l)}$$

The hydrides of the p-block elements are covalent, e.g.

$$
\begin{array}{llll}
CH_4 & NH_3 & H_2O & HF \\
SiH_4 & PH_3 & H_2S & HCl \\
 & & & HBr \\
 & & & HI
\end{array}
$$

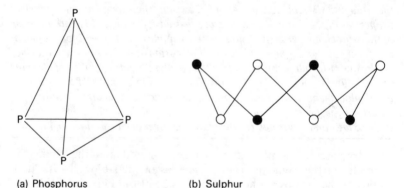

(a) Phosphorus   (b) Sulphur

Fig. 8.28 The phosphorus (P_4) and sulphur (S_8) molecules

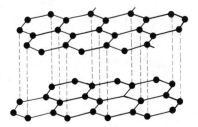

Fig. 8.29 The structure of graphite

and thus differ from the ionic hydrides of the s-block, e.g.

$$2Na + H_{2(g)} \xrightarrow{\text{heat}} 2Na^+H^-_{(s)}$$
$$\text{sodium hydride}$$
$$\downarrow H_2O$$
$$2NaOH_{(aq)} + H_{2(g)}$$

The hydrides of the p-block elements vary from neutral compounds, such as methane; weak bases and weak acids, such as ammonia and hydrogen sulphide respectively; to the strong acids of the hydrogen halides, e.g. hydrogen chloride and hydrogen bromide.

In contrast to those of the s-block, the p-block elements display variable valencies and their compounds are able to act as oxidising agents or reducing agents. For example, sulphur has valency states of 1 in S_2Cl_2, 2 in SCl_2 or H_2S, 4 in SO_2 and 6 in SO_3 and H_2SO_4. Sulphuric(VI)acid acts as an oxidising agent in its reaction with copper:

$$2H_2SO_4 + Cu \longrightarrow CuSO_4 + SO_2 + 2H_2O$$

while sulphur dioxide is a reducing agent in its reaction with potassium dichromate(VI) in acid solution:

$$3SO_{2(g)} + Cr_2O^{2-}_{7(aq)} + 2H^+_{(aq)} \longrightarrow 3SO^{2-}_{4(aq)} + 2Cr^{3+}_{(aq)} + H_2O_{(l)}$$

All the p-block elements are able to form covalent compounds, while the more electronegative elements, especially those of Group VI and Group VII, form anions with electropositive elements, such as the metals of Groups IA and IIA. Examples of such compounds are listed in Table 8.16. This ability to form either anions or covalent bonds is demonstrated by the halogens. The ease of anion formation is represented by the *electron affinity* of an element. This is defined as the enthalpy change in kJ mol^{-1} of the reaction:

$$X_{(g)} + e^- \longrightarrow X^-_{(g)}$$

where X is an atom of the element. The second electron affinity is the

Table 8.16   *Examples of ionic and covalent compounds of the p-block*
              elements

Element	Ionic compounds	Covalent compounds
Nitrogen	$Li_3^+ N^{3-}$, $Mg_3^{2+} N_2^{3-}$	NH_3
Oxygen	$Na_2^+ O^{2-}$, $Mg^{2+} O^{2-}$	CO_2, SO_2 and H_2O
Sulphur	$Na_2^+ S^{2-}$	H_2S, CS_2
Halogen	$Li^+ F^-$ $K^+ Cl^-$	CCl_4, CF_4, NF_3, PCl_3

enthalpy change for the process:

$$X_{(g)}^- + e^- \longrightarrow X_{(g)}^{2-}$$

The electron affinities of a number of elements are given in Table 8.17. The difference in reactivity of the halogens is also represented by their oxidising ability, thus a halogen will displace a less electronegative halogen from a solution of its ions, e.g.

$$Cl_{2(g)} + 2Br_{(aq)}^- \longrightarrow 2Cl_{(aq)}^- + Br_{2(aq)}$$
oxidising   reducing
agent   agent

$\uparrow$ electrons

$$Br_{2(aq)} + 2I_{(aq)}^- \longrightarrow 2Br_{(aq)}^- + I_{2(aq)}$$
oxidising   reducing
agent   agent

$\uparrow$ electrons

Fluorine will oxidise water to oxygen:

$$F_2 + H_2O \longrightarrow \tfrac{1}{2}O_2 + 2HF$$

Chlorine and bromine form an aqueous solution of the unstable hypo-halous acid, chloric(I) (hypochlorous) acid (HClO) and bromic(I) (hypo-bromous) acid (HOBr) respectively, e.g.

$$Cl_{2(aq)} + 2H_2O \longrightarrow H_3O_{(aq)}^+ + Cl_{(aq)}^- + HOCl_{(aq)}$$

and iodine does not react.

There are also differences in the products obtained by reaction of concentrated sulphuric acid with the metal halides. Sodium fluoride and sodium chloride yield hydrogen fluoride and hydrogen chloride respectively:

$$NaF + H_2SO_4 \longrightarrow NaHSO_4 + HF$$
$$NaCl + H_2SO_4 \longrightarrow NaHSO_4 + HCl$$

while sodium bromide and sodium iodide yield bromine and iodine. This is due to the fact that hydrogen bromide and hydrogen iodide are progressively stronger reducing agents:

$$2HBr + H_2SO_4 \longrightarrow SO_2 + 2H_2O + Br_2$$
$$6HI + H_2SO_4 \longrightarrow S + 4H_2O + 3I_2$$

Thus there is a far greater variability in the chemistry of the p-block elements and their compounds than in that of the s-block. Although a number of trends are apparent, the p-block elements are more difficult to characterise. The principal differences compared with the s-block elements which illustrate the diversity of p-block behaviour are:
1. The p-block elements may be metals, non-metals or metalloids.
2. They may be solids, liquids (e.g. bromine) or gases.
3. They show variability of valency.
4. They form both ionic and covalent compounds.
5. Their oxides are not strong bases.
6. Their chlorides are covalent and are hydrolysed by water (see Section 8.3).
7. Their hydrides are covalent.

The diversity of behaviour of the p-block elements is illustrated by the properties and reactions of aluminium and sulphur and of their oxides, and chlorides. The chemical reactions of these two elements are sum-

Table 8.17 *Electron affinities* (/kJ mol^{-1})

H						
-72						
Li	B	C	N	O	O$^-$	F
-50	-25	-121	-3	-141	$+791$	-333
Na			P	S	S$^-$	Cl
-68			-70	-200	$+649$	-364
						Br
						-342
						I
						-296

marised in fig. 8.30 and 8.31 respectively. The chemical properties of chlorine (as an example of the halogens) are summarised in fig. 8.32.

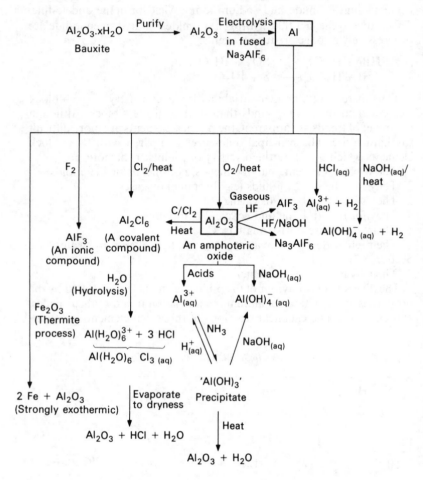

Fig. 8.30 Preparation and chemical reactions of aluminium

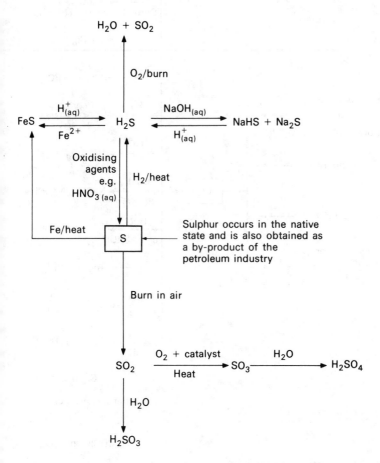

Fig. 8.31 Summary of the chemical reactions of sulphur

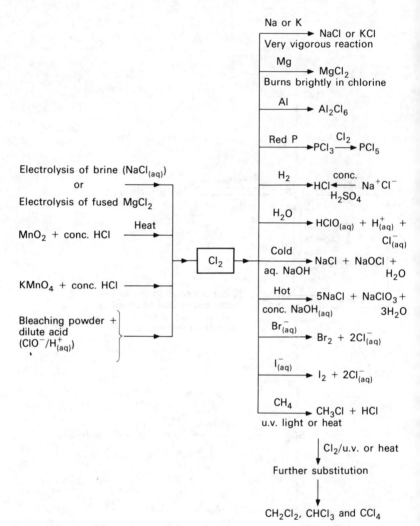

Fig. 8.32 Preparation and reactions of chlorine

Experiment 8.6
Reactions of aluminium and some of its compounds

(i) Add some dilute hydrochloric acid to a few aluminium turnings in a test-tube. Repeat the experiment using aqueous sodium hydroxide. Warm the mixture and identify the gas which is evolved.

(ii) Heat small amounts of hydrated and anhydrous aluminium chloride in a test-tube and compare the results. Add a little anhydrous aluminium chloride to water. Determine the pH of the solution with indicator paper.

Prepare a solution of hydrated aluminium chloride $(Al(H_2O)_6Cl_3)$ in water and determine its pH. Note the effect of adding (a) warm sodium carbonate solution, (b) aqueous ammonia and (c) aqueous sodium hydroxide to samples of this solution.

(iii) Heat small amounts of freshly prepared aluminium oxide with (a) aqueous hydrochloric acid and (b) aqueous sodium hydroxide. Compare your results with the effect of this reagent on samples of magnesium oxide.

Experiment 8.7
Comparison of the action of concentrated sulphuric acid on chlorides, bromides and iodides

Add 2–3 cm^3 of concentrated sulphuric acid (*Care*) to small amounts of sodium chloride, sodium bromide and sodium iodide in clean, dry test-tubes. Warm the tubes gently over a Bunsen burner. Test any gases evolved by smell (*Care!*) and with moist litmus paper, and compare the changes which occur. Write equations for these reactions.

8.7
The d-block elements

Specific objectives: *The expected learning outcome of this section is that the student:* (i) *states that the characteristic properties of the d-block elements are:*
(a) *metallic character (physical and chemical)*
(b) *variable valency*
(c) *formation of co-ordination complexes*
(d) *formation of coloured ions*
(e) *paramagnetism*
(ii) *describes examples to illustrate these properties by reference to at least two elements and their compounds.*

The d-block elements are also known as the *transition elements*. This group forms a transition in properties between the highly electropositive s-block metals and the more electronegative elements of the p-block (see fig. 8.13). The electronic configurations of the elements in the first transition series and a number of their common ions are listed in Table 8.18. When they form ions the 3d-block elements all lose the 4s

Table 8.18   Electronic configurations of the elements and common ions of the 3d-block (scandium—zinc)

Element	Symbol	Electronic configuration	Common ions	Electronic configuration
Potassium	K	$(Ar)4s^1$	K^+	(Ar)
Calcium	Ca	$(Ar)4s^2$	Ca^{2+}	(Ar)
Scandium	Sc	$(Ar)3d^14s^2$	Sc^{3+}	(Ar)
Titanium	Ti	$(Ar)3d^24s^2$	Ti^{3+}	$(Ar)3d^1$
			Ti^{4+}	(Ar)
Vanadium	V	$(Ar)3d^34s^2$	V^{3+}	$(Ar)3d^2$
Chromium	Cr	$(Ar)3d^54s^1$	Cr^{2+}	$(Ar)3d^4$
			Cr^{3+}	$(Ar)3d^3$
Manganese	Mn	$(Ar)3d^54s^2$	Mn^{2+}	$(Ar)3d^5$
Iron	Fe	$(Ar)3d^64s^2$	Fe^{2+}	$(Ar)3d^6$
			Fe^{3+}	$(Ar)3d^5$
Cobalt	Co	$(Ar)3d^74s^2$	Co^{2+}	$(Ar)3d^7$
Nickel	Ni	$(Ar)3d^84s^2$	Ni^{2+}	$(Ar)3d^8$
Copper	Cu	$(Ar)3d^{10}4s^1$	Cu^+	$(Ar)3d^{10}$
			Cu^{2+}	$(Ar)3d^9$
Zinc	Zn	$(Ar)3d^{10}4s^2$	Zn^{2+}	$(Ar)3d^{10}$

electrons from the outermost orbital before they lose electrons from the inner 3d shell. As the chemical properties of an element are largely determined by the electrons in the outermost shell, there is considerable similarity in the properties of the transition elements. These typical properties are demonstrated by elements having at least one ion with partly filled d-orbitals. Thus, zinc differs in many of its properties from the other members of the transition series as neither the metal nor its ion contain a partly filled d-orbital. The general characteristics of these elements are:

(a) Metallic properties

The d-block elements are all metals with similar physical properties. Their hardness, strength and high melting points and boiling points indicate the strength of the metallic bond in elements with 4s and 3d electrons available for bonding, compared with the s-block metals (see Table 8.19). The metals (especially chromium and copper) can be polished and show many of the other typical metallic characteristics. They are malleable and ductile and are good conductors of heat and electricity.

The d-block elements also show the chemical properties of a metal. They are moderately electropositive and, except for copper ($E_H^\circ = +0.34$ V), they all yield hydrogen on treatment with an acid. Chromium reacts only very slowly with aqueous acid owing to the presence of a protective film of oxide on the metal surface. Iron and steel objects are frequently chromium plated to protect them from corrosion. Iron reacts with steam to yield a compound oxide of iron(II) and iron(III)oxides:

$$3Fe_{(s)} + 4H_2O_{(g)} \rightleftharpoons Fe_3O_{4(s)} + 4H_{2(g)}$$
$$(FeOFe_2O_3)$$

The cations of the d-block elements are smaller than those of the s-block metals and frequently have a higher charge. Their compounds therefore have lower thermal stability, they are less ionic and are more easily reduced to the metal. For example, the green precipitate of basic copper carbonate obtained by adding aqueous sodium carbonate to a solution of a copper(II) salt is converted into black copper(II)oxide by boiling. Copper compounds may be reduced to the metal by heating with carbon, by electrolysis, or by adding iron to an aqueous solution of the salt. The oxides of d-block metals in the lower oxidation states are weakly basic or amphoteric, e.g.

FeO	NiO	CuO	Fe_2O_3	Cr_2O_3
basic	basic	basic	amphoteric	amphoteric

Table 8.19   Comparison of s-block and d-block metals

	s-block				d-block		
Metal	Melting point (/°C)	Boiling point (/°C)	Density (/g cm^{-3})	Metal	Melting point (/°C)	Boiling point (/°C)	Density (/g cm^{-3})
Ca	840	1484	1.54	Ti	1660	3290	4.50
Rb	39	688	1.53	Cr	1860	2670	7.20
Ba	725	1640	3.51	Fe	1535	2750	7.86

while those in the highest oxidation state are acidic. For example, chromium(VI)oxide, CrO_3, is obtained as deep red crystals on adding concentrated sulphuric(VI)acid to a solution of sodium dichromate(VI). The oxide dissolves readily in water to yield chromic acid:

$$CrO_3 \xrightarrow{\text{H}_2\text{O}} H_2CrO_{4(aq)} + H_2O(CrO_3)_n$$
chromic acid

(b) Variable valency

Because of the similarity in energy level, electrons can be lost from both the 3d and 4s orbitals when the metal forms a cation. All the metals of the 3d block from titanium to copper therefore show variable valency. For example, iron can show valencies of two and three, copper one and two, while chromium has stable valency states of two, three and six. The common oxides and chlorides of a number of the 3d-block metals illustrate the wide range of valencies displayed by these elements (see Table 8.20).

Table 8.20   Common oxides and chlorides of a number of 3d-block metals

Element	Valency states	Oxides	Chlorides	Other compounds
Chromium	2	CrO	$CrCl_2$	$CrSO_4$
	3	Cr_2O_3	$CrCl_3$	$Cr_2(SO_4)_3$
	6	CrO_3		K_2CrO_4, $K_2Cr_2O_7$
Manganese	2	MnO	$MnCl_2$	$MnSO_4$
	3	Mn_2O_3		
	4	MnO_2		
	7	Mn_2O_7		$KMnO_4$
Iron	2	FeO	$FeCl_2$	$FeSO_4$
	3	Fe_2O_3	Fe_2Cl_6	$Fe_2(SO_4)_3$
Copper	1	Cu_2O	$CuCl$	
	2	CuO	$CuCl_2$	$CuSO_4$

(b) The formation of coloured compounds is probably the most characteristic feature of the transition metals. In many cases, these colours,

especially of aqueous solutions, provide an easy means of identifying a particular cation. For example, hydrated copper(II) salts are blue, nickel(II) is green, chromium(III) is violet, manganese(II) is pink, iron(II) is pale-green, while iron(III) is yellow-brown and zinc(II) – which has filled 3d-orbitals and according to the definition is not a transition metal – is colourless. The colours of transition metal cations are sensitive to changes in their chemical environment. For example, an aqueous solution of copper(II)nitrate changes from blue to green and then yellow on adding concentrated hydrochloric acid.

(d) Complex formation

A *complex* or *co-ordination compound* differs from a mixture or double salt, such as $(NH_4)_2SO_4FeSO_46H_2O$ or the alums, in displaying properties which are different from those of the ions or molecules of which it is composed. For example, crystals of chrome alum, $K_2SO_4Cr_2(SO_4)_3$ $24H_2O$, dissolve in water to yield a solution which shows the characteristic reactions of hydrated potassium, chromium and sulphate ions. If however, an excess of sodium cyanide solution is added to aqueous iron(II) sulphate, the colour changes from green to yellow and an ion is obtained whose properties differ from those of the Fe^{2+} and CN^- ions from which it is derived:

$$Fe^{2+}_{(aq)} + 6CN^-_{(aq)} \longrightarrow [Fe(CN)_6]^{4-}$$
$$\text{hexacyanoferrate(II) ion}$$
$$\text{(ferrocyanide)}$$

Complex anions and cations are formed both from ions of opposite charges and by combination with neutral molecules, e.g.

$$[AlF_6]^{6-}, [Ag(NH_3)_2]^+, [Cu(NH_3)_4]^{2+} \text{ and } [Zn(OH)_4]^-.$$

The groups surrounding the central atom are known as *ligands* and are attached by dative covalent (or co-ordinate) bonds (see Section 8.1(c)). The ligands act as electron donors and the extent of electron sharing (cf Section 8.3) can vary from a pure covalency to ion–dipole or ion–ion attraction.

Complex formation is a characteristic property of the transition metals because of the presence of partly filled d-orbitals to accommodate the donated electrons. For example, the deep-blue colour obtained by the addition of ammonia to an aqueous solution of a copper(II)salt is due to the formation of the tetrammine copper(II) (or cuproammonium) ion:

$$Cu^{2+}_{(aq)} + 4NH_{3(aq)} \longrightarrow [Cu(NH_3)_4]^{2+}$$

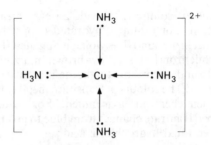

Although the central copper ion has achieved greater stability by complex formation it does not have a noble gas configuration. Iron achieves the noble gas configuration of krypton in the hexacyanoferrate(II) (ferrocyanide) ion, but is one electron short of this noble gas configuration in hexacyanoferrate(III) (ferricyanide) (see fig. 8.33).

A hydrated ion is also an example of complex formation, e.g. $[Cu(H_2O)_4]^{2+}$ and $[Ni(H_2O)_6]^{2+}$. It is the colour of these *aquo complexes* in which water molecules are acting as a neutral ligand which is responsible for the characteristic colours of many of the transition metal salts. In many cases the colour changes, or is lost, when the salt is heated. For example, hydrated copper(II)sulphate, $CuSO_4 5H_2O$, first loses the four water molecules attached to the copper ion on heating:

$$CuSO_4 5H_2O \xrightarrow{\text{heat}} CuSO_4 H_2O + 4H_2O$$
$$\text{blue} \qquad\qquad\qquad \text{white}$$

The final water molecule is attached to the sulphate ion and is lost at a higher temperature to yield the anhydrous salt. Similarly, crystals of $MnSO_4 5H_2O$ (pink) and $FeSO_4 7H_2O$ (green) form a white anhydrous salt on heating. With a few important exceptions, such as the hydrated ions and ammines, e.g. $[Mg(H_2O)_6]^{2+}$ and $[Mg(NH_3)_6]^{2+}$, the s-block elements do not form stable co-ordination compounds.

Iron, copper and other heavy metal ions are usually present in complexed form when these substances occur in living tissues. This increases their solubility and promotes their chemical activity. For example, iron is co-ordinated to nitrogen atoms forming part of complex ring structures in the haem groups of haemoglobin. This substance transports oxygen in the blood stream. Haem groups also play an important part in electron transfer reactions.

(e) Paramagnetism
Transition metals and their compounds which have partly filled d-orbitals (i.e. those which have unpaired electrons) are attracted by a magnetic field and are said to be *paramagnetic*. This effect in salts, such as Fe^{2+}, Fe^{3+}, Cr^{3+} and Cu^{2+}, is considerably smaller than the ferro-

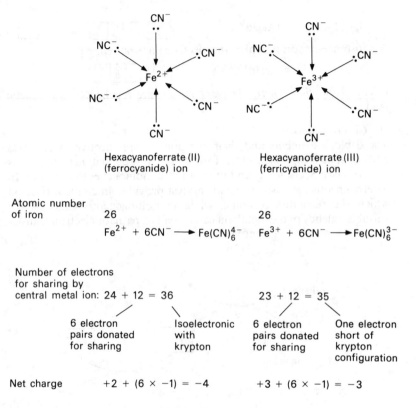

Fig. 8.33 Structure and formation of hexacyanoferrate(II) (ferrocyanide) and hexacyanoferrate(III) (ferricyanide) complex ions

magnetism of iron, steel, nickel or cobalt and is detected by weighing a sample of the salt in the magnetic field above the poles of a powerful magnet. A decrease in weight when the magnet is removed indicates that the substance is paramagnetic. The magnitude of the effect increases with the number of unpaired electrons in the ion. Orbitals are first occupied singly before pairing occurs (see Section 7.5) so iron(III) and cobalt(II) salts with five and three unpaired electrons respectively:

	Electronic configuration	3d	4s
Fe^{3+}	$(Ar)3d^5$	↑ ↑ ↑ ↑ ↑	☐
Co^{2+}	$(Ar)3d^7$	↑↓ ↑↓ ↑ ↑ ↑	☐

have a higher magnetic moment than copper(II) which has only one:

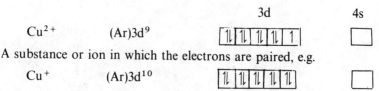

Cu^{2+} (Ar)3d^9

A substance or ion in which the electrons are paired, e.g.

Cu^+ (Ar)3d^{10}

is said to be *diamagnetic*. These materials are repelled by a magnetic field.

(f) Catalytic activity

The d-block elements and their compounds are effective as catalysts both as solids (especially in the form of fine powders) in heterogeneous catalysis (see Section 3.1) and in solution in homogeneous catalysis. In heterogeneous catalysis the solid catalyst provides an active surface on which the reactants combine, while in homogeneous catalysis the variable valency of the metal ion can provide a path for electron transfer between a number of intermediates:

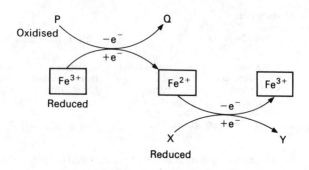

The catalytic effects of iron in the Haber process and of vanadium pentoxide in the Contact process were described in Section 3.7(*b*). Traces of cobalt salts catalyse the evolution of oxygen from aqueous suspensions of bleaching powder or other chlorate(I) salts (hypochlorites):

$$2ClO^-_{(aq)} \xrightarrow{Co^{2+}} 2Cl^-_{(aq)} + O_{2(g)}$$

Manganese(IV)oxide is used as a catalyst in the preparation of oxygen from potassium chlorate(V):

$$2KClO_{3(s)} \xrightarrow[\text{heat}]{MnO_2} 2KCl_{(s)} + 3O_{2(g)}$$

Other examples of the catalytic effect of the d-block elements and their compounds are given in Chapters 9 and 10.

Assignment
The d-block metals are of great commercial importance. What are the main uses of iron, chromium, copper, titanium and vanadium? To what extent are these applications related to the typical properties of the transition metals?

Experiment 8.8
To examine the typical properties of the d-block elements and their compounds

(a) Note the colours of the hydrated sulphates of cobalt(II), manganese(II), nickel(II), chromium(III), iron(II) and iron(III). Heat small samples of these salts in dry test-tubes and note any colour changes which occur. Allow the residue to cool to room temperature and then add 2–3 cm^3 of distilled water.

(b) *Solutions required:* 0.1 M aqueous solutions of titanium(III)sulphate, ammonium vanadium(III)sulphate, chromium(III)sulphate, manganese (II)sulphate, iron(II)sulphate, iron(III)sulphate, cobalt(II)nitrate, nickel (II)nitrate, copper(II)sulphate and zinc(II)sulphate.

Method
Carry out the following tests on 3–4 cm^3 samples of the above solutions. Tabulate your results.

(i)   Add 1 M aqueous ammonia drop by drop until it is present in excess.

(ii) Add 2 M aqueous sodium hydroxide until it is in excess. Note any changes which occur when the mixture is then boiled.

(iii) Add 2–3 cm^3 of 1 M aqueous sodium carbonate solution. Note any changes which occur when the mixture is boiled.

(iv) Add 0.1 M aqueous ammonium thiocyanate drop by drop until it is present in excess.

(c) *Change in oxidation state.* Add aqueous 1 M potassium iodide solution to tubes containing (i) 1% aqueous potassium manganate(VII) acidified with dilute sulphuric acid, (ii) aqueous potassium dichromate (VI) acidified with dilute sulphuric acid. Repeat this experiment using a 0.1 M aqueous solution of iron(II)sulphate instead of the potassium iodide. Write equations for the reactions which occur.

Summary

1. Atoms attain a stable electronic configuration *either* by gaining or losing electrons to form an ionic (or electrovalent) bond *or* by sharing electrons to form a covalent bond.

2. A dative covalent bond is a covalent bond in which *both* the shared electrons forming the bond are donated by a single atom, e.g. $H_3N \rightarrow BF_3$, NH_4^+ and H_3O^+ contain a dative covalent bond.

3. Atoms, ions or molecules which have the same number of electrons are said to be *isoelectronic*.

4. The general properties of metals are summarised in Table 8.7. In metallic bonding the valency electrons move about freely in a lattice of cations.

5. The shapes of simple covalent molecules are explained in terms of the repulsion of bonding and non-bonding electron pairs. In the gas phase simple $BeCl_2$ molecules are linear, BF_3 is planar, CH_4 is tetrahedral, NH_3 is pyramidal and H_2O is bent.

6. Unequal sharing of electrons in bonds is due to the different extent to which the atoms attract electrons. Such a bond is said to be *polarised* and the separation of charges produces a *dipole*.

7. Ionic and covalent bonds are extreme forms of bond polarisation.

8. The principal types of intermolecular forces are (a) van der Waals' forces, (b) dipole–dipole interaction, (c) hydrogen bonding, (d) ion–ion electrostatic attraction.

9. Hydrogen bonding affects the boiling point, melting point, solubility and structure of substances. It is a special type of dipole–dipole interaction in molecules in which hydrogen is linked to nitrogen, oxygen or fluorine atoms.

10. The order of increasing magnitude of these forces: van der Waals', dipole–dipole interaction, hydrogen bonding and ion–ion electrostatic attraction is illustrated by the melting-points and boiling-points of oxygen, hydrogen chloride, water and sodium chloride.

11. The s-block elements have similar physical and chemical properties: they are all light reactive metals, they are powerful reducing agents, virtually all their chlorides are ionic, they have an invariable ionic valency and they give a characteristic flame colour.

12. The p-block elements show far greater diversity of behaviour than the s-block and d-block elements. This diversity is apparent in:
   (a) their physical properties (e.g. the p-block elements are solids, liquids or gases, metals or non-metals, conducting or non-conducting etc.);
   (b) their chemical properties:
   (i) the p-block elements are less electropositive than those of the s-block and show a greater range of electronegativity;

(ii) they form covalent chlorides which are generally hydrolysed by cold water;

(iii) their oxides are less basic than those of the s-block elements; some are amphoteric, some are neutral and the rest are acidic. The oxides of the p-block elements (except aluminium, for example) are covalent;

(iv) they form covalent hydrides;

(v) many of the p-block elements show variable valency;

(vii) all the p-block elements form covalent bonds, some (e.g. nitrogen, oxygen, sulphur and the halogens) can also form anions.

13. Variations in oxidising ability of the halogens are illustrated by displacement reactions of chlorine, bromine and iodine.

14. The diversity of behaviour of the p-block elements is illustrated by the chemical properties of aluminium, sulphur and chlorine. The principal reactions of these elements are summarised in figs. 8.30, 8.31 and 8.32 respectively.

15. The typical properties of the d-block elements (or transition metals) are demonstrated by elements having at least one ion with partly filled d-orbitals. The characteristic properties are:

(a) Metallic character (both physical and chemical).

(b) Variable valency. Because of the small difference in energy levels, electrons may be lost from the 3d and 4s orbitals thus giving a range of different valency states.

(c) They form stable complexes (co-ordination compounds) owing to the availability of partly filled d-orbitals to accommodate electrons donated by ligand ions or neutral molecules.

(d) They form coloured ions.

(e) Compounds containing ions with partly filled d-orbitals (i.e. those with unpaired d-electrons) are paramagnetic. Paramagnetic substances are attracted into a magnetic field.

(f) The d-block elements and their compounds show great catalytic activity.

Questions

1. By reference to two examples of each, distinguish between an ionic and a covalent bond.

2. List and explain three different general physical properties of ionic and covalent compounds.

3. The Al^{3+} and O^{2-} ions have the same electronic configuration. How do you account for the difference in their ionic radii? (0.050 and 0.140 nm respectively).

4. What is a dative covalent bond? Give *three* examples of molecules containing a dative covalent bond.

5. What is meant by the term 'isoelectronic'?

6. What is the metallic bond? Describe how this explains two typical properties of metals.

7. What is meant by a lattice?

8. Explain the shapes of gaseous molecules of $BeCl_2$, BF_3, CH_4, NH_3, H_2O and CH_3OH.

9. What is a giant molecule? Describe the structure of one example and explain how this accounts for the substance's physical properties.

10. What is meant by the polarisation of a covalent bond?

11. How do you account for the fact that a fine jet of water or trichloromethane is attracted by a negatively or positively charged metal plate, but tetrachloromethane is not?

12. How do you account for the difference in physical properties of aluminium chloride and aluminium fluoride?

13. Compare and contrast the action of water on the chlorides of the elements of the second period of the Periodic Table.

14. What are (a) van der Waals' forces and (b) dipole–dipole interactions?

15. What is hydrogen bonding? Explain how these forces arise and describe two examples of their effect.

16. Arrange the following intermolecular forces in order of increasing magnitude: ion–ion electrostatic attraction, van der Waals' forces, hydrogen bonding and dipole–dipole interaction. Give examples of compounds whose physical properties illustrate the relative strength of these forces.

17. Describe examples from two different elements and their compounds which illustrate six different general properties of the s-block.

18. How do you explain the difference in the thermal stability of the carbonates and nitrates of the s-block elements?

19. The chemical and physical properties of the p-block elements show greater diversity than those of the s-block. Discuss this statement with reference to suitable examples.

20. Compare and contrast the structure, bonding and properties of (a) the oxides, (b) the chlorides and (c) the hydrides of the s-block and p-block elements.

21. Describe and explain the reactions you would carry out to demonstrate the difference in oxidising ability of chlorine, bromine and iodine.

22. What is a transition metal? Illustrate your answer by reference to copper, nickel, zinc and calcium.

23. Discuss the general properties of the d-block elements with reference to suitable examples from the first transition series, scandium–zinc.

24. What is a complex (or co-ordination) compound?

25. What is paramagnetism? How would you demonstrate that cobalt(II)sulphate(VI) is paramagnetic?

26. Give five examples (with equations) of the use of the d-block elements or their compounds as catalysts.

27. Compare and contrast the general properties of the s-block and d-block metals.

28. Give examples from the chemistry of chromium, manganese or iron to illustrate (a) the variable valency, (b) the formation of coloured salts and (c) complex formation by the d-block elements.

F   Carbon chemistry

9   Introduction to organic chemistry

General objective: *The expected learning outcome of this chapter is that the student is able to describe the structure, properties and reactions of some selected carbon compounds.*

9.1
Introduction: The scope of carbon chemistry

As its name indicates, carbon chemistry is concerned with the preparation, structure, properties and reactions of the compounds of carbon. This branch of science is also referred to as *organic chemistry* to distinguish it from the study of the hundred or so other elements of the Periodic Table and their compounds which comes within the province of *inorganic chemistry*.

Organic chemistry began as the study of the sugars, alcohols, oils, pigments and other compounds formed within the living tissues of plants and animals. However this distinction is no longer made and tens of thousands of new compounds are synthesised every year in the laboratory. Synthetic organic substances are widely used as solvents, man-made fibres, drugs, plastics, detergents, fuels, lubricants and other essential materials of everyday life.

Far more carbon compounds are known than the compounds of all the other elements of the Periodic Table put together. This is due to a number of special properties of the carbon atom. Carbon has an electronic configuration of $1s^2 2s^2 2p^2$ and a Pauling electronegativity value of 2.5 (see fig. 8.13). It exerts a covalency of four in virtually all of its compounds and forms *strong covalent bonds* with hydrogen, halogens, oxygen, nitrogen and a number of other elements, e.g.

$$
\begin{array}{ccc}
\text{H} & \text{H} \quad \text{O} & \text{NH}_2 \\
| & | \quad \diagup\!\!\diagup & \diagup \\
\text{H—C—Cl} & \text{H—C—C} & \text{O=C} \\
| & | \quad \diagdown & \diagdown \\
\text{H} & \text{H} \quad \text{O–H} & \text{NH}_2 \\
\text{chloromethane} & \text{ethanoic acid} & \text{carbamide (urea)}
\end{array}
$$

The mean bond strengths of a number of these bonds are listed in Table 9.1. The most important and unique property of the carbon atom is its ability to form strong single and multiple bonds with other carbon atoms to yield chains, e.g. hexane

$$
\begin{array}{ccccccc}
& H & H & H & H & H & H \\
& | & | & | & | & | & | \\
H- & C- & C- & C- & C- & C- & C-H \\
& | & | & | & | & | & | \\
& H & H & H & H & H & H \\
\end{array}
$$

hexane

and rings, e.g. cyclohexane.

$$
\begin{array}{c}
\quad\quad CH_2 \\
\diagup \quad\quad \diagdown \\
CH_2 \quad\quad CH_2 \\
| \quad\quad\quad | \\
CH_2 \quad\quad CH_2 \\
\diagdown \quad\quad \diagup \\
\quad\quad CH_2
\end{array}
$$

cyclohexane

Isomerism is very common in organic chemistry, i.e. the same molecular formula may apply to two or more different compounds. For example, two structural formulae may be drawn for the molecular formula C_2H_6O using the valencies of carbon(4), hydrogen(1) and oxygen(2):

$$
\begin{array}{cc}
H \quad H \\
| \quad | \\
H-C-C-O-H \\
| \quad | \\
H \quad H
\end{array}
\qquad and \qquad
\begin{array}{cc}
H \quad\quad H \\
| \quad\quad | \\
H-C-O-C-H \\
| \quad\quad | \\
H \quad\quad H
\end{array}
$$

ethanol   methoxymethane
(dimethyl ether)

b.p. 78°   b.p. −25°

These two isomers are readily distinguished by their boiling points and chemical properties. The enormous difference in the volatility of these two substances is due to hydrogen bonding in the alcohol.

The number of possible isomers increases enormously as the number of carbon atoms in the molecule increases. For example, there are three isomers of formula C_5H_{12} (pentane):

$$
\begin{array}{ccccc}
H & H & H & H & H \\
| & | & | & | & | \\
H-C- & C- & C- & C- & C-H \\
| & | & | & | & | \\
H & H & H & H & H \\
\end{array}
\qquad
\begin{array}{cccc}
H & H & H & H \\
| & | & | & | \\
H-C- & C- & C- & C-H \\
| & | & | & | \\
H & H & & H \\
& & H-C-H \\
& & | \\
& & H \\
\end{array}
$$

$$
\begin{array}{c}
H \\
| \\
H-C-H \\
\end{array}
$$

eighteen isomers of C_8H_{18} and 4×10^9 possible structures of $C_{30}H_{62}$.

Carbon compounds have the physical properties expected of covalent substances (see Section 8.1(b)). Thus they are usually gases, volatile liquids or solids of comparatively low melting point which – other than hydroxy or amino compounds (see Sections 8.1(b) and 8.4(c)) – are insoluble in water but dissolve readily in organic solvents. Except for the salts of organic acids and a few other ionic derivations, carbon compounds do not conduct electricity and, as covalent bonds are directional, organic molecules have a definite shape. The reactions of organic compounds are usually slower than those of inorganic salts and other ionic compounds as they involve breaking and forming covalent bonds.

Assignment

Draw structural formulae for the different isomers of formulae:

C_3H_8O, C_6H_{14} and $C_4H_{10}O$.

Table 9.1   Mean bond energies

Bond	$\Delta H/kJ\ mol^{-1}$
C—C	348
C=C	610
C≡C	837
C—H	412
C—Cl	338
C—Br	276
C—N	305
C—O	360
C=O	745
O—H	463
N—H	388
Si—Si	176

9.2
The hydrocarbons

Specific objectives: *The expected learning outcome of this section is that the student:* (i) *Recognises the existence of cyclic hydrocarbons such as cyclohexane, cyclo-hexene and benzene;* (ii) *Represents the formulae for benzene and methylbenzene as* ◎ *and* CH_3 *respectively;* (iii) *Defines a homologous series as consisting of compounds with the same functional group but with each successive member differing by* $-CH_2-$; (iv) *States that members of a homologous series show a gradation of physical properties.*

(a) *Saturated and unsaturated hydrocarbons*
The hydrocarbons are the simplest class of organic compounds. As their name indicates, they consist of carbon and hydrogen only. They are classified as *saturated* or *unsaturated* compounds depending respectively on whether the compound contains single bonds only, or whether it possesses a double or triple carbon–carbon bond. The saturated hydrocarbons are known as the *alkanes* (or paraffins), e.g.

$$\begin{array}{cc} H & H \\ | & | \\ H-C-C-H \\ | & | \\ H & H \end{array} \quad \text{ethane}$$

while compounds with double and triple bonds, e.g.

$$\begin{array}{cc} H & H \\ \diagdown & \diagup \\ C=C \\ \diagup & \diagdown \\ H & H \end{array} \quad \text{and} \quad H-C\equiv C-H$$

ethene   ethyne (acetylene)

are known as *alkenes* and *alkynes* respectively.

The formulae and structures of the alkanes may be deduced from the valencies of carbon(4) and hydrogen(1) (see Table 9.2). Alkanes containing four or more carbon atoms can exist as a number of different isomers. For example, there are two isomeric butanes (C_4H_{10}) and three isomeric pentanes (C_5H_{12}). The names and formulae of the alkanes are important as these compounds provide the basis for naming many other classes of organic compound.

(b) *Cyclic hydrocarbons*
Cyclic hydrocarbons are compounds in which a chain of carbon atoms is joined into a ring. Thus cyclohexane and cyclohexene are examples of cyclic alkanes and cyclic hexenes respectively:

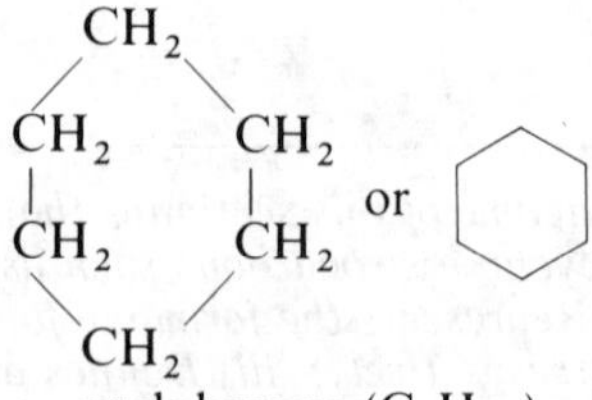

CH$_2$
CH$_2$ CH$_2$
CH$_2$ CH$_2$ or
CH$_2$

cyclohexane (C$_6$H$_{12}$)

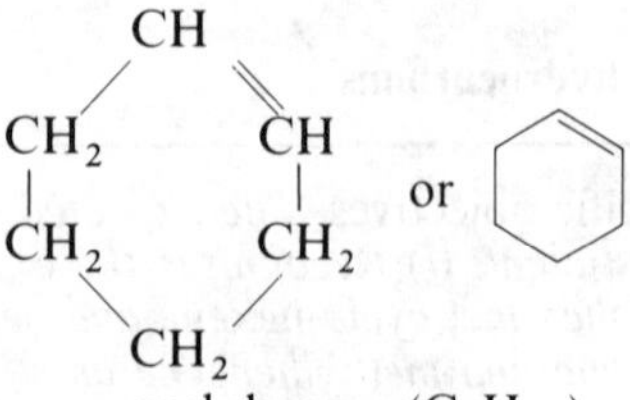

CH
CH$_2$ CH
CH$_2$ CH$_2$ or
CH$_2$

cyclohexene (C$_6$H$_{10}$)

Benzene is the most important of the unsaturated cyclic hydrocarbons. Its molecular formula is C$_6$H$_6$ and as neither of the ring structures:

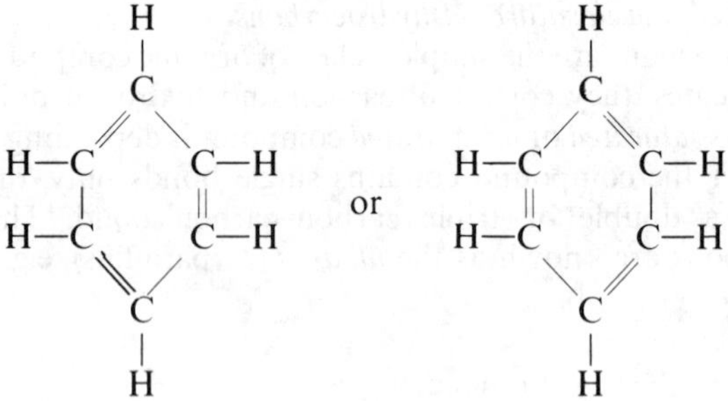

H
|
C
H—C   C—H
H—C   C—H
C
|
H

or

H
|
C
H—C   C—H
H—C   C—H
C
|
H

i.e

or

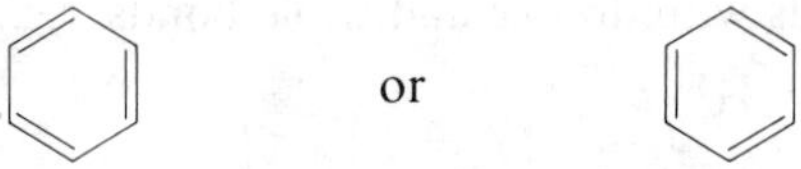

adequately describe its bonding, the compound is usually written as:

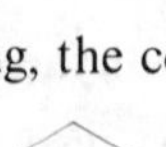

where, unless otherwise indicated, the carbon atom at the corner of the hexagon is linked to a hydrogen atom. Thus chlorobenzene (C$_6$H$_5$Cl) and methylbenzene (toluene) (C$_6$H$_5$CH$_3$) are:

Cl

and

CH$_3$

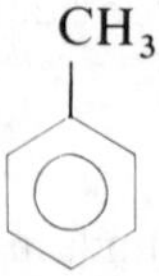

respectively

Compounds containing the benzene ring or other similarly stable unsaturated ring structures are said to be *aromatic*.

Table 9.2 Names and formulae of the alkanes

Number of carbon atoms		Formula	Name
1	$\begin{array}{c} \quad H \\ \quad | \\ H-C-H \\ \quad | \\ \quad H \end{array}$	CH_4	methane
2	$\begin{array}{c} H \quad H \\ | \quad | \\ H-C-C-H \\ | \quad | \\ H \quad H \end{array}$	C_2H_6	ethane
3	$\begin{array}{c} H \quad H \quad H \\ | \quad | \quad | \\ H-C-C-C-H \\ | \quad | \quad | \\ H \quad H \quad H \end{array}$	C_3H_8	propane
4	$\begin{array}{c} H \quad H \quad H \quad H \\ | \quad | \quad | \quad | \\ H-C-C-C-C-H \\ | \quad | \quad | \quad | \\ H \quad H \quad H \quad H \end{array}$ or $\begin{array}{c} H \quad H \quad H \\ | \quad | \quad | \\ H-C-C-C-H \\ | \quad | \quad | \\ H \quad | \quad H \\ \quad H-C-H \\ \quad\quad | \\ \quad\quad H \end{array}$	C_4H_{10}	butane
5		C_5H_{12}	pentane
6		C_6H_{14}	hexane
7		C_7H_{16}	heptane
8		C_8H_{18}	octane

(c) *Homologous series*

The compounds listed in Table 9.2 form part of a *homologous series*. A homologous series has the following characteristics:

1. All the compounds in the series have the same reactive (or *functional*) group and therefore have similar methods of preparation and similar chemical properties.

2. Each member of the series has the same *general formula*. For example, it should be apparent from Table 9.2 that the general formula of the alkane homologous series is C_nH_{2n+2}, where n is the number of carbon atoms and $2n + 2$ is the number of hydrogen atoms in the alkane.

3. Each member of the series differs from the next by a $-CH_2-$ group. As the relative atomic masses of carbon and hydrogen are 12 and 1 respectively, this means that there is a difference of 14 in the relative molecular mass of successive members of a homologous series.

4. There is a progressive change in the physical properties of the members of the series. This gradation of physical properties in the alkane homologous series is illustrated by the uniform increase in boiling point with increasing number of carbon atoms in the unbranched alkanes (see fig. 9.1).

The similarity of chemical properties and the gradation of the physical properties of the compounds within a given homologous series provide a systematic framework for the study of organic chemistry. This makes it possible to predict the properties of a particular compound, to name it and to suggest possible methods of synthesising it. This greatly reduces the amount of factual material which needs to be memorised for an adequate mastery of organic chemistry.

9.3
Functional groups and the main classes of organic compounds

Specific objectives: *The expected learning outcome of this section is that the student: (i) names and draws the structures of the functional groups alkane, alkene, alkyne, alcohol, halide, carboxylic acid, carbonyl; (ii) recognises the presence of the functional groups listed above in given structural formulae; (iii) states that the chemical properties of carbon compounds are largely determined by the functional groups present in the molecule.*

The other classes of carbon compound may be regarded as derivatives of the hydrocarbons in which one or more hydrogen atoms are replaced by atoms of other elements, such as halogen or oxygen, or by groups of atoms, such as hydroxyl ($-OH$), amino ($-NH_2$) or nitro ($-NO_2$) groups. For example, chloromethane (CH_3Cl) and bromobenzene (C_6H_5Br):

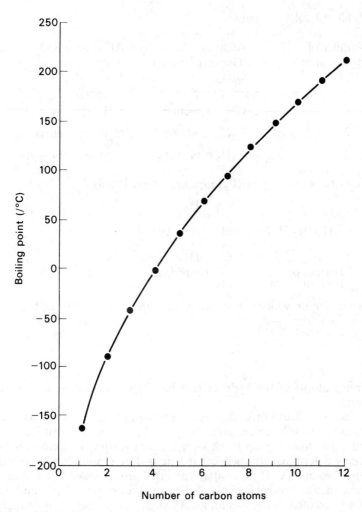

Fig. 9.1 The boiling-points of the unbranched alkanes

are derived by substituting a hydrogen in the methane and benzene molecules by atoms of chlorine and bromine respectively. Similarly, ethanol (C_2H_5OH) is a derivation of ethane in which one of the hy-

Table 9.3   Alkyl groups

Number of carbon atoms	Alkanes (General formula = C_nH_{2n+2})		Alkyl groups (R-) (General formula = C_nH_{2n+1})	
1	CH_4	methane	CH_3-	methyl
2	C_2H_6	ethane	C_2H_5-	ethyl
3	C_3H_8	propane	C_3H_7-	propyl

The two isomeric propyl groups are referred to as

$$CH_3CH_2CH_2- \quad \text{and} \quad \begin{array}{c} CH_3 \\ \diagdown \\ CH- \\ \diagup \\ CH_3 \end{array}$$

normal or   *iso*-propyl
n-propyl

depending on which carbon atom the substituent is attached

drogen atoms of the hydrocarbon has been replaced by a hydroxyl group.

The monosubstituted alkanes are compounds of an *alkyl group* containing one less hydrogen atom than the alkane from which it is derived and a *functional group* (such as halogen, hydroxyl or amino) which largely determines its chemical reactions. For example, bromoethane (ethyl bromide) C_2H_5Br contains an ethyl group linked to an atom of bromine. The general formula of the alkyl groups is C_nH_{2n+1} and they are represented by the symbol R-. Alkyl groups are named by changing the *-ane* of the final syllable of the corresponding alkane to *-yl*. The names and formulae of alkyl groups containing up to three carbon atoms are listed in Table 9.3. Similarly, the *aryl* group (Ar) contains one hydrogen atom less than an aromatic hydrocarbon.

The main classes of organic compounds are:

(a) The alkenes and alkynes
The functional group in the unsaturated hydrocarbons is the multiple bond itself. Alkenes contain a carbon–carbon double bond which replaces two hydrogen atoms in the alkane:

$$-\overset{\underset{\displaystyle H}{|}}{\underset{\underset{\displaystyle H}{|}}{C}}-\overset{\underset{\displaystyle H}{|}}{\underset{\underset{\displaystyle H}{|}}{C}}- \quad \xrightarrow{-2H} \quad \overset{\diagdown}{\diagup}C{=}C\overset{\diagup}{\diagdown}$$

alkane	alkene
(General formula	(General formula
C_nH_{2n+2})	C_nH_{2n})

Thus the general formula of the alkene homologous series is C_nH_{2n}. The alkynes have a carbon–carbon triple bond:

$$-\overset{\underset{\displaystyle H}{|}}{\underset{\underset{\displaystyle H}{|}}{C}}-\overset{\underset{\displaystyle H}{|}}{\underset{\underset{\displaystyle H}{|}}{C}}- \quad \xrightarrow{-4H} \quad -C{\equiv}C-$$

alkane	alkyne
(C_nH_{2n+2})	(C_nH_{2n-2})

and their general formula is C_nH_{2n-2}.

The alkenes and alkynes are named by changing the *-ane* at the end of the name of the corresponding alkane having the same number of carbon atoms to *-ene* and *-yne* respectively. Thus,

CH_3CH_3	$CH_2{=}CH_2$	$HC{\equiv}CH$
ethane	ethene	ethyne
(C_2H_6)	(C_2H_4)	(C_2H_2)

$CH_3CH_2CH_3$	$CH_3CH{=}CH_2$	$CH_3C{\equiv}CH$
propane	propene	propyne
(C_3H_8)	(C_3H_6)	(C_3H_4)

(b) The halogenoalkanes

Halogenoalkanes are obtained by substituting one of the hydrogen atoms of an alkane by a halogen atom. The general formula of the homologous series is thus $C_nH_{2n+1}X$ or RX, where X is an atom of fluorine, chlorine, bromine or iodine. These substances are also known as the *alkyl halides*. For example, CH_3Br is bromomethane (or methyl bromide), while C_2H_5I is iodoethane (or ethyl iodide). There are two isomeric halogenopropanes, C_3H_7X; they are $CH_3CH_2CH_2X$ and CH_3CHXCH_3. Such compounds are named by numbering the carbon atoms in the longest carbon chain to indicate the position of the substituent. The carbon chain is numbered in such a direction as to keep the numbers as small as possible. Thus,

$$CH_3CH_2CH_2Cl \text{ is 1- chloropropane (and not 3-chloropropane}$$
$$3 \quad 2 \quad 1$$

$$CH_3CH_2CH_2Cl) \text{ and } CH_3CHClCH_3 \text{ is 2-chloropropane.}$$
$$1 \quad 2 \quad 3$$

(c) The alcohols

The general formula of the alcohol (or alkanol) homologous series is $C_nH_{2n+1}OH$, or ROH. They are named by substituting the suffix *-ol* for the final *-e* of the alkane which has the same number of carbon atoms. Thus the first three members of the series are: methanol, ethanol and propanol, see Table 9.4.

Table 9.4   The alcohols

Number of carbon atoms, n	Formula of alcohol $C_nH_{2n+1}OH$	Name	Alternative name
1	CH_3OH	methanol	methyl alcohol
2	CH_3CH_2OH or C_2H_5OH	ethanol	ethyl alcohol
3	$CH_3CH_2CH_2OH$ or $CH_3CHOHCH_3$ $\Big\}$ C_3H_7OH	propan-1-ol	*n*-propyl alcohol
		propan-2-ol	*iso*-propyl alcohol

(d) The ethers

These compounds have the general formula R-O-R'. The two alkyl groups may be the same or different, e.g.

$$CH_3OCH_3 \text{ is methoxymethane (or dimethyl ether)}$$

$$CH_3OC_2H_5 \text{ is methoxyethane (or ethyl methyl ether)}$$

(e) The carboxylic acids

The functional group in the carboxylic acids has the structure

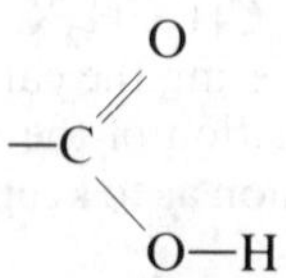

$$-C \overset{\displaystyle O}{\underset{\displaystyle O-H}{\big\langle}}$$

The general formula of the carboxylic acid homologous series is thus $C_nH_{2n+1}CO_2H$, or RCO_2H.

According to the recommendations of the IUPAC (International Union of Pure and Applied Chemists), these compounds are named after the alkane having the same number of carbon atoms; however, their unsystematic names, e.g. acetic acid and formic acid, are still in common use (see Table 9.5).

Table 9.5   Formulae of carboxylic acids (General formula
$$= C_nH_{2n+1}CO_2H)$$

n	Formula	Systematic name	Trivial name
0	HCO_2H	Methanoic acid	Formic acid
1	CH_3CO_2H	Ethanoic acid	Acetic acid
2	$CH_3CH_2CO_2H$	Propanoic acid	Propionic acid

In esters the acid hydrogen of the carboxy group is replaced by an alkyl (or aryl) group, e.g. $HCO_2C_2H_5$ (ethyl methanoate). The general formula of the esters is RCO_2R' and these compounds are named as alkyl alkanoates.

(*f*) *Carbonyl compounds*
A carbon atom linked by a double bond to an oxygen atom is known as the *carbonyl group*:

$$\diagdown C = O \quad \text{carbonyl group}$$

The two main classes of carbonyl compound are the *aldehydes* and *ketones*. The carbonyl group is attached to at least one hydrogen atom in the aldehydes and to none in the ketones, thus the general formulae of these two classes of compound are:

R—C$\overset{H}{\underset{O}{}}$ and $\overset{R}{\underset{R}{}}$C=O

RCHO   RCOR
aldehydes   ketones

The nomenclature (i.e. the method of naming) of these compounds is described in Section 10.6.

The functional groups and general formulae of these classes of organic compounds are summarised in Table 9.6. The information in the table is sufficient to assign these substances to their class.

An organic compound can contain more than one functional group, for example $CH_3CHNH_2CO_2H$ is an aminocarboxylic acid (i.e. an amino acid). The chemical properties of any compound are largely determined by the functional groups present in the molecule.

The general formulae in Table 9.6 apply to alkane derivatives. Aromatic compounds are derived by replacing the hydrogen atoms attached to carbon atoms of the benzene ring or other aromatic hydrocarbon (ArH, where Ar is the *aryl group*) by chlorine, hydroxy, amino and other functional groups. For example, aromatic halogen compounds have the general formula ArX, e.g. chlorobenzene C_6H_5Cl, and aromatic hydroxy compounds have the general formula ArOH, e.g. C_6H_5OH. Aromatic compounds are discussed in Section 9.7.

*Table 9.6　Principal classes of organic compounds
　　　　　　(alkane derivatives)*

Class of compound	Functional group	General formula
Alkanes	—H	C_nH_{2n+2} or RH
Alkenes	C=C	C_nH_{2n}
Alkynes	—C≡C—	C_nH_{2n-2}
Halogenoalkanes (alkyl halides)	—X (X = halogen)	$C_nH_{2n+1}X$ or RX
Alcohols	—OH	$C_nH_{2n+1}OH$ or ROH
Ethers	—OR	ROR′
Aldehydes	—CHO	RCHO
Ketones	C=O	RCOR′
Carboxylic acids	—CO_2H	$C_nH_{2n+1}CO_2H$ or RCO_2H
Esters	—CO_2R'	RCO_2R'
Alkyl amines	—NH_2	RNH_2 (a primary amine)
Nitro compounds	—NO_2	RNO_2

9.4
Petroleum

Specific objective: *The expected learning outcome of this section is that the student states, with examples, the importance of oil as a source of hydrocarbons.*

Petroleum was formed over millions of years by the decomposition of billions of tiny marine plants and animals. This decaying organic matter accumulated over a long period of time at the bottom of oceans and former seas and was gradually covered with layers of sand and silt which subjected it to considerable pressure and heat. The oil and gases, such as that under the North Sea and in the petroleum deposits of the Middle East and America, became trapped under layers of salt from the dried up sea bed or other impervious strata. Pockets of oil or gas are often discovered under folds in the rock layers, known as *anticlines*, or other faults produced by earthquake activity (see fig. 9.2).

Oil wells are drilled and the crude petroleum is brought to the surface, see fig. 9.2(a), and transported to the refinery where it is separated into fractions by distillation. The fractionating columns are often more than 40 m in height and contain a large number of bubble caps to bring the vapour and liquid into contact (see fig. 9.3). The approximate boiling points and names of the main fractions, with examples of their applications, are shown in Table 9.7.

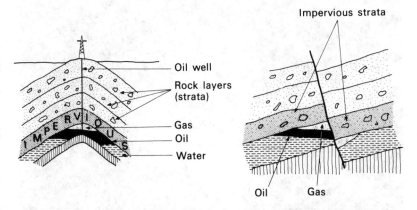

(a) An anticline

(b) Oil trapped by geological fault resulting from earthquake activity

Fig. 9.2 Natural oil traps

Fig. 9.2(a) BP's drilling rig Sea Conquest at well 3/29–2 east of the Shetland Islands, with supply vessel alongside. Photograph by BP Oil Limited

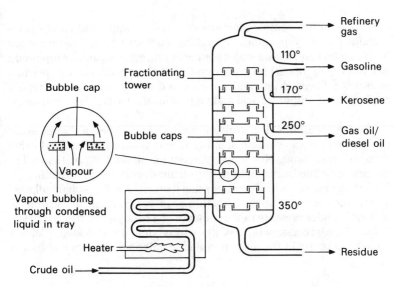

Fig. 9.3 Fractional distillation of crude petroleum

Table 9.7 *Fractional distillation of crude petroleum*

Fraction	Name	Boiling point /°C	Number of carbon atoms	Applications
I	Gas fraction	<40°	1–4	As a fuel, e.g. refinery gas and LPG (Calor gas etc.)
II	Gasoline	40–110	4–7	Petrol and solvents
III	Naphtha	110–170	7–10	Synthesis of organic compounds
IV	Kerosene	170–250	10–16	Heating oil, catalytic cracking, jet fuel
V	Gas oil	250–350	16–30	Fuel oil (diesel), catalytic cracking
VI	Residue	>350	>30	Grease, lubricating oils, wax, asphalt and coke

Petroleum is a complex mixture of gaseous, liquid and solid hydro-carbons with varying amounts of sulphur compounds etc. It is important both as a fuel and as the major source of synthetic organic compounds. About 90% of all carbon compounds and their products, e.g. plastics, man-made fibres, drugs and ethanol, and many inorganic materials, e.g. hydrogen, sulphuric acid and ammonia, are derived from petroleum sources.

The hydrocarbons in petroleum are mostly alkanes, although some petroleum deposits contain significant amounts of benzene and other cyclic hydrocarbons. North Sea gas contains about 95% methane. The gas and gasoline fractions from petroleum distillation are used mainly for heating purposes and as motor fuel (petrol). The long-chain alkanes in the kerosene and gas oil fractions can be 'cracked' by heating at 400–600° under pressure in the presence of a catalyst, see figs. 9.3(a) and 9.3(b). This process, which is known as *catalytic cracking*, yields a complex mixture of the more useful lower alkanes, alkenes and hydrogen, e.g.

$$-C-C-C-C-C-C-C-C-C-C-C- \xrightarrow{\text{catalytic cracking}}$$

$$CH_3CH{=}CH_2, \ C_2H_4, \ CH_4, \ C_2H_6, \ H_2 \ \text{etc.}$$

Hydrogen is used to manufacture ammonia by the Haber process (see Section 3.7(a)) and the alkenes are the starting material for the pre-paration of alcohols, e.g. ethanol (see Section 3.7(c)), and many useful polymers (see Section 9.6(c)(v)).

9.5
The alkanes

Specific objectives: *The expected learning outcome of this section is that the student:* (i) *describes the effect of increasing chain length and chain branching on the boiling point of alkanes;* (ii) *makes models and sketches of alkanes to show the spatial distribution of bonds;* (iii) *states the conditions and possible products for the halogenation of simple alkanes.*

(a) Physical properties

The general formula of the alkane homologous series is C_nH_{2n+2}. The names and formulae of the first eight members of the series were given in Table 9.2. The boiling points of the alkanes increase uniformly with chain length (see fig. 9.1). This is mainly a result of the increase in van der Waals' forces with increasing relative molecular mass as the number of electrons available for polarisation in the molecule increases (see

Section 8.4(a)). Each alkane in the series differs from the next by a $-CH_2-$ group, or 14 RMM units. The first four alkanes are gases at room temperature. Those alkanes with between five and seventeen carbon atoms are liquids while the higher alkanes are waxy solids.

Chain branching in isomeric alkanes lowers the boiling point as it makes the molecule more compact, thereby reducing the surface available for polarisation and interaction by van der Waals' forces. For example, the boiling points of the three isomeric pentanes are:

$$CH_3CH_2CH_2CH_2CH_3 \qquad CH_3CH_2\underset{\overset{|}{CH_3}}{CH}CH_3 \qquad CH_3-\underset{\overset{|}{CH_3}}{\overset{\overset{CH_3}{|}}{C}}-CH_3$$

pentane	2-methylbutane	2,2-dimethylpropane
b.p. 36.3°	b.p. 28°	b.p. 9°

interaction between molecules decreases

⟶

boiling-point decreases

(b) Shape of molecules

The four covalent bonds in a saturated carbon compound are arranged tetrahedrally round the central atom as this is the spatial distribution which gives maximum separation of the electron pairs (see Section 8.2). Methane is thus a tetrahedral molecule (see fig. 9.4(a)). Similarly, the covalent bonds are arranged tetrahedrally around the carbon atoms in ethane and the higher alkanes (see fig. 9.4(b) and (c)). Alkanes containing more than two carbon atoms have a zig-zag skeleton in which there is free rotation about any carbon–carbon single bond.

Experiment 9.1
Building molecular models

Use a molecular model kit to build models of methane, ethane, propane, butane and its isomers, hexane and cyclohexane. Draw the models to show the spatial arrangement of the bonds and the shape of the carbon skeleton.

Fig. 9.3(a) Vacuum unit furnace and fractionating column of hydrocracker complex at BP's Grangemouth Refinery, Scotland. Photograph by BP Oil Limited

Fig. 9.3(b) BP Oil Kent Refinery Ltd. Isle of Grain, catalytic cracker unit. Photograph by BP Oil Limited

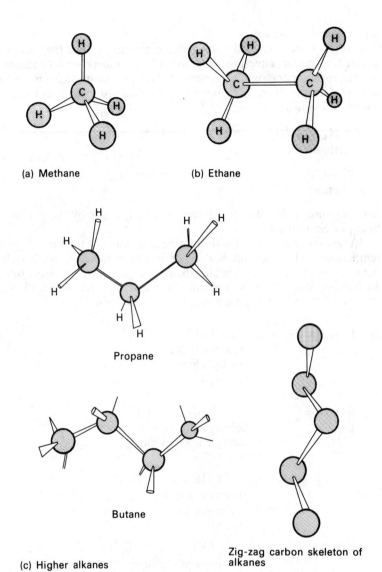

(a) Methane

(b) Ethane

Propane

Butane

Zig-zag carbon skeleton of alkanes

(c) Higher alkanes

Fig. 9.4 Shapes of alkane molecules

(c) Chemical properties

The alkanes are chemically unreactive compounds, thus they are un-affected by water, aqueous acids and alkalis, and powerful oxidising agents, such as potassium manganate(VII) or potassium dichromate(VI) at room temperature. They burn readily in air to yield a mixture of carbon dioxide and water:

$$CH_{4(g)} + 2O_{2(g)} \longrightarrow CO_{2(g)} + 2H_2O_{(l)}$$
methane

$$2C_4H_{10(g)} + 13O_{2(g)} \longrightarrow 8CO_{2(g)} + 10H_2O_{(l)}$$
butane

and the long-chain alkanes are cracked catalytically by the action of heat (see Section 9.4).

The alkanes do not react with chlorine or bromine in the dark at room temperature. However, on heating or in the presence of ultra-violet light the hydrogen atoms in the alkane are progressively substituted by halogen atoms. For example, methane and chlorine yield a mixture of mono-, di-, tri- and tetrachloromethanes on irradiation:

$$CH_4 + Cl_2 \xrightarrow[\text{heat}]{\text{u.v. or}} \quad CH_3Cl \quad + HCl$$
chloromethane
(methyl chloride)
b.p. $-24°$

$$CH_3Cl + Cl_2 \longrightarrow \quad CH_2Cl_2 \quad + HCl$$
dichloromethane
(methylene dichloride)
b.p. $40°$

$$CH_2Cl_2 + Cl_2 \longrightarrow \quad CHCl_3 \quad + HCl$$
trichloromethane
(chloroform)
b.p. $61°$

$$CHCl_3 + Cl_2 \longrightarrow \quad CCl_4 \quad + HCl$$
tetrachloromethane
(carbon tetrachloride)
b.p. $77°$

The mixture may be separated by fractional distillation. By using an excess of chlorine tetrachloromethane may be obtained as the major product, while chloromethane is the major product if an excess of methane is employed.

9.6
The alkenes

Specific objectives: *The expected learning outcome of this section is that the student: (i) draws the structural formulae of simple alkenes and names them; (ii) states that alkenes undergo addition reactions as a result of the presence of the carbon–carbon double bond; (iii) represents the reaction of a simple alkene with (a) bromine, (b) hydrogen bromide, (c) hydrogen by means of chemical equations; (iv) describes the use of bromine as a test for unsaturation.*

(*a*) *Structure and nomenclature*
The general formula of the alkenes is C_nH_{2n} (see Section 9.3(*a*)). The structure, formulae and names of the first three members of the homologous series are shown in Table 9.8.

(*b*) *Preparation and properties*
Most of the ethene required for industrial purposes is obtained as a product of petroleum cracking (see Section 9.4). It may be prepared in the laboratory by the dehydration of ethanol, either by heating it with an excess of concentrated sulphuric(VI)acid at temperatures in excess of 170°, or by passing the ethanol vapour over heated aluminium oxide:

$$
\begin{array}{c}
\text{H H}\\
\ \ |\ \ |\\
\text{H--C--C--OH}\\
\ \ |\ \ |\\
\text{H H}\\
\text{ethanol}
\end{array}
\xrightarrow[\text{or Al}_2\text{O}_3/350°]{\overset{-\text{H}_2\text{O}}{\text{conc. H}_2\text{SO}_4/>170°}}
\begin{array}{c}
\text{H}\qquad\ \ \text{H}\\
\ \diagdown\qquad\diagup\\
\ \ \ \text{C}=\text{C}\\
\ \diagup\qquad\diagdown\\
\text{H}\qquad\ \ \text{H}\\
\text{ethene}
\end{array}
$$

Propene may be prepared by the dehydration of propanol.
  Ethene (b.p. −104°) and propene (b.p. −48°) are both gases at room temperature. Cyclohexene is a colourless liquid, b.p. 83°.

(*c*) *Reactions*
Alkenes are unsaturated compounds and their typical reactions involve *addition* to the double bond to yield a saturated product. This addition occurs with:

(i) Hydrogen
An alkene is reduced to the corresponding alkane by heating with hydrogen in the presence of a catalyst, such as finely powdered platinum or nickel:

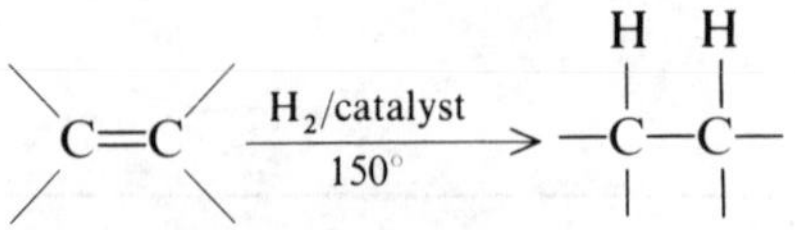

$$\diagdown C = C \diagup \xrightarrow[150°]{H_2/catalyst} \begin{matrix} H & H \\ | & | \\ -C-C- \\ | & | \end{matrix}$$

e.g. $CH_3CH{=}CH_2 \xrightarrow[150°]{H_2/catalyst} CH_3CH_2CH_3$
      propene   propane

(ii) Bromine

Bromine water, or a solution of bromine in tetrachloromethane, is decolorised by ethene or propene owing to the formation of 1,2-dibromoethane and 1,2-dibromopropane respectively:

$$CH_2{=}CH_2 + Br_2 \longrightarrow CH_2BrCH_2Br$$
$$1,2\text{-dibromoethane}$$

$$CH_3CH{=}CH_2 + Br_2 \longrightarrow CH_3CHBrCH_2Br$$
$$1,2\text{-dibromopropane}$$

This decolorisation of bromine by formation of the addition product is used as a test for carbon–carbon unsaturation and is given by alkynes as well as alkenes, including cyclic compounds such as cyclohexene:

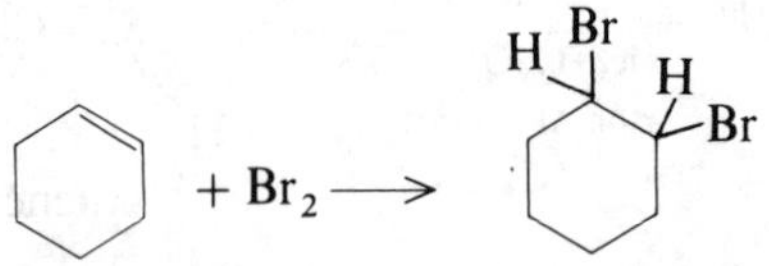

C_6H_{10} $C_6H_{10}Br_2$
cyclohexene   1,2-dibromocyclohexane

(iii) Hydrogen bromide

Ethene reacts readily with hydrogen bromide to yield bromoethane:

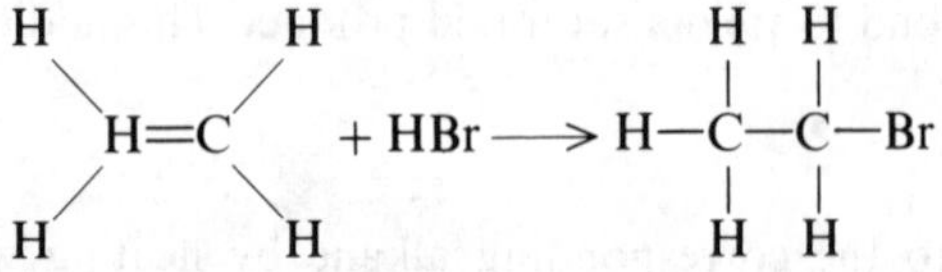

The other hydrogen halides react in the same way and the order of increasing ease of addition is HF < HCl < HBr < HI. Propene reacts

Table 9.8 Structural formulae of alkenes

Formula	Structure	Name
C_2H_4		Ethene
C_3H_6		Propene
C_4H_8 (3 isomers)		But-1-ene
		But-2-ene
		2-Methylpropene

with hydrogen bromide to yield 2-bromopropane rather than the 1-isomer:

$$CH_3CH=CH_2 \xrightarrow{\text{HBr}} \begin{cases} \longrightarrow CH_3CHBrCH_3 \\[2ex] \xrightarrow{\times} CH_3CH_2CH_2Br \end{cases}$$

(iv) Water
The hydration of ethene to yield ethanol was discussed in Section 3.7(c).

(v) Other alkene molecules
This addition reaction to the double bond of an alkene molecule produces a *polymeric* chain composed of a large number of alkene *monomer* units. For example, ethene yields the useful plastic poly(ethene) (or polythene):

$$CH_2=CH_2 \quad CH_2=CH_2 \quad CH_2=CH_2$$
$$\longrightarrow -CH_2CH_2-CH_2CH_2-CH_2CH_2- \text{ etc.}$$

i.e. $nCH_2=CH_2 \xrightarrow{\text{polymerisation}} [-CH_2CH_2-]_n$

     ethene   poly(ethene)
     monomer   polymer

Other polymers with useful properties are obtained by the polymerisation of substituted alkenes, e.g.

$$n\underset{\underset{Cl}{|}}{CH_2=CH} \xrightarrow{\text{polymerisation}} [-\underset{\underset{Cl}{|}}{CH_2CH_2}-]_n$$

    chloroethene   poly(chloroethene)
   (vinyl chloride)   (polyvinyl chloride or PVC)

The polymerisation reactions are carried out by heating the monomer under pressure in the presence of a catalyst, e.g. triethylaluminium and titanium(III)chloride.

Experiment 9.2
Reactions of alkenes

Cyclohexene is a liquid alkene (b.p. 83°) and is therefore a convenient compound for carrying out the following tests. Alternatively the tests may be carried out on the ethene prepared in Demonstration 10.2 by bubbling the gas through 4–5 cm^3 of the reagent in test-tubes.

1. Action of bromine (test for unsaturation)
Add a few drops of cyclohexene to 2–3 cm³ of a solution of bromine in tetrachloromethane. How do you account for any changes which occur?

2. Oxidation

(a) Acidified $KMnO_4$
Add a few drops of cyclohexene to 2–3 cm³ of 1% aqueous potassium manganate(VII) acidified with dilute sulphuric acid.

(b) Alkaline $KMnO_4$
Add a few drops of cyclohexene to 2–3 cm³ of 1% aqueous potassium manganate(VII) containing about 0.3 g of potassium carbonate. In each case note what changes occur. Compare the results with tests carried out on hexane (*Care: This liquid is highly flammable*) or other suitable liquid alkane.

9.7
Benzene

Specific objectives: *The expected learning outcome of this section is that the student: (i) states that the benzene ring is planar; (ii) states that the carbon–carbon bonds in benzene are all equivalent; (iii) states that benzene shows both addition and substitution reactions; (iv) states possible products for addition reactions resulting from hydrogen/catalyst and halogen/ultra violet treatment of benzene; (v) compares the relative ease with which alkenes and benzene undergo addition reactions; (vi) writes formulae of the products, and states the reagents, catalysts and conditions for (a) nitration, (b) sulphonation, (c) alkylation of benzene (monosubstitution only).*

(a) *Properties*
Benzene is a colourless liquid (m.p. 5°, b.p. 80°). It is immiscible with water and as its density (0.88 g cm⁻³) is less it forms a second layer on top of water. It dissolves readily in organic solvents and is used as a solvent itself. It burns with a smoky flame which indicates the relatively high carbon content of the compound. Benzene has a characteristic odour and is *poisonous*. Exposure to benzene vapour over a period of time can produce anaemia and possibly leukaemia. A less dangerous alternative, e.g. methylbenzene (m.p. −95°, b.p. 111°), should therefore be used instead of benzene wherever possible.

(b) *Structure of benzene*
Benzene, C_6H_6, is a planar, hexagonal molecule in which all the carbon–

carbon bonds are identical. Carbon–carbon double bonds are shorter than carbon–carbon single bonds (see Table 9.9) so although benzene is an unsaturated compound its molecule cannot be represented as a structure containing alternating double and single bonds (see Section 9.2(*b*)). The benzene ring is extremely stable, thus benzene is unaffected by aqueous solutions of oxidising agents, aqueous acids, bromine water or cold concentrated sulphuric(VI)acid. Benzene does undergo some of the addition reactions described for the alkenes (e.g. with halogen or hydrogen), but its principal reactions involve *substitution*. These two classes of reaction are now considered separately.

Table 9.9   Comparison of bond lengths

Bond	Compound	Bond length (/nm)
C—C	ethane	0.154
C=C	ethene	0.133
C≡C	ethyne	0.120
carbon/carbon	benzene	0.139

(*c*) *Addition reactions of benzene (cf alkenes, Section 9.6(c))*

(i) Hydrogenation
More vigorous reaction conditions are required for the hydrogenation of the benzene molecule than for the corresponding addition to the double bond of an alkene. Thus benzene has to be heated with the nickel catalyst at about 200° under a pressure of approx. 40 atm to yield cyclohexane:

$$\text{C}_6\text{H}_6 + 3\text{H}_2 \xrightarrow{\text{Ni/200°/40 atm}} \text{C}_6\text{H}_{12}$$

benzene   cyclohexane

(ii) Addition of chlorine or bromine
Unlike the alkenes or alkynes, benzene does not react with bromine at room temperature, thus it does not give the unsaturation test described in Section 9.6(*c*)(ii). This test may be used to distinguish aromatic hydrocarbons from alkenes or alkynes. More vigorous conditions are required for addition to occur. This again reflects the greater stability of the aromatic ring. Benzene reacts with chlorine or bromine in the presence of ultra-violet light to yield 1,2,3,4,5,6-hexachloro (or

hexabromo) cyclohexane:

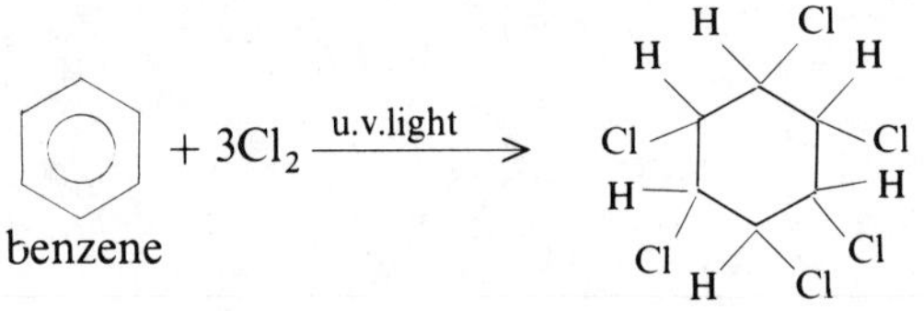

1,2,3,4,5,6-hexachlorocyclohexane

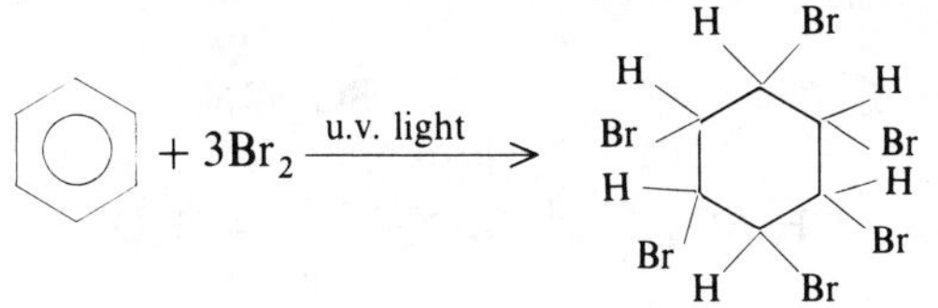

1,2,3,4,5,6-hexabromocyclohexane

Benzene can also undergo substitution by chlorine or bromine (see Section 9.7(*d*)(iv)).

(*d*) *Substitution reactions of benzene*

The characteristic reactions of the aromatic hydrocarbons involve *substitution* of the hydrogen atom attached to the carbon forming part of the benzene ring. The most important substitution reactions are:

(i) Nitration

Benzene reacts with a mixture of concentrated nitric(V) and sulphuric(VI)acids to yield nitrobenzene:

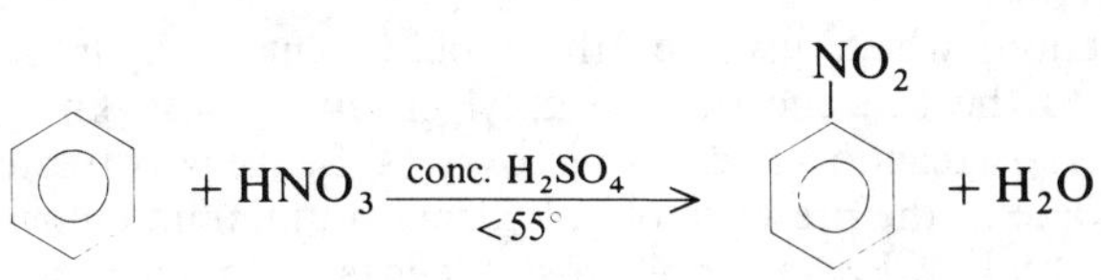

$$C_6H_5NO_2$$
nitrobenzene
b.p. 211°

The concentrated sulphuric(VI)acid acts as a catalyst by forming the *nitronium ion* by reaction with the concentrated nitric(V)acid:

$$HNO_3 + 2H_2SO_4 \longrightarrow H_3O^+ + NO_2^+ \quad + 2HSO_4^-$$
nitronium
ion

It is this ion which undergoes reaction with benzene:

$$\text{C}_6\text{H}_6 + NO_2^+ \longrightarrow \text{C}_6\text{H}_5NO_2 + H^+$$

(ii) Sulphonation

Benzene sulphonic acid, $C_6H_5SO_3H$, is obtained when benzene is heated with concentrated sulphuric(VI)acid:

$$\text{C}_6\text{H}_6 + H_2SO_4 \xrightarrow{\text{heat}} \text{C}_6\text{H}_5SO_2{\cdot}OH + H_2O$$

$$C_6H_5SO_3H$$
benzene sulphonic acid

The reaction is considerably faster if fuming sulphuric(VI)acid, i.e. a solution of sulphur trioxide in concentrated sulphuric(VI)acid, is used. Benzene sulphonic acid is a strong acid and is very soluble in water. It effervesces with sodium carbonate and forms salts on reaction with bases, e.g.

$$C_6H_5SO_3H_{(aq)} + Na_2CO_{3(aq)}$$
benzene sulphonic
acid
$$\longrightarrow C_6H_5SO_3^-Na^+_{(aq)} + H_2O_{(l)} + CO_{2(aq)}$$

(iii) Alkylation

This reaction, which involves the replacement of hydrogen atoms attached to the benzene ring by alkyl groups, is also known as the *Friedel–Crafts* reaction after its discoverers. Benzene is treated with a chloroalkane in the presence of anhydrous aluminium chloride which acts as a catalyst. For example, methylbenzene (toluene) may be prepared by the reaction:

$$\text{C}_6\text{H}_6 + CH_3Cl \xrightarrow{\text{anhydrous } Al_2Cl_6} \text{C}_6\text{H}_5CH_3 + HCl$$
methylbenzene

(iv) Halogenation

In the presence of a catalyst (known as a *halogen carrier*) benzene undergoes substitution by chlorine or bromine:

chlorobenzene

bromobenzene

Suitable catalysts for this reaction include anhydrous aluminium chloride or iron(III)chloride for chlorination and aluminium bromide, iron filings or iron(III)bromide for bromination. This reaction and its conditions should be compared with the addition of halogen to the benzene ring in the presence of ultra-violet light (see Section 9.7(c)(ii)).

The reactions of benzene are summarised in fig. 9.5.

Experiment 9.3
Reactions of aromatic hydrocarbons

(i) *Solubility*. Test the solubility of a few drops of methylbenzene in (a) water, (b) tetrachloromethane and (c) propanone (acetone).

(ii) *Combustion*. Ignite a few drops of methylbenzene on a crucible lid and note the colour of the flame. (*Note: methylbenzene is highly inflammable so the container should not be placed anywhere near a naked flame.*)

(iii) *Action of bromine*. Add a few drops of methylbenzene to 2–3 cm^3 of a solution of bromine in tetrachloromethane. Compare the result with that obtained for cyclohexene (see Experiment 9.2). Add some iron filings to the mixture and note whether any change occurs. Test any gas evolved with litmus.

(iv) *Oxidation*. Note the effect of (a) acidified $KMnO_4$ and (b) alkaline $KMnO_4$ (see Experiment 9.2) on 3–4 drops of methylbenzene. Compare your results with those obtained for cyclohexene.

(v) *Nitration*. Add about 1.5 cm^3 of methylbenzene to a mixture of 3 cm^3 of concentrated sulphuric(VI)acid and 3 cm^3 of concentrated nitric(V)acid (*Care!*). Mix well for 2–3 minutes and allow the mixture to stand for about 5 minutes before pouring into a beaker of cold water. Note the colour, odour and appearance of the product.

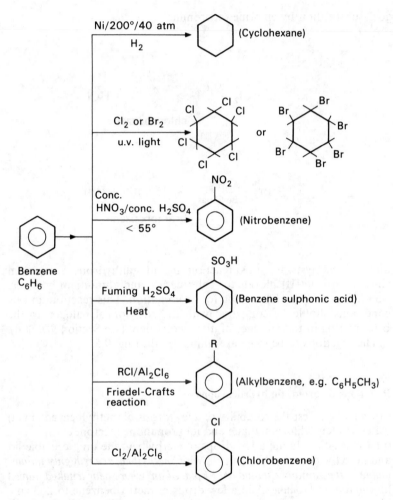

Fig. 9.5 Summary of the reactions of benzene

Summary

1. Two or more compounds which have the same molecular formula are said to be *isomeric*.

2. The different classes of hydrocarbon are summarised in fig. 9.6.

3. The names and formulae of the alkanes are listed in Table 9.2.

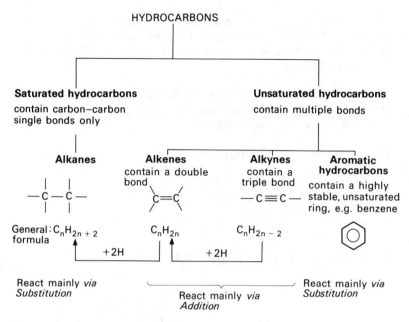

Fig. 9.6   The principal classes of hydrocarbon

4. Compounds in a *homologous series* (a) have the same functional group and the same general formula, (b) have similar chemical properties and similar methods of preparation, (c) differ from the next member of the series by a $-CH_2-$ group and 14 units of RMM, (d) show a gradation of physical properties.

5. The chemical properties of an organic compound are largely determined by the functional groups which are present in the molecule.

6. The general formula of the alkyl group is C_nH_{2n+1}. The alkyl group is denoted by the symbol R$-$. The aryl group is denoted by the symbol Ar$-$.

7. The functional groups and general formulae of the main classes of organic compounds are summarised in Table 9.6.

8. Petroleum is a complex mixture of gaseous, liquid and solid hydrocarbons.

9. Chain branching lowers the boiling point of isomeric alkanes.

10. The hydrogen atoms in an alkane are progressively substituted by chlorine or bromine on heating or if the mixture is exposed to ultra-violet light. For example, methane yields a mixture of CH_3Cl, CH_2Cl_2, $CHCl_3$ and CCl_4.

11. Alkenes (general formula C_nH_{2n}) are unsaturated compounds. Their principal reactions involve addition to the double bond. The reactions of ethene are summarised in fig. 9.7.

12. The decolorisation of bromine:

$$\begin{array}{c}\diagup\\C=C\\\diagup\end{array}\xrightarrow[CCl_4]{Br_2\ in}\begin{array}{c}\mid\ \ \ \mid\\-C-C-\\\mid\ \ \ \mid\\Br\ \ \ Br\end{array}$$

may be used as a test for carbon–carbon unsaturation.

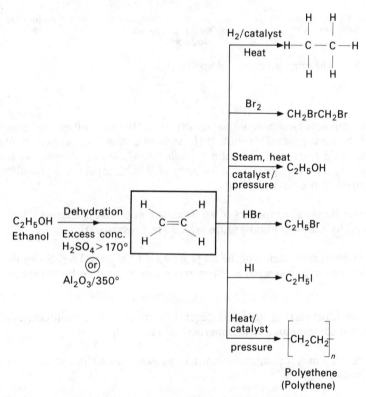

Fig. 9.7 Summary of the preparation and reactions of ethene

13. Benzene is a stable, unsaturated compound. The benzene molecule, C_6H_6, is a planar, regular hexagon.

14. Benzene's principal reactions involve substitution of the hydrogen atoms attached to carbon atoms forming part of the ring. Benzene can also undergo addition reactions with (a) chlorine or bromine in the presence of ultra-violet light and (b) hydrogen. The reactions of benzene are summarised in fig. 9.5.

Questions

1. Discuss two characteristics of the carbon atom which account for the existence of such a large number of carbon compounds compared with the compounds of other elements in the Periodic Table.

2. Discuss three general differences between organic and inorganic compounds.

3. Explain what is meant by the term 'isomerism'.

4. What is the difference between a saturated and an unsaturated hydrocarbon? Give *two* examples of each.

5. What is (a) a cyclic hydrocarbon, (b) an aromatic hydrocarbon?

6. Explain by reference to *two* different classes of organic compound what is meant by a homologous series. Give *four* different characteristics of such a series.

7. What is a functional group? Give *four* different examples.

8. What is (a) an alkyl, (b) an aryl group?

9. What are the molecular formulae of (a) the alkanes, (b) the alkenes, (c) the alkynes, (d) the alcohols and (e) the carboxylic acids which contain ten carbon atoms?

10. Name the following compounds: (a) $CH_3CHOHCH_2CH_3$, (b) $C_3H_7CO_2H$, (c) CHI_3, (d) C_6H_5I, (e) CH_3NO_2.

11. Identify the functional groups in the following molecules: (a) C_3H_4, (b) C_2H_4, (c) $CH_3CH(OH)CO_2H$, (d) CH_2O, (e) $(CH_3)_2CO$, (f) $ClCH_2CH_2OH$.

12. What is petroleum? Why is petroleum so important?

13. What is meant by (a) the fractional distillation and (b) the catalytic cracking of petroleum?

14. Describe the effect of (a) increasing chain length and (b) chain branching on the boiling points of alkanes.

15. Sketch the shapes of the following molecules to show the spatial distribution of the bonds (a) methane, (b) ethane, (c) benzene, (d) propane.

16. What is the shape of the carbon skeleton in an unbranched alkane such as butane?

17. State the reaction conditions and name the products of the bromination of methane.

18. Draw the structural formulae and name the first *three* members of the alkane and alkene homologous series.

19. Write equations and give the conditions for the reaction of (a) bromine, (b) hydrogen and (c) hydrogen bromide with ethene.

20. Describe *one* chemical test you would use to distinguish between the following pairs of compounds: (a) ethane and ethene, (b) benzene and cyclohexene.

21. How do you account for the fact that benzene (or methylbenzene) usually burns with a smoky flame but methane does not?

22. Why is it advisable to use methylbenzene instead of benzene as a solvent wherever possible?

23. What is (a) a monomer, (b) a polymer? Give *two* examples of each.

24. What is the structure of benzene?

25. Give *two* examples of (a) the addition reactions and (b) the substitution reactions of benzene.

26. How and under what conditions does benzene react with (a) hydrogen, (b) chlorine, (c) sulphuric(VI)acid, (d) chloromethane? Write equations for the reactions and name the products which are obtained.

27. Give *three* examples of the use of catalysts in organic reactions.

28. Why is it necessary to add concentrated sulphuric(VI)acid to the reaction mixture when preparing nitrobenzene? Write equations for the reactions which take place.

29. Compare the relative ease with which benzene and the alkenes undergo addition reactions.

10 Reactions of functional groups

General objective: *The expected learning outcome of this chapter is that the student is able to describe a limited range of reactions to illustrate the behaviour of some functional groups.*

10.1
Hydroxy-compounds

Specific objective: *The expected learning outcome of this section is that the student names and draws the structural formulae of simple primary, secondary and tertiary alcohols and of phenols.*

The two principal groups of hydroxy-compounds are classified as the *alcohols* and the *phenols*, depending on whether the hydroxyl group is attached to the carbon atom of an alkyl group or to one forming part of an aromatic ring, such as that of benzene. The general formulae of the two classes are thus:

Alcohols
R—OH
where R is the alkyl group
(C_nH_{2n+1})
e.g. CH_3OH methanol
(methyl alcohol)

Phenols
Ar—OH
where Ar is the aryl group
e.g. C_6H_5 (the phenyl group)
OH

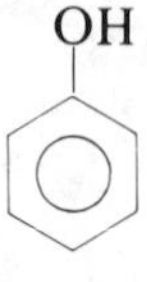

phenol (C_6H_5OH)

The position of substituents in the benzene ring of phenols and other benzene derivatives is indicated by numbering the carbon atoms, e.g.

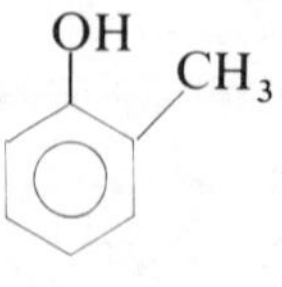

2-methylphenol 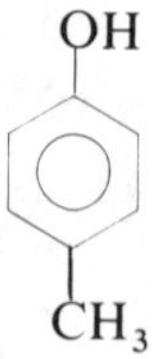   4-methylphenol 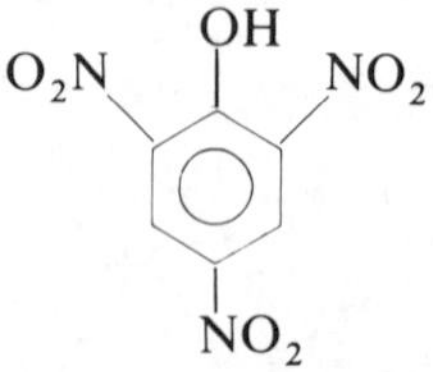   2,4,6-trinitrophenol
(picric acid)

Phenylmethanol (benzyl alcohol), $C_6H_5CH_2OH$, is not a phenol as the hydroxyl group is not attached directly to the aromatic nucleus:

$$CH_2OH$$

Alcohols are classified as primary, secondary or tertiary according to the number of hydrogen atoms linked to the carbon atom to which the hydroxyl group is attached. In a *primary* (or 1°) *alcohol* this carbon atom is linked to at least two hydrogen atoms and the compound contains the group:

—CH_2OH (1° alcohol)

while in *secondary* (2°) and *tertiary* (3°) alcohols the number of hydrogen atoms linked to the carbon atom is one and zero respectively:

CHOH   (2° alcohol)

—COH   (3° alcohol)

The general formulae of the three classes of alcohol are:

$$RCH_2OH \qquad \begin{matrix} R \\ R \end{matrix}\!\!\diagdown\!\!CHOH \qquad R'\!\!-\!\!COH$$

(including methanol CH_3OH)

1°   2°   3°

where the alkyl groups, R, R' and R" may be the same, as in 2-methyl-propan-2-ol (tertiary or *tert*-butyl alcohol), $(CH_3)_3COH$, or different as in butan-2-ol (secondary or *sec*-butyl alcohol), $CH_3CH_2CHOHCH_3$.

Alcohols and phenols are both hydroxy-compounds, but although there are some similarities the chemical properties of the two classes of compound are so different that it is more convenient to consider them separately.

Assignment

Draw the structural formulae of the alcohols containing 1–4 carbon atoms. Name them and classify them as primary, secondary or tertiary alcohols.

10.2
Alcohols

Specific objective: *The expected learning outcome of this section is that the student states the conditions and writes equations for the following reactions of alcohols:*
1. *substitution by halogen,*
2. *esterification,*
3. *oxidation (for primary and secondary alcohols only),*
4. *dehydration.*

(a) *Preparation*
Alcohols are now usually manufactured by the hydration of alkenes obtained from cracked petroleum (see Section 9.4), e.g.:

$$CH_2{=}CH_2 + H_2O \xrightarrow[320°/70 \text{ atm}]{H_3PO_4/\text{celite}} C_2H_5OH$$
$$\text{ethene} \qquad \text{steam} \qquad\qquad\qquad \text{ethanol}$$

$$CH_3CH{=}CH_2 + H_2O \longrightarrow CH_3CHOHCH_3$$
$$\text{propene} \qquad \text{steam} \qquad \text{propan-2-ol}$$

Some ethanol, particularly as wine, beer, whisky etc., is prepared by the fermentation of sugars or other carbohydrates under anaerobic conditions (i.e. in the absence of air):

$$C_6H_{12}O_6 \xrightarrow[\text{anaerobic fermentation}]{\text{yeast}} 2C_2H_5OH + 2CO_2$$
$$\text{fructose}$$
$$\text{or glucose}$$

(b) *Properties of alcohols*
The lower alcohols are colourless, volatile liquids which are completely miscible with water. The boiling points of the first members of the homologous series are listed in Table 10.1. These boiling points are considerably higher than those of the ethers with which the alcohols are isomeric. For example, ethanol (CH_3CH_2OH), boils at 78.5° while its isomer, methoxymethane (dimethyl ether) CH_3OCH_3, b.p. $-24°$, is a gas at room temperature. This decreased volatility and the greater solubility of the alcohols in water are due to the ability of the hydroxyl group to form hydrogen bonds (see Section 8.4(c)). The solubility of the alcohols in water decreases with increasing relative molecular mass as the number of carbon atoms and hence the hydrophobic part of the molecule (see Sections 6.5 and 8.1(b)) increases (see Table 10.2).

Table 10.1 Boiling points of alcohols

Compound	Formula	b.p. (/°C)
Methanol	CH_3OH	64.5
Ethanol	CH_3CH_2OH	78.5
Propan-1-ol	$CH_3CH_2CH_2OH$	97.2
Propan-2-ol	$CH_3CHOHCH_3$	82.4
Butan-1-ol	$CH_3CH_2CH_2CH_2OH$	117

Table 10.2 Solubility of unbranched chain primary alcohols in water

Alcohol	Solubility (/g in 100 cm^3 of water)
CH_3OH	∞
C_2H_5OH	∞ completely miscible
C_3H_7OH	∞
C_4H_9OH	8.3
$C_5H_{11}OH$	2.0
$C_6H_{13}OH$	0.5
$C_7H_{15}OH$	0.12

(c) *Reactions*
The principal reactions of the alcohols are:

(i) Action of sodium
Effervescence occurs and hydrogen is evolved when metallic sodium is added to an anhydrous alcohol, e.g.

$$2C_2H_5OH + 2Na \longrightarrow 2C_2H_5O^-Na^+ + H_{2(g)}$$
ethanol　　　　　　　sodium ethoxide

An ionic metal alkoxide is obtained. The evolution of hydrogen in this reaction confirms the presence of a hydroxyl group in a compound, *cf.*

$$2H_2O + 2Na \longrightarrow 2NaOH_{(aq)} + H_{2(g)}$$

(ii) Substitution by halogen

The hydroxyl group in an alcohol may be replaced by a halogen by the following reactions:

1. The action of a phosphorus or sulphur halide, e.g.

$$ROH + PCl_5 \longrightarrow RCl + HCl_{(g)} + POCl_3$$
  alcohol   phosphorus   chloroalkane
            pentachloride

$$ROH + SOCl_2 \longrightarrow RCl + SO_{2(g)} + HCl_{(g)}$$
  alcohol   sulphur dichloride   chloroalkane
            oxide
          (thionyl chloride)

For example, chloroethane (ethyl chloride) may be prepared by the action of phosphorus pentachloride, or of sulphur dichloride oxide, on ethanol:

$$C_2H_5OH + PCl_5 \longrightarrow C_2H_5Cl + HCl + POCl_3$$
$$C_2H_5OH + SOCl_2 \longrightarrow C_2H_5Cl + SO_2 + HCl$$

The evolution of hydrogen chloride in the reaction with phosphorus pentachloride, or of sulphur dioxide and hydrogen chloride on treatment with sulphur dichloride oxide (thionyl chloride), is used as a test for the presence of a hydroxyl group in a compound.

Bromoalkanes and iodoalkanes are obtained by the action of phosphorus tribromide (PBr_3) or a mixture of red phosphorus and iodine on the alcohol respectively. For example,

$$3C_2H_5OH + PBr_3 \longrightarrow 3C_2H_5Br + P(OH)_3$$
      ethanol   bromoethane
                             (ethyl bromide)

$$2P + 3I_2 \longrightarrow 2PI_3$$
red phosphorus

$$3C_2H_5OH + PI_3 \longrightarrow 3C_2H_5I + P(OH)_3$$
      ethanol   iodoethane
                           (ethyl iodide)

2. The action of a hydrogen halide

Ethanol reacts with anhydrous hydrogen chloride in the presence of anhydrous zinc chloride to yield chloroethane (*Grove's process*):

$$C_2H_5OH_{(l)} + HCl_{(g)} \xrightarrow{\text{anhydrous } ZnCl_2} C_2H_5Cl_{(g)} + H_2O_{(l)}$$

A catalyst is not required for the preparation of a bromoalkane:

$$ROH_{(l)} + HBr_{(aq)} \longrightarrow RBr_{(l)} + H_2O_{(l)}$$

and the hydrogen bromide for the reaction may be prepared *in situ* (i.e. in the reaction flask) by the action of concentrated sulphuric(VI)acid on sodium bromide, e.g.

$$NaBr + H_2SO_4 \longrightarrow NaHSO_4 + HBr$$
$$C_2H_5OH + HBr \longrightarrow C_2H_5Br + H_2O.$$

(iii) Esterification

The formation of an ester by the reaction between a carboxylic acid and an alcohol in the presence of a strong acid catalyst was described in Section 3.2(*b*) as an example of a reversible reaction. The general reaction for the process is:

$$\underset{\substack{\text{carboxylic}\\\text{acid}}}{R-C{\overset{O}{\underset{OH}{}}}} + \underset{\text{alcohol}}{R'OH} \underset{}{\overset{H^+_{(aq)} \text{ (catalyst)}}{\rightleftharpoons}} \underset{\text{ester}}{R-C{\overset{O}{\underset{O-R'}{}}}} + \underset{\text{water}}{H_2O}$$

For example, methyl ethanoate is prepared by gently warming a mixture of methanol and ethanoic acid containing a few drops of concentrated sulphuric(VI)acid:

$$\underset{\substack{\text{ethanoic}\\\text{acid}}}{CH_3CO_2H} + \underset{\text{methanol}}{CH_3OH} \overset{H_2SO_4}{\rightleftharpoons} \underset{\substack{\text{methyl}\\\text{ethanoate}}}{CH_3CO_2CH_3} + \underset{\text{water}}{H_2O}$$

Esters are colourless liquids with a pleasant, 'fruity' odour. For example, amyl ethanoate (acetate), $CH_3CO_2C_5H_{11}$, smells of pear-drops and methyl 2-hydroxy-benzoate (methyl salicylate) smells of oil of wintergreen. Esters are widely used as solvents.

methyl 2-hydroxy-benzoate
(methyl salicylate)

The esterification reaction is reversible and esters are hydrolysed by boiling with aqueous acids or alkalis, e.g.

$$CH_3CO_2C_2H_5 + H_2O \underset{}{\overset{H_{(aq)}^+}{\rightleftharpoons}} CH_3CO_2H + C_2H_5OH$$
ethyl ethanoate   ethanoic acid   ethanol

$$CH_3CO_2C_2H_5 + NaOH_{(aq)} \xrightarrow{boil} CH_3CO_2^- Na_{(aq)}^+ + C_2H_5OH$$
    ethyl   sodium   ethanol
 ethanoate   ethanoate

Many naturally occurring fats and oils are esters of the trihydric alcohol propane-1,2,3-triol (glycerol), $CH_2OHCHOHCH_2OH$, and long chain carboxylic acids, such as hexadecanoic acid (palmitic acid) $CH_3(CH_2)_{14}CO_2H$ and octadecanoic acid (stearic acid) $CH_3(CH_2)_{16}CO_2H$. The sodium or potassium salts obtained by the alkaline hydrolysis (or *saponification*) of these fats with aqueous sodium or potassium hydroxide are used as soaps (see Section 6.5):

$$
\begin{array}{l}
CH_2OCOR \\
| \\
CHOCOR \\
| \\
CH_2OCOR
\end{array}
+ 3NaOH_{(aq)} \xrightarrow{boil}
\begin{array}{l}
CH_2OH \\
| \\
CHOH \\
| \\
CH_2OH
\end{array}
+ 3RCO_2^- Na_{(aq)}^+
$$

a glyceride
fat or oil

where **R** is the alkyl group (hydrophobic chain) of a long chain carboxylic acid.

(iv) Oxidation

The products obtained on the oxidation of an alcohol are determined by the class of alcohol (i.e. primary, secondary or tertiary) which is being oxidised. A primary alcohol is oxidised in two stages to yield first an aldehyde and then a carboxylic acid:

$$R-CH_2OH \xrightarrow{oxidation} R-C\overset{H}{\underset{O}{\diagup}} \xrightarrow{further\ oxidation} R-CO_2H$$

1° alcohol   aldehyde   carboxylic acid e.g.

$$CH_3CH_2OH \xrightarrow{\text{oxidation}} CH_3CHO \xrightarrow[\text{oxidation}]{\text{further}} CH_3CO_2H$$

ethanol   ethanal   ethanoic
               (acetaldehyde)   acid

Secondary alcohols yield ketones on oxidation which are difficult to oxidise further. The use of powerful oxidising agents causes the ketone molecule to break up to yield a mixture of acids, each containing less carbon atoms than the original alcohol or ketone:

$$\begin{array}{c}R \\ \diagdown \\ \diagup \\ R\end{array}CHOH \xrightarrow{\text{oxidation}} \begin{array}{c}R \\ \diagdown \\ \diagup \\ R\end{array}C{=}O \xrightarrow[\text{oxidation}]{\text{powerful}} \begin{array}{c}\text{molecule} \\ \text{breaks up}\end{array}$$

2° alcohol   ketone

For example, propan-2-ol yields propanone (acetone) on oxidation:

$$CH_3CHOHCH_3 \xrightarrow{\text{oxidation}} CH_3COCH_3$$

propan-2-ol   propanone

Tertiary alcohols are difficult to oxidise and the molecule breaks up to yield a mixture of acids and other fragmentation products.

The oxidation of primary or secondary alcohols may be carried out using aqueous sodium (or potassium) dichromate(VI) acidified with dilute sulphuric(VI)acid as the oxidising agent, or with air or oxygen and a catalyst such as platinum or copper. The dichromate solution changes colour from orange to green in the course of the reaction as the chromium is reduced from the $+6$ to the $+3$ oxidation state, e.g.

$$3C_2H_5OH + Cr_2O_{7(aq)}^{2-} + 8H_{(aq)}^{+} \rightarrow 3CH_3CHO + 2Cr_{(aq)}^{3+} + 7H_2O$$

ethanol   (orange)   ethanal   (green)

This reaction is the same as that used in the breathalyser or alcohol detector to measure the alcohol content of a driver's bloodstream.

(v) Dehydration

Alcohols undergo dehydration when they are heated with concentrated sulphuric(VI) or phosphoric(V)acid or if their vapour is passed over heated alumina (aluminium oxide). The product which is obtained depends on the reaction conditions. For example, ethoxyethane (diethyl ether), b.p. 35°, is obtained by the action of an excess of ethanol on concentrated sulphuric(VI) acid at 140°:

$$2C_2H_5OH \xrightarrow{\text{conc } H_2SO_4/140°} (C_2H_5)_2O + H_2O$$

(excess of ethanol)   ethoxyethane

while with an excess of concentrated sulphuric(VI)acid at temperatures above 170° ethene is obtained:

$$C_2H_5OH \xrightarrow[>170°]{\text{excess of conc } H_2SO_4} C_2H_4 + H_2O$$
$$\text{ethene}$$

Similarly, the temperature employed determines the product which is obtained from the catalytic dehydration over heated alumina:

$$C_2H_5OH \begin{cases} \xrightarrow[-H_2O]{Al_2O_3/260°} (C_2H_5)_2O \\ \\ \xrightarrow[-H_2O]{Al_2O_3/350°} C_2H_4 \end{cases}$$

Other alcohols react similarly, e.g.

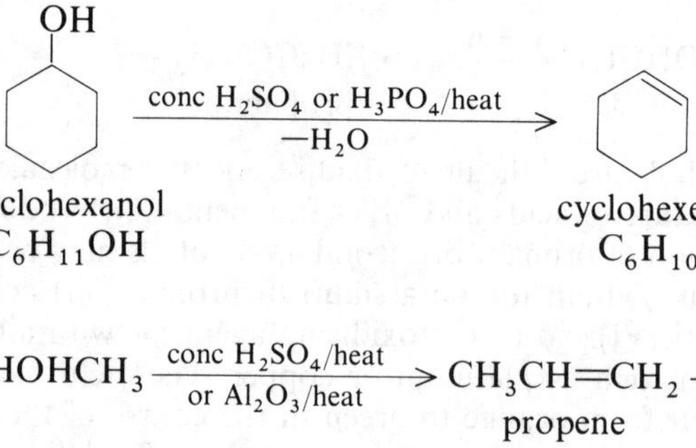

OH

$$\xrightarrow[-H_2O]{\text{conc } H_2SO_4 \text{ or } H_3PO_4/\text{heat}}$$

cyclohexanol
$C_6H_{11}OH$

cyclohexene
C_6H_{10}

$$CH_3CHOHCH_3 \xrightarrow[\text{or } Al_2O_3/\text{heat}]{\text{conc } H_2SO_4/\text{heat}} CH_3CH{=}CH_2 + H_2O$$
$$\text{propene}$$

Experiment 10.1
Reactions of alcohols

(a) *Action of sodium*
Add a small pellet of sodium to about 1 cm³ of anhydrous methanol or ethanol in a dry test-tube. Note the evolution of hydrogen.

(b) *Action of phosphorus pentachloride*
Add about 0.1 g of phosphorus pentachloride (*Care!*) to 1–2 cm³ of anhydrous methanol, ethanol or propanol in a dry test-tube. Test the gas evolved with (i) moist blue litmus paper, (ii) gaseous ammonia from an open bottle of aqueous ammonia (density 0.880 g cm⁻³).

(c) *Esterification*
Warm about 1 cm³ of ethanol (industrial methylated spirit (IMS)) with about 0.5 cm³ of ethanoic acid containing 2–3 drops of concentrated

sulphuric(VI)acid gently for 2–3 minutes in a test-tube and then pour the mixture into a 100 cm³ beaker containing about 20 cm³ of 2 M aqueous sodium hydroxide. Note the pleasant odour of the ethyl ethanoate which is obtained. Repeat the experiment using (i) amyl alcohol, $C_5H_{11}OH$, instead of the ethanol, (ii) about 1 cm³ of methanol, 0.5 g of 2-hydroxybenzoic (salicylic) acid and 2–3 drops of concentrated sulphuric(VI)acid.

(d) Oxidation
Add about 1 cm³ of ethanol (IMS) to 1–2 cm³ of aqueous potassium dichromate(VI) solution acidified with an equal volume of dilute sulphuric(VI)acid. Warm the mixture gently and note the odour of the product and the change in the colour of the solution. Repeat the experiment using methanol or propan-2-ol.

Demonstration 10.1
Catalytic oxidation of methanol

Heat a spiral of platinum or copper wire in a Bunsen burner flame until it is red hot and then immediately place it in the vapour from about 10 cm³ of methanol contained in a 100 cm³ beaker (see fig. 10.1). Note the pungent odour of the methanal which is obtained as a product of the oxidation:

$$2CH_3OH + O_2 \xrightarrow[\text{heat}]{\text{Pt or Cu catalyst}} 2CH_2O + 2H_2O$$
$$\text{methanol} \qquad\qquad\qquad\qquad\quad \text{methanal}$$

The wire frequently continues to glow as this reaction is strongly exothermic ($\Delta H = -157$ kJ mol^{-1}).

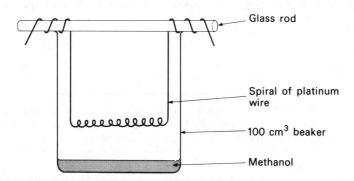

Fig. 10.1 Catalytic oxidation of methanol

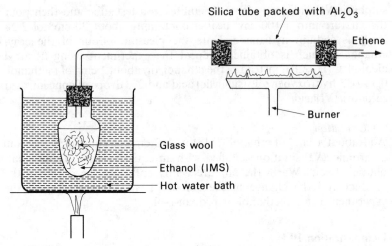

Fig. 10.2 Catalytic dehydration of ethanol: preparation of ethene

Demonstration 10.2
Catalytic dehydration of ethanol

Place 10 cm³ of ethanol (IMS) in a 25 cm³ pear-shaped flask containing glass wool to ensure even boiling and then set up the apparatus
as shown in fig. 10.2. Heat the silica tube containing the alumina
catalyst to approx. 350° (this is well below red heat) and then gently
boil the alcohol in the flask to drive the alcohol vapour over the heated
catalyst. Collect the ethene obtained in test-tubes over water, or bubble
the gas through test-tubes containing 2–3 cm³ of (a) bromine in tetrachloromethane, (b) acidified 1% aqueous potassium manganate(VII),
(c) alkaline 1% aqueous potassium manganate(VII) solution to demonstrate the general reactions of alkenes (see Section 9.6 and Experiment
9.2).

10.3
Phenols

Specific objective: *The expected learning outcome of this section is that
the student states that the phenolic hydroxyl group is acidic, and illustrates
this statement by reference to the reaction with alkali.*

(a) Properties of phenol
The general properties of the phenols (see Section 10.1) are illustrated
by those of phenol itself. Phenol (m.p. 42°, b.p. 181°) is a colourless,

crystalline solid when pure. It slowly becomes tinged with pink on storage and exposure to air owing to the formation of traces of oxidation products. Phenol is also known as carbolic acid. It has a sharp, 'disinfectant-like' odour and is moderately soluble in cold water, but completely miscible above 65.8°. It dissolves readily in aqueous sodium hydroxide and in organic solvents. The compound is caustic (i.e. it has a corrosive action on the skin and can produce severe burns) and is poisonous. Phenol is used for the manufacture of resins (e.g. Bakelite), it is a starting material for the preparation of nylon and is also used as a disinfectant and antiseptic (carbolic acid).

(b) Chemical reactions

(i) As an acid

The hydroxyl group is considerably more acidic in phenols than in alcohols (see Table 10.3):

$$C_6H_5OH_{(aq)} + H_2O \rightleftharpoons C_6H_5O^-_{(aq)} + H_3O^+_{(aq)}$$

The figures in Table 10.3 are based on the relative magnitude of the equilibrium constants for the dissociation:

$$HX_{(aq)} \rightleftharpoons H^+_{(aq)} + X^-_{(aq)}$$
$$\text{acid}$$

Phenol dissolves in alkalis, such as aqueous sodium hydroxide, to yield salts, e.g.

phenol + NaOH$_{(aq)}$ $\longrightarrow$ sodium phenoxide + H$_2$O

However, it does not liberate carbon dioxide from carbonates as phenol is a much weaker acid than carbonic acid (see Table 10.3):

$$CO_3^{2-}{}_{(aq)} + 2H^+_{(aq)} \rightleftharpoons [H_2CO_{3(aq)}] \rightleftharpoons H_2O_{(l)} + CO_{2(aq)}$$

Table 10.3   Relative acidic strengths of methanol, phenol, carbonic acid and ethanoic (acetic) acid

Substance:	CH_3OH	C_6H_5OH	'H_2CO_3'	CH_3CO_2H
Relative acidic strength:	1	10^6	10^9	10^{11}

$[H^+_{(aq)}]$ from phenol is too low to displace the equilibrium to the right to produce gaseous carbon dioxide.

(ii) Action of iron(III)chloride solution
A violet coloration is obtained when a few drops of neutral aqueous iron(III)chloride (ferric chloride) solution are added to a dilute solution of phenol. This test is given by compounds containing an *enol group*, i.e. a hydroxyl group linked to an unsaturated carbon atom:

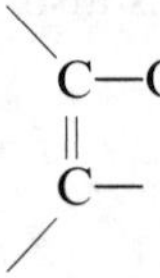

enol group

(iii) Ester formation
Unlike the alcohols (see Section 10.2(c)(iii)), phenols do not form esters by direct reaction with carboxylic acids. Esters are obtained, however, by treating the phenol with the acid anhydride or acyl halide which are considerably more reactive than the free acid (see Section 10.4(c)(ii) and Experiment 10.3), e.g.

$$(CH_3CO)_2O + C_6H_5OH \longrightarrow CH_3CO_2C_6H_5 + CH_3CO_2H$$

ethanoic   phenyl ethanoate
anhydride   (phenyl acetate)

$$CH_3COCl + C_6H_5OH \longrightarrow CH_3CO_2C_6H_5 + HCl$$

ethanoyl
chloride

(iv) Substitution of the aromatic ring
The presence of the hydroxyl group activates the ring and makes substitution of phenol much easier than in benzene. For example, bromine water gives an immediate precipitate of 2,4,6-tribromophenol with aqueous phenol:

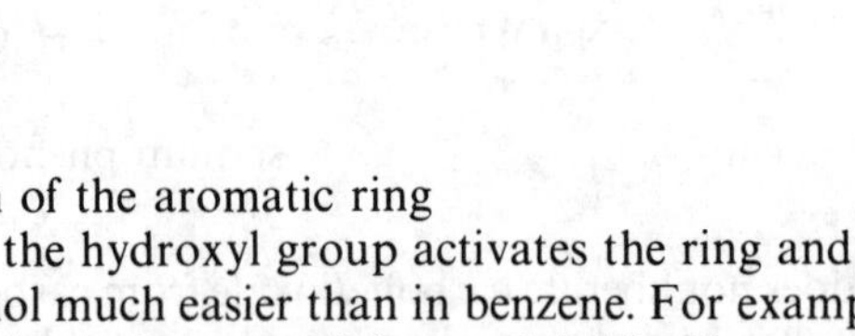

phenol   2,4,6-tribromophenol
C_6H_5OH $C_6H_2Br_3OH$

while dilute aqueous nitric(V)acid gives a mixture of the isomeric 2- and 4-nitrophenols:

| phenol | 2-nitrophenol | 4-nitrophenol |

Benzene requires considerably more vigorous reaction conditions, thus bromination to yield the monobrominated product requires a catalyst or halogen carrier (see Section 9.7(d)(iv)), while nitration of benzene requires a mixture of concentrated nitric(V)acid and sulphuric(VI)acid at about 50° (see Section 9.7(d)(i)).

Experiment 10.2
Reactions of phenol

(*a*) *Solubility*
Compare the solubility of phenol in (i) distilled water, (ii) aqueous 2 M sodium hydroxide and (iii) aqueous sodium carbonate. Determine the pH of a cold saturated aqueous solution of phenol with indicator papers. (*Care: phenol is caustic and poisonous. Do not allow the substance or its aqueous solution to come into contact with the skin.*) Note the odour of phenol.

(*b*) *Action of neutral iron(III)chloride solution*
Add 2–3 drops of neutral iron(III)chloride solution (see Appendix VI) to a dilute aqueous solution of phenol.

(*c*) *Action of bromine water*
Add bromine water drop by drop to about 1–2 cm^3 of a cold aqueous solution of phenol. Note the formation of a precipitate of 2,4,6-tribromophenol.

The reactions of ethanol and phenol are summarised in figs. 10.3 and 10.4 respectively.

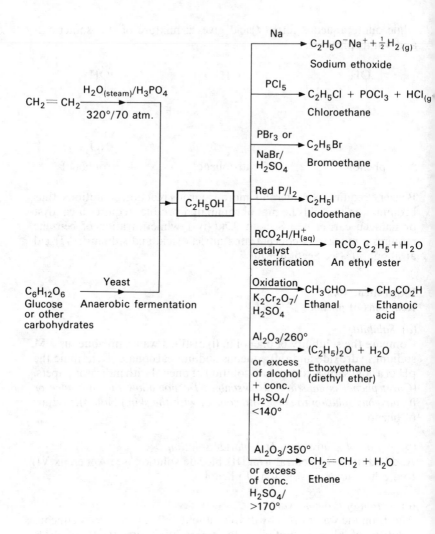

Fig. 10.3 The manufacture and reactions of ethanol

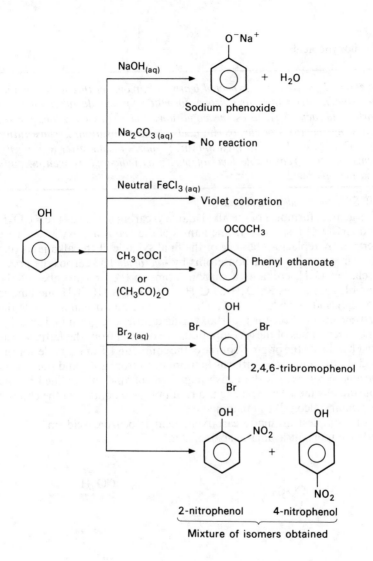

Fig. 10.4 The reactions of phenol

10.4
Carboxylic acids

Specific objectives: *The expected learning outcome of this section is that the student: (i) names and draws formulae for simple alkyl and aryl carboxylic acids (ii) states the conditions and writes equations for the following reactions of carboxylic acids: 1. neutralisation, 2. substitution of —OH by —Cl, 3. esterification (iii) prepares a solid ester (e.g. phenyl benzoate) to a reasonable level of purity as indicated by melting point and in good yield.*

(a) Structure and nomenclature

The general formulae of the alkyl and aryl carboxylic acids are RCO_2H and $ArCO_2H$ respectively. The names of the alkyl carboxylic acids are derived by replacing the *-ane* of the final syllable of the alkane having the same number of carbon atoms by *-oic acid*. The carboxylic group itself, $—CO_2H$, contains a carbon atom, so the first member of the homologous series RCO_2H or $C_nH_{2n+1}CO_2H$ is HCO_2H, methanoic (formic) acid, for which n = 0. The systematic and trivial names of the first members of the alkyl carboxylic acid series are given in Table 9.5. The older names of these compounds are derived from the Latin words which indicate the original source of the compound. For example, formic acid (Latin, *formica* = ant) was first obtained from ants, and acetic acid (*acetum* = vinegar) is the active ingredient of vinegar obtained by the souring of wines. This souring is a result of the oxidation of the ethanol (a primary alcohol) to ethanoic acid.

The simplest aromatic carboxylic acid is benzoic acid (m.p. 121°). Other important aromatic acids include:

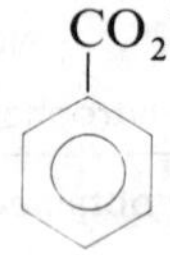

benzoic acid 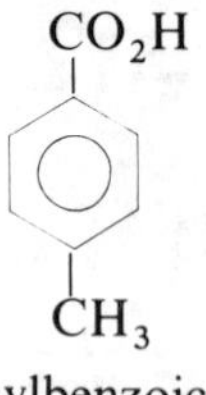   4-methylbenzoic acid

Benzene-1,2
dicarboxylic acid
(phthalic acid)

Benzene-1,4-
dicarboxylic acid
(terephthalic acid)

(b) Physical properties

The first members of the alkanoic acid homologous series are liquids with boiling points which are considerably higher than those of alkanes or esters of similar relative molecular mass (see Table 10.4). This decreased volatility is due to inter-molecular hydrogen bonding and reflects the greater energy required to separate the associated molecules. Anhydrous ethanoic acid (m.p. 16.7°) is known as glacial ethanoic (or acetic) acid as it freezes to a colourless, ice-like solid in a cold room.

Methanoic and ethanoic acids have sharp, vinegar-like odours. In fact, vinegar itself is a dilute aqueous solution of ethanoic acid containing caramel and other colouring and flavouring materials. Carboxylic acids containing up to four carbon atoms are completely soluble in water, but this solubility decreases as the number of carbon atoms in the molecule increases. The alkyl carboxylic acids are miscible with organic solvents. The aromatic carboxylic acids are colourless, crystalline solids which are slightly soluble in cold water and reasonably soluble in hot water.

Table 10.4   Comparison of volatility of alkanes, esters and carboxylic acids of similar relative molecular mass

Compound	Formula	RMM	Intermolecular forces	b.p. (/°C)
Butane	$CH_3CH_2CH_2CH_3$	58	van der Waals'	−0.5
Methyl methanoate	HCO_2CH_3	60	dipole–dipole	31.5
Ethanoic acid	CH_3CO_2H	60	hydrogen bonding	118

(*c*) *Chemical properties*
Methanoic acid differs from the other members of the alkanoic acid homologous series in many of its chemical properties. The chemistry of ethanoic acid is therefore described as illustrating the typical properties of these compounds.

(i) Neutralisation
The carboxylic acids are weak acids (see Section 4.1(*b*)):

$$RCO_2H + H_2O \rightleftharpoons RCO^-_{2(aq)} + H_3O^+_{(aq)}$$

They react with sodium carbonate with effervescence, liberating carbon dioxide (*cf* phenols Section 10.3(*b*)(i)) and are neutralised by alkalis to yield salts, e.g.

$$\underset{\text{ethanoic acid}}{2CH_3CO_2H} + Na_2CO_3 \longrightarrow \underset{\text{sodium ethanoate}}{2CH_3CO_2^-Na^+} + H_2O + CO_2$$

$$\underset{\text{benzoic acid}}{C_6H_5CO_2H_{(s)}} + NaOH_{(aq)} \longrightarrow \underset{\text{sodium benzoate}}{C_6H_5CO_2^-Na^+_{(aq)}} + H_2O_{(l)}$$

(ii) Substitution of —OH by —Cl
The hydroxyl group of carboxylic acids is substituted by chlorine to yield an acyl chloride when the compound is treated with phosphorus pentachloride or sulphur dichloride oxide (thionyl chloride):

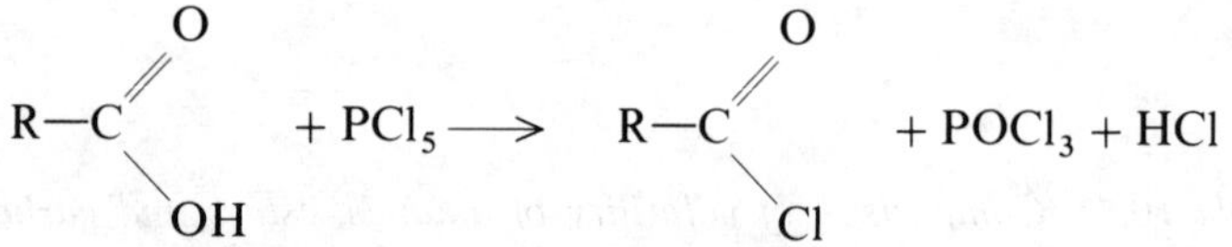

carboxylic acid an acyl chloride

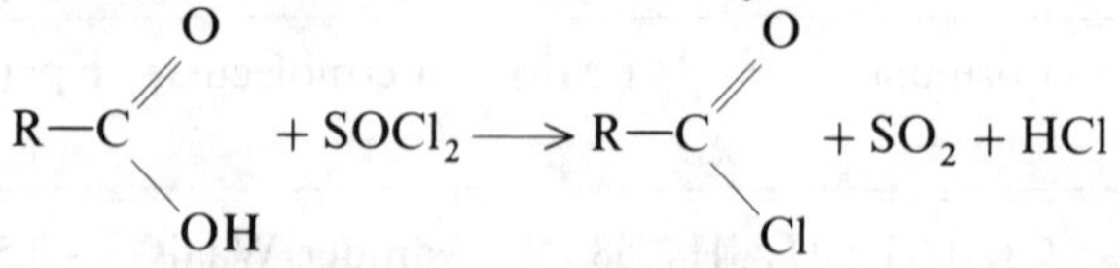

where R = alkyl or aryl groups.
For example, ethanoyl chloride, CH_3COCl, and benzoyl chloride, C_6H_5COCl, may be prepared by the reactions:

$$CH_3CO_2H + PCl_5 \longrightarrow CH_3COCl + POCl_3 + HCl$$

$$CO_2H \qquad\qquad COCl$$

benzoic acid   benzoyl chloride

Hydrogen chloride is evolved in these reactions, thus confirming the presence of a hydroxyl group in the carboxylic acid (*cf* Section 10.2(*c*)(ii) where this reaction was used to demonstrate the presence of a hydroxyl group in alcohols).

The acyl chlorides are fuming liquids with a sharp irritating odour. They are highly reactive compounds and are rapidly hydrolysed by cold water, e.g.

$$CH_3COCl + H_2O \longrightarrow CH_3CO_2H + HCl$$

They react with alcohols or phenols to yield esters, e.g.

$$C_6H_5COCl + C_6H_5OH \xrightarrow{\text{NaOH}_{(aq)}} C_6H_5CO_2C_6H_5 + HCl$$
benzoyl   phenyl
chloride   benzoate

$$CH_3COCl + C_6H_5OH \longrightarrow CH_3CO_2C_6H_5 + HCl$$
ethanoyl   phenyl
chloride   ethanoate

and with the anhydrous salt of a carboxylic acid to yield an acid anhydride:

acid anhydride

For example, ethanoic anhydride, $(CH_3CO)_2O$, may be prepared by the action of ethanoyl (acetyl) chloride on sodium ethanoate:

$$CH_3COCl + CH_3CO_2^- Na^+ \longrightarrow (CH_3CO)_2O + Na^+Cl^-$$
ethanoic
anhydride

Methanoic acid does not yield the corresponding acyl halide on treatment with phosphorus pentachloride or sulphur dichloride oxide, nor does it form an anhydride. Methanoyl chloride, HCOCl, and methanoic anhydride, $(HCO)_2O$, are unknown.

Acid anhydrides are hydrolysed to the carboxylic acid by water:

$$(RCO)_2O + H_2O \longrightarrow 2RCO_2H$$

and react with alcohols or phenols to yield an ester:

$$(RCO)_2O + R'OH \longrightarrow RCO_2R' + RCO_2H$$

(iii) Esterification (see Section 10.2(*c*)(iii))
The formation of a solid ester by treating an alcohol or a phenol with benzoyl or 3,5-dinitrobenzoyl chloride:

$$\underset{\substack{\text{aromatic acyl}\\\text{chloride}}}{ArCOCl} + \underset{\text{alcohol}}{ROH} \xrightarrow{\text{NaOH}_{(aq)}} \underset{\text{ester}}{ArCO_2R} + HCl$$

e.g.

$$\text{3,5-dinitrobenzoyl chloride} + C_2H_5OH \longrightarrow \text{ethyl 3,5-dinitrobenzoate} + HCl$$

is often used as a method of identifying a particular hydroxy-compound. The solid derivative obtained is purified by recrystallisation and its melting point is then determined. The hydroxy-compound may be identified by referring to tables listing the melting points of the benzoates and 3,5-dinitrobenzoates of known alcohols and phenols.

Experiment 10.3
The preparation of phenyl benzoate

Note: Benzoyl chloride is an unpleasant, fuming liquid and phenol is a toxic, corrosive solid. These materials should therefore be dispensed in a fume cupboard and should not be allowed to come into contact with the skin. Safety spectacles or goggles *must* be worn.
Method
Add about 1 cm^3 of benzoyl chloride to 1 g of phenol in 15 cm^3 of aqueous sodium hydroxide contained in a thick-walled glass boiling-

tube. Stopper the tube securely with a cork or rubber bung and shake the mixture vigorously for 5–10 minutes. Filter off the precipitate of phenyl benzoate, wash well with water and recrystallise from hot ethanol (IMS). Weigh the dry, purified product and determine the melting point of a sample. Calculate the percentage yield of phenyl benzoate.

Example 10.1
Calculation of percentage yields
A 3.9 g sample of pure, dry phenyl benzoate was obtained by treating 2.5 g of phenol with an excess of benzoyl chloride. What is the percentage yield of the product?

Solution
The equation for the reaction is:

$$C_6H_5COCl + C_6H_5OH + NaOH_{(aq)} \longrightarrow C_6H_5CO_2C_6H_5 + NaCl + H_2O$$

<table>
<tr><td>1 mole</td><td>1 mole</td><td>1 mole</td></tr>
<tr><td>RMM of phenol = 94</td><td></td><td>RMM of phenyl benzoate = 198</td></tr>
</table>

If the reaction proceeds to completion and no phenyl benzoate is lost in the preparation and purification, 1 mole (198 g) of phenyl benzoate would be obtained from 1 mole (94 g) of phenol. The theoretical yield from 2.5 g of phenol is thus $\frac{198}{94} \times 2.5 = 5.27$ g.

In any preparation,

$$\text{Percentage yield} = \frac{\text{Actual yield}}{\text{Theoretical yield}} \times 100$$

$$\therefore \text{ Percentage yield of phenyl benzoate} = \frac{3.9}{5.27} \times 100 = 74\%$$

Experiment 10.4
General reactions of carboxylic acids

(*a*) *Solubility*
(i) Compare the solubility of ethanoic acid (glacial) and benzoic acid in water. Determine the approximate pH of the aqueous solution with Universal indicator paper.
(ii) Add an excess of cold aqueous sodium hydroxide to 0.3–0.5 g of benzoic acid and observe what happens when 1–2 cm^3 of concentrated hydrochloric acid is now added. Boil the mixture gently for 1–2 minutes and allow it to cool.

(*b*) *Action of sodium carbonate*
Add 3–4 cm^3 of aqueous sodium carbonate solution to small quantities

of ethanoic and benzoic acids. Note the effervescence which occurs and test the gas evolved with lime water. A convenient small-scale method of testing for carbon dioxide is described in fig. 10.5.

(c) Action of phosphorus pentachloride
Add about 0.1 g of phosphorus pentachloride (*Care!*) to about 1 cm^3 of anhydrous (glacial) ethanoic acid in a test-tube. Test the fumes evolved with (i) moist blue litmus paper and (ii) gaseous ammonia from an open bottle of 0.880 aqueous ammonia.

Repeat the experiment with about 0.3–0.5 g of benzoic acid.

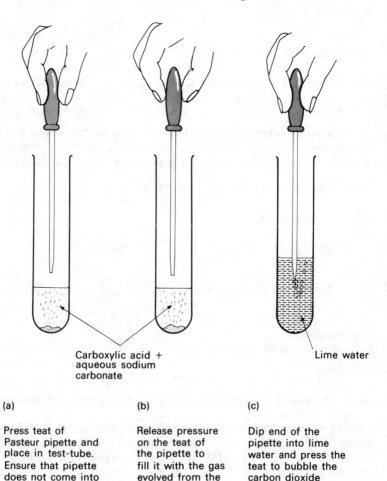

Carboxylic acid + aqueous sodium carbonate

Lime water

(a)

Press teat of Pasteur pipette and place in test-tube. Ensure that pipette does not come into contact with the liquid

(b)

Release pressure on the teat of the pipette to fill it with the gas evolved from the effervescing liquid

(c)

Dip end of the pipette into lime water and press the teat to bubble the carbon dioxide through the liquid

Fig. 10.5 Small scale method of testing for carbon dioxide

(*d*) *Esterication* (see Experiment 10.1(*c*))

10.5
Amines

Specific objectives: *The expected learning outcome of this section is that the student: (i) names and draws the formulae of examples of primary, secondary and tertiary amines, including aromatic primary amines; (ii) describes the reactions of amines with water and acids to illustrate their basic nature.*

(*a*) *Formula and nomenclature*
The amines may be regarded as ammonia derivatives in which one or more hydrogen atoms of the ammonia molecule have been replaced by alkyl or aryl groups. The amines are classified as primary ($1°$), secondary ($2°$) or tertiary ($3°$) according to the number of hydrogen atoms which have been replaced:

Formula	Class
NH_3 (ammonia)	
RNH_2	Primary amine
$\begin{array}{c} R \\ \diagdown \\ NH \text{ or } R_2NH \\ \diagup \\ R'' \end{array}$	Secondary amine
$\begin{array}{c} R' \\ \diagdown \\ R'' -N \text{ or } R_3N \\ \diagup \\ R''' \end{array}$	Tertiary amine

The amines are usually named by adding the word *amine* to the names of the alkyl or aryl groups which are attached to the nitrogen atom. Alternatively, the compounds may be named as alkane derivatives by adding the prefix *amino* to the name of the corresponding alkane. The names and formulae of a number of simple amines are listed in Table 10.5.

Aromatic amines contain at least one aryl group linked directly to the

Table 10.5   Nomenclature and classification of amines

Formula	Class	Name
CH_3NH_2	1°	Methylamine or aminomethane
$C_2H_5NH_2$	1°	Ethylamine or aminoethane
$(CH_3)_2NH$	2°	Dimethylamine
$CH_3CH_2CH_2NH_2$	1°	*n*-Propylamine or 1-aminopropane
$CH_3CHNH_2CH_3$	1°	*iso*-Propylamine or 2-aminopropane
$C_2H_5NHCH_3$	2°	Ethylmethylamine
$(CH_3)_3N$	3°	Trimethylamine
$C_2H_5N(CH_3)_2$	3°	Ethyldimethylamine

nitrogen atom. The most important aromatic amine is phenylamine (or aniline), $C_6H_5NH_2$:

This compound is an example of a primary aromatic amine. Other examples of aromatic amines are:

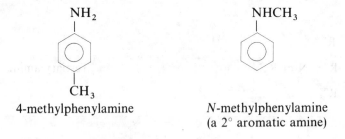

4-methylphenylamine

N-methylphenylamine
(a 2° aromatic amine)

(b) Preparation of alkyl amines
The alkylamines may be obtained by the action of ammonia on a halogenoalkane (alkyl halide):

$$RBr + NH_3 \longrightarrow RNH_2 + HBr$$
$$1° \text{ amine}$$

The primary amine also reacts with the alkyl halide and a mixture of the primary, secondary and tertiary amines is obtained as well as the tetra-alkylammonium salt in which all the hydrogen atoms in the ammonium ion have been replaced by alkyl groups:

$$RBr + RNH_2 \longrightarrow R_2NH + HBr$$
$$2° \text{ amine}$$

$$RBr + R_2NH \longrightarrow R_3N + HBr$$
$$3° \text{ amine}$$

$$RBr + R_3N \longrightarrow R_4N^+Br^-$$
tetra-alkylammonium bromide
(a quaternary salt)

The products are obtained as salts because amines are basic compounds and react with the acid to yield the corresponding alkylammonium halide, $[RNH_3]^+Br^-$, $[R_2NH_2]^+Br^-$, and $[R_3NH]^+Br^-$. The free amine is obtained by treating these salts with aqueous sodium hydroxide, e.g.

$$[(CH_3)_2NH_2]^+Br^- + NaOH_{(aq)} \xrightarrow{\text{warm}} (CH_3)_2NH + NaBr + H_2O$$
dimethylammonium   dimethylamine
bromide

Phenylamine is obtained by the reduction of nitrobenzene (see Section 9.7(d)(i)) using hydrogen and a catalyst, or with tin or iron and aqueous hydrochloric acid:

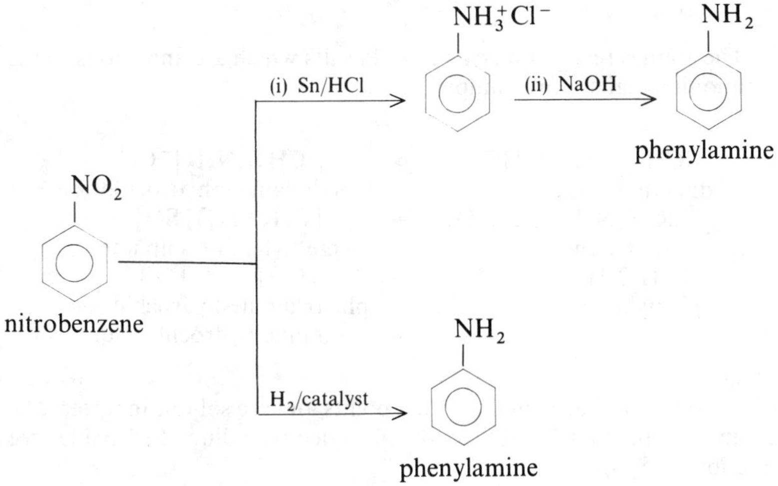

(c) Physical properties of amines

The lower alkylamines are either gases or readily volatile liquids. They are extremely soluble in water and in organic solvents and have a 'fishy' odour. Amines, in fact, are among the products of the putrefaction of fish.

Phenylamine (b.p. 184°) is a colourless, oily liquid when pure. It slowly turns yellow and brown on exposure to air and light owing to the formation of coloured oxidation products. Phenylamine vapour has a characteristic odour and is poisonous. The liquid is slightly soluble in water but dissolves readily in organic solvents or aqueous acids.

(d) Basic properties of amines

The amines are weak bases (see Section 4.1(*b*)) and yield low concentrations of hydroxide ions in aqueous solution:

$$RNH_2 + H_2O \rightleftharpoons RNH_{3(aq)}^+ + OH_{(aq)}^-$$
1° amine

$$R_2NH + H_2O \rightleftharpoons R_2NH_{2(aq)}^+ + OH_{(aq)}^-$$
2° amine

The aromatic amines, e.g. phenylamine

$$C_6H_5NH_2 + H_2O \rightleftharpoons C_6H_5NH_{3(aq)}^+ + OH_{(aq)}^-$$

are considerably weaker bases than ammonia or the alkylamines. This is indicated in Table 10.6. These relative basicity values are based on the magnitude of the equilibrium content for the reactions:

$$B: + H_2O \rightleftharpoons BH_{(aq)}^+ + OH_{(aq)}^-$$
base

The amines react with acids to yield salts which are analogous to the ammonium salts. For example,

$$(CH_3)_2NH + HCl \longrightarrow [(CH_3)_2NH_2]^+Cl^-$$
dimethylamine   dimethylamine hydrochloride

$$2CH_3NH_2 + H_2SO_4 \longrightarrow [CH_3NH_3]_2^+SO_4^{2-}$$
methylamine   methylamine sulphate

$$C_6H_5NH_2 + HCl \longrightarrow [C_6H_5NH_3]^+Cl^-$$
phenylamine   phenylamine hydrochloride
                                     (aniline hydrochloride)

These salts have fairly high melting points and are soluble in water. The amine is liberated by the action of aqueous sodium hydroxide (see Section 10.5(*b*)).

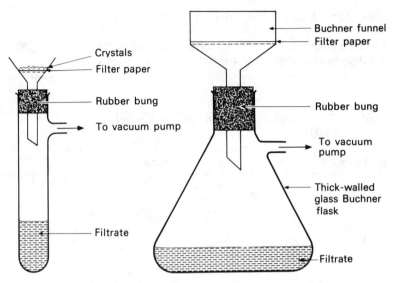

Fig. 10.6(a) A Hirsch funnel and filter tube (left)
Fig. 10.6(b) A Buchner funnel and flask (right)

10.6
Carbonyl compounds

Specific objectives: *The expected learning outcome of the following section is that the student is able to:* (i) *name and draw structural formulae of simple carbonyl compounds;* (ii) *state the conditions and write equations for the reactions of carbonyl compounds with:* 1. *two of the following:* HCN, NH_3, $NaHSO_3$, *and* 2. *phenylhydrazine or 2,4-dinitrophenylhydrazine (2,4-DNPH) and semicarbazide;* (iii) *describe oxidation reactions of carbonyl compounds which illustrate a method of distinguishing between aldehydes and ketones.*

(a) General formulae and nomenclature
The general formulae of the aldehydes and ketones are $RCHO$ and $R'COR$ respectively (see Section 9.3). The carbonyl group ($\diagup C{=}O$) is linked to at least one hydrogen atom in the aldehydes. The first members of the aldehyde (or *alkanal*) homologous series, $C_nH_{2n+1}CHO$, are listed in Table 10.7. The compounds are named according to the recommendations of the I.U.P.A.C. by replacing the final *-e* of the alkane with the same number of carbon atoms with the suffix *-al*.

The carbonyl group in ketones is linked directly to alkyl or aryl groups

Table 10.6   Relative basic strengths of amines

Formula of amine:	$(CH_3)_2NH$	CH_3NH_2	NH_3	$C_6H_5NH_2$
Relative basic strength:	1.4×10^6	1×10^6	4×10^4	1

Table 10.7   Nomenclature of aldehydes of general formula $C_nH_{2n+1}CHO$

n	Formula		Name
0	H⧵C=O / H⧸	or CH_2O	Methanal (formaldehyde)
1	$CH_3—C$ with H and O	or CH_3CHO	Ethanal (acetaldehyde)
2	$CH_3CH_2—C$ with H and O	or C_2H_5CHO	Propanal (propionaldehyde)

Table 10.8   Nomenclature of ketones (or alkanones)

Formula	I.U.P.A.C. recommended name	Alternative name(s)
CH_3COCH_3	Propanone	acetone or dimethyl ketone
$CH_3CH_2COCH_3$	Butanone	ethyl methyl ketone (methylethyl ketone or M.E.K.)
$CH_2CH_2COCH_2CH_3$	Pentan-3-one	diethyl ketone
$CH_3CH_2CH_2COCH_3$	Pentan-2-one	methyl-*n*-propyl ketone

and not to hydrogen atoms. The ketones (or *alkanones*) are named by replacing the final *-e* of the corresponding alkane by the suffix *-one*. The carbon atoms are numbered to indicate the position of the carbonyl carbon in the chain. The formulae and I.U.P.A.C. recommended names of the first members of the series are given in Table 10.8 along with their common names. Aromatic aldehydes and ketones contain at least one aryl group attached to the carbonyl groups e.g.

benzaldehyde

phenylethanone
(acetophenone)

diphenylmethanone
(benzophenone)

(b) Preparation
The aldehydes and ketones are obtained as products of the oxidation of primary and secondary alcohols respectively:

$$RCH_2OH \xrightarrow{\text{oxidation}} RCHO$$

1° alcohol   aldehyde

2° alcohol   ketone

This oxidation may be carried out using acidified sodium or potassium dichromate(VI) (see Section 10.2(*c*)(iv)). With primary alcohols the aldehyde vapour is distilled off before further oxidation can take place to yield the carboxylic acid, e.g.

$$CH_3CH_2OH \xrightarrow{\text{oxidation}} CH_3CHO \xrightarrow{\text{further oxidation}} CH_3CO_2H$$

ethanol   ethanal   ethanoic acid
b.p. 78.5°   b.p. 21°   b.p. 118°

Alcohols may also be oxidised catalytically by oxygen (see Section 10.2(*c*)(iv) and Demonstration 10.1) or by vapour-phase dehydrogenation using a catalyst of heated copper in the absence of air. For example, propanone (acetone) may be prepared by passing propan-2-ol vapour over copper gauze at 400°:

$$\begin{array}{c} CH_3 \\ \diagdown \\ CHOH \\ \diagup \\ CH_3 \end{array} \xrightarrow[400]{Cu} \begin{array}{c} CH_3 \\ \diagdown \\ C=O + H_2 \\ \diagup \\ CH_3 \end{array}$$

propan-2-ol   propanone

(c) Properties of carbonyl compounds

Methanal is a pungent gas, b.p. $-21°$, which is readily soluble in water. Its aqueous solution is known as formalin and is used as a preservative for biological specimens. Ethanal, b.p. $21°$, and propanone, b.p. $56°$, are completely miscible with water and organic solvents. They are both highly flammable. The solubility of the higher aldehydes and ketones in water decreases with increasing relative molecular mass. Propanone is widely used as a solvent for grease, plastics and varnish. It is also a starting material for the manufacture of Perspex.

(d) Reactions of aldehydes and ketones

The principal reactions of these two classes of compounds may be subdivided into the *addition* and *condensation* reactions of the carbonyl group.

(i) Addition reactions

The general equation for addition of a molecule XY to the double bond of the carbonyl group is:

$$\begin{array}{c} \diagdown \\ C=O + XY \longrightarrow \end{array} \begin{array}{c} OX \\ \diagdown \diagup \\ C \\ \diagup \diagdown \\ Y \end{array} \qquad \text{addition product}$$

where Y is the more electronegative atom or group in the added molecule XY (e.g. HCN, $NaHSO_3$, NH_3 and H_2) and X is usually hydrogen.

1. Action of hydrogen cyanide

Aldehydes and ketones readily add hydrogen cyanide across the double bond of the carbonyl groups to yield a 2-hydroxynitrile (or *cyanohydrin*):

$$\begin{array}{c} \diagdown \\ C=O \xrightarrow{HCN} \end{array} \begin{array}{c} OH \\ \diagdown \diagup \\ C \\ \diagup \diagdown \\ CN \end{array}$$

aldehyde or   2-hydroxynitrile
ketone   (a cyanohydrin)

For example,

$$CH_3CHO \xrightarrow{\text{HCN}} CH_3CH\begin{smallmatrix}\diagup OH \\ \diagdown CN\end{smallmatrix}$$

ethanal · 2-hydroxypropanonitrile
(ethanal cyanohydrin)

$$CH_3COCH_3 \xrightarrow{\text{HCN}} \underset{CH_3}{\overset{CH_3}{\diagup}}C\underset{CN}{\overset{OH}{\diagdown}}$$

propanone · 2-hydroxy-2-methylpropanonitrile
(propanone cyanohydrin)

The reaction is usually carried out using an alkaline solution of potassium cyanide in water; however, this experiment should not be attempted owing to the high toxicity of cyanides.

2. Action of sodium hydrogen sulphate(IV) (sodium bisulphite)
An exothermic reaction occurs when a saturated solution of sodium hydrogen sulphate(IV) is added to an aldehyde or many ketones:

$$\diagdown{C}{=}O + NaHSO_3 \longrightarrow \diagdown{C}\begin{smallmatrix}\diagup OH \\ \diagdown OSO_2^- Na^+\end{smallmatrix}$$

For example, with propanone a colourless, crystalline solid is obtained as the mixture cools to room temperature:

$$CH_3COCH_3 + NaHSO_3 \longrightarrow \underset{CH_3}{\overset{CH_3}{\diagup}}C\underset{OSO_2^- Na^+}{\overset{OH}{\diagdown}}$$

propanone · propanone-sodium hydrogen sulphate(IV) adduct

Except for methanal and ethanal where the adduct is extremely soluble in water, the precipitation of this crystalline product may be used as a test for the presence of the carbonyl group.

3. Addition of ammonia
An unstable, white addition compound is formed when ammonia is bubbled through a cold solution of an aldehyde in ether. For example,

1-aminoethanol (ethanal-ammonia) is obtained from the reaction:

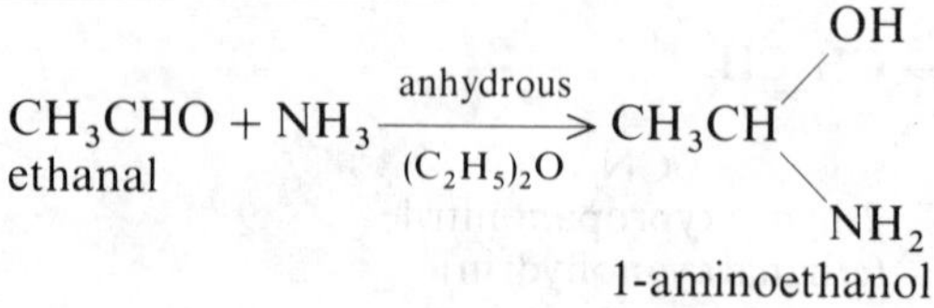

$$CH_3CHO + NH_3 \xrightarrow[\text{(C}_2\text{H}_5)_2\text{O}]{\text{anhydrous}} CH_3CH \underset{NH_2}{\overset{OH}{\Big<}}$$

ethanal

1-aminoethanol

These carbonyl adducts readily undergo polymerisation or condensation (see Section 10.6(*d*)(ii) for definition of a condensation reaction). For example, methanal yields hexamethylenetetramine

$$6CH_2O + 4NH_3 \longrightarrow (CH_2)_6N_4 + 6H_2O$$

hexamethylene-
tetramine

and propanone reacts with ammonia according to the following equation, but only at $-65°$:

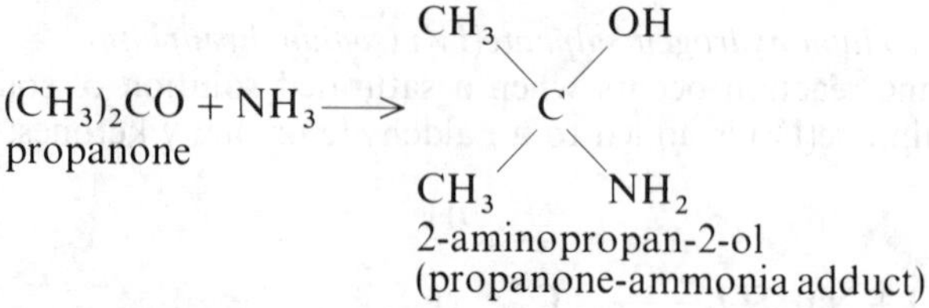

$$(CH_3)_2CO + NH_3 \longrightarrow \underset{CH_3 \quad NH_2}{\overset{CH_3 \quad OH}{C}}$$

propanone

2-aminopropan-2-ol
(propanone-ammonia adduct)

At higher temperatures water is eliminated to yield complex condensation products.

4. Reduction

Aldehydes and ketones yield primary and secondary alcohols respectively on reduction, thus reversing the reaction used for their preparation described in Section 10.6(*b*):

$$RCHO \underset{\text{oxidation}}{\overset{\text{reduction}}{\rightleftarrows}} RCH_2OH$$

aldehyde   1° alcohol

$$\underset{R^1}{\overset{R}{\Big>}}C{=}O \underset{\text{oxidation}}{\overset{\text{reduction}}{\rightleftarrows}} \underset{R^1}{\overset{R}{\Big>}}CHOH$$

ketone   2° alcohol

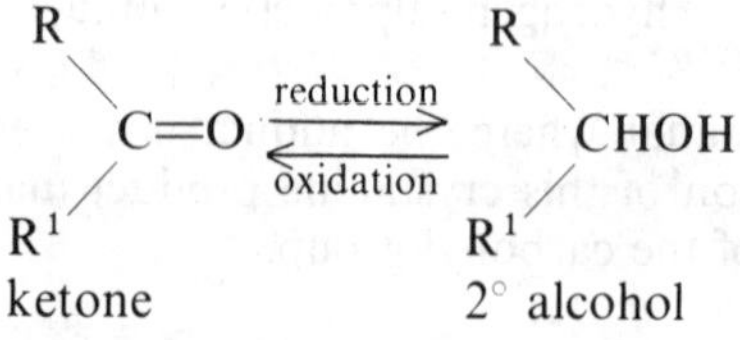

This reduction may be carried out catalytically using hydrogen in the presence of finely divided nickel e.g.

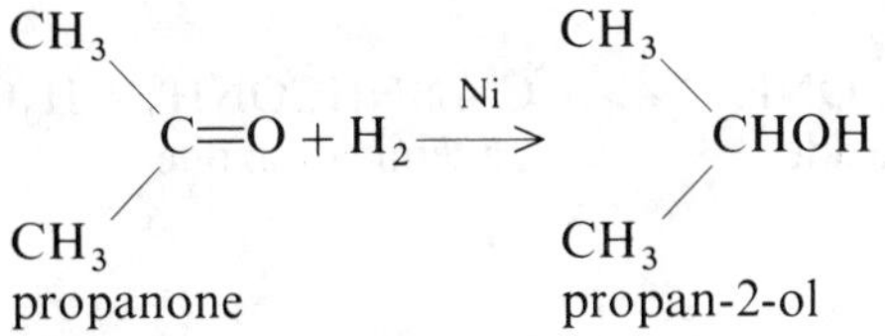

$$CH_3 \diagdown$$
$$\qquad C=O + H_2 \xrightarrow{Ni}$$
$$CH_3 \diagup$$

propanone

$$CH_3 \diagdown$$
$$\qquad CHOH$$
$$CH_3 \diagup$$

propan-2-ol

or by sodium amalgam in water, e.g.,

$$CH_3CHO \xrightarrow[H_2O]{Na/Hg} CH_3CH_2OH$$

ethanal ethanol

$$Na \xrightarrow{H_2O} Na^+ + e^-$$

sodium
dissolves

$$\diagdown$$
$$C=O + 2e^- + 2H^+ \longrightarrow$$
$$\diagup$$
electrons act
as reducing
agent

$$\diagdown \quad OH$$
$$\qquad C$$
$$\diagup \quad \diagdown H$$
an alcohol

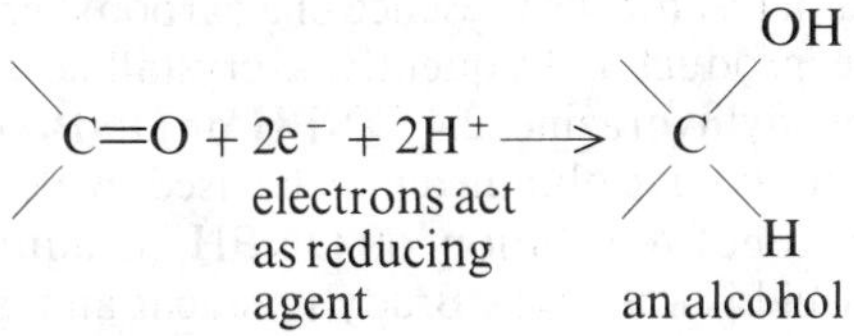

(ii) Condensation reactions

A condensation reaction is one in which two or more molecules combine to form a larger molecule, and a smaller molecule (or molecules), such as water or ammonia, is eliminated.

Aldehydes and ketones readily undergo condensation with compounds containing an —NH_2 group. The most important of these substances are hydrazine, NH_2NH_2, and its substituted derivatives such as phenylhydrazine, $C_6H_5NHNH_2$, and semicarbazide, $H_2NNHCONH_2$. In each case, a molecule of water is eliminated by reaction with one molecule of the carbonyl compound:

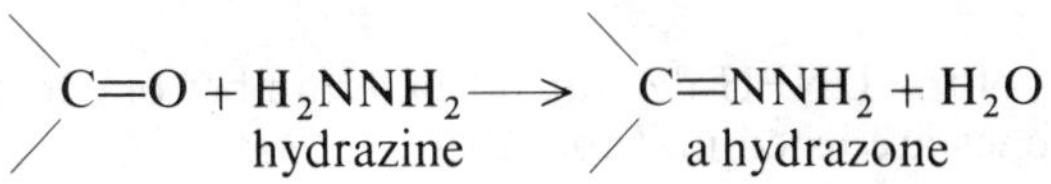

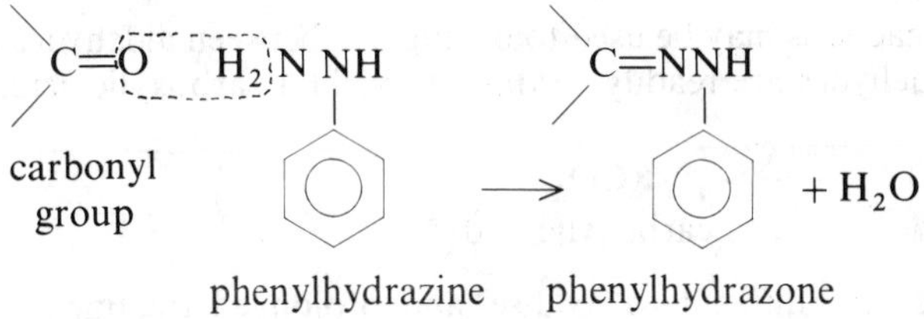

$$\diagdown \qquad\qquad\qquad \diagdown$$
$$C=O + H_2NNH_2 \longrightarrow C=NNH_2 + H_2O$$
$$\diagup \qquad\qquad\qquad \diagup$$
hydrazine a hydrazone

$$\diagdown \qquad\qquad\qquad\qquad \diagdown$$
$$C=O \quad H_2N\,NH \qquad\qquad C=NNH$$
$$\diagup \qquad\qquad | \qquad\qquad\qquad \diagup \qquad |$$

carbonyl
group

$\longrightarrow \qquad\qquad + H_2O$

phenylhydrazine phenylhydrazone

$$\diagdown C{=}O + H_2NNHCONH_2 \longrightarrow \diagdown C{=}NNHCONH_2 + H_2O$$

semicarbazide   a semicarbazone

For example,

$$CH_3CHO + C_6H_5NHNH_2 \longrightarrow CH_3CH{=}NNHC_6H_5 + H_2O$$

ethanal   phenyl-   ethanal
       hydrazine   phenylhydrazone

$$(CH_3)_2CO + H_2NNHCONH_2 \longrightarrow (CH_3)_2C{=}NNHCONH_2 + H_2O$$

propanone   semicarbazide   propanone
                          semicarbazone

These reactions are used as a test for the presence of a carbonyl group in a compound and as the product is frequently a crystalline solid (especially with 2,4-dinitrophenylhydrazine, 2,4-DNPH or DNPH) the melting point of the purified derivative obtained may be used to identify the original aldehyde or ketone. A solution of DNPH in aqueous methanol and sulphuric(VI)acid is known as Brady's reagent and gives a yellow or orange precipitate of the corresponding 2,4-dinitrophenyl-hydrazone with an aldehyde or ketone. For example,

CH₃CHO +   H₂N NH   NO₂   CH₃CH=N NH   NO₂
ethanal

$$+ H_2O$$

NO₂   NO₂
2,4-DNPH   ethanal 2,4-dinitrophenyl
                            hydrazone
                            m.p. 168°

The melting-points of the DNPH-derivatives of a number of common aldehydes and ketones are listed in Table 10.9.

(iii) Oxidation

Oxidation reactions may be used to distinguish between aldehydes and ketones. Aldehydes are readily oxidised to yield a carboxylic acid:

$$RCHO \xrightarrow{\text{oxidation}} RCO_2H$$

aldehyde   carboxylic acid

Ketones are very difficult to oxidise, and prolonged treatment with

Table 10.9 *Melting-points of 2,4-dinitrophenylhydrazones of carbonyl compounds*

Compound	Formula	m.p. of DNPH derivatives ($/°C$)
Methanal	CH_2O	166
Ethanal	CH_3CHO	168
Propanal	CH_3CH_2CHO	154
Propanone	CH_3COCH_3	126
Butanone	$C_2H_5COCH_3$	115
Pentan-2-one	$CH_3CH_2CH_2COCH_3$	130
Pentan-3-one	$CH_3CH_2COCH_2CH_3$	156

powerful oxidising agents, such as nitric(V)acid or alkaline potassium manganate(VII), causes the molecule to break up and produces a mixture of carboxylic acids, each containing fewer carbon atoms than the original ketone.

The oxidising agents which are commonly used to distinguish between the two classes of carbonyl compound are: cold aqueous sodium (or potassium) dichromate(VI) acidified with dilute sulphuric(VI)acid, e.g.

$$3CH_3CHO + Cr_2O_7^{2-} + 8H^+ \longrightarrow 3CH_3CO_2H + 2Cr^{3+} + 4H_2O$$

ethanal   (orange)   ethanoic   (green)
                                    acid

ammoniacal silver nitrate(V) (*Tollen's reagent*) which is reduced to a silver mirror:

$$RCHO \xrightarrow[\text{warm}]{[Ag(NH_3)_2]^+_{(aq)}} RCO_2H + silver$$

or Fehling's solution which yields an orange-red precipitate of copper(I)oxide:

$$RCHO \xrightarrow[\text{warm}]{\text{Fehling's solution}} RCO_2H + Cu_2O$$

Ketones do *not* react with cold acidified dichromate solution, ammoniacal silver nitrate(V) (Tollen's reagent) or with Fehling's solution and are thus readily distinguished from aldehydes.

The preparation of ammoniacal silver nitrate(V) (Tollen's reagent) is described in Experiment 10.5(*c*). The solution should be prepared in small quantities as required and washed away down the sink immediately after use as it may explode when dry or on prolonged storage.

Fehling's solution contains the deep blue copper(II)-dihydroxybutane-dioate (tartrate) complex ion. The reagent is prepared as required by mixing equal volumes of Fehling's solution I and II (see Appendix VI).

Experiment 10.5
Reactions of carbonyl compounds

(a) *Action of sodium hydrogen sulphate(IV)*
Add 1 cm^3 of propanone to 1 cm^3 of a saturated solution of sodium hydrogen sulphate(IV)(see Appendix VI). Shake the mixture and allow it to stand. Record your observations in your practical book.

(b) *Condensation with 2,4-DNPH*
Add about 0.5 cm^3 of propanone to 2–3 cm^3 of Brady's reagent (see Appendix VI). Note the formation of an orange precipitate of the 2,4-dinitrophenylhydrazone. Repeat this test with an aqueous solution of methanal or ethanal. The derivative may be filtered off using a small Buchner or Hirsch funnel (see fig. 10.6) and recrystallised from the minimum amount of hot ethanol (IMS) and water (1:1 by volume). Compare the melting-point of the dry, purified solid product with the values listed in Table 10.9.

(c) *Action of ammoniacal silver nitrate(V)* (*Tollen's reagent*)
Preparation of reagent: Add 1–2 drops of dilute sodium hydroxide solution to 3–4 cm^3 of aqueous silver nitrate(V) solution. Add dilute aqueous ammonia drop by drop until the brown precipitate of silver(I)oxide has almost dissolved. Use the reagent immediately.
Divide the reagent between two scrupulously clean test-tubes and add 2–3 drops of ethanal or an aqueous solution of methanal to one and 2–3 drops of propanone to the other. Place the test-tubes in a beaker of boiling water to warm for about 5 minutes.

(d) *Action of Fehling's solution*
Add about 0.5 cm^3 of ethanal or an aqueous solution of methanal or other suitable aldehyde to a mixture of about 1 cm^3 each of Fehling's solution I and II and boil gently for 2–3 minutes. Repeat the test using about 0.5 cm^3 of propanone and compare the result.

The reactions of ethanal and propanone are summarised in figs. 10.7 and 10.8.

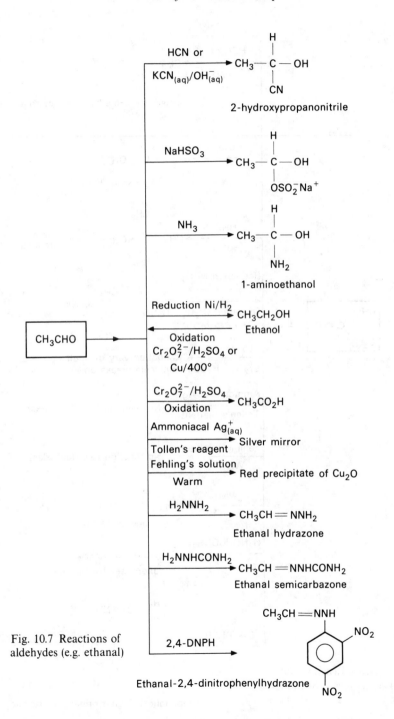

Fig. 10.7 Reactions of aldehydes (e.g. ethanal)

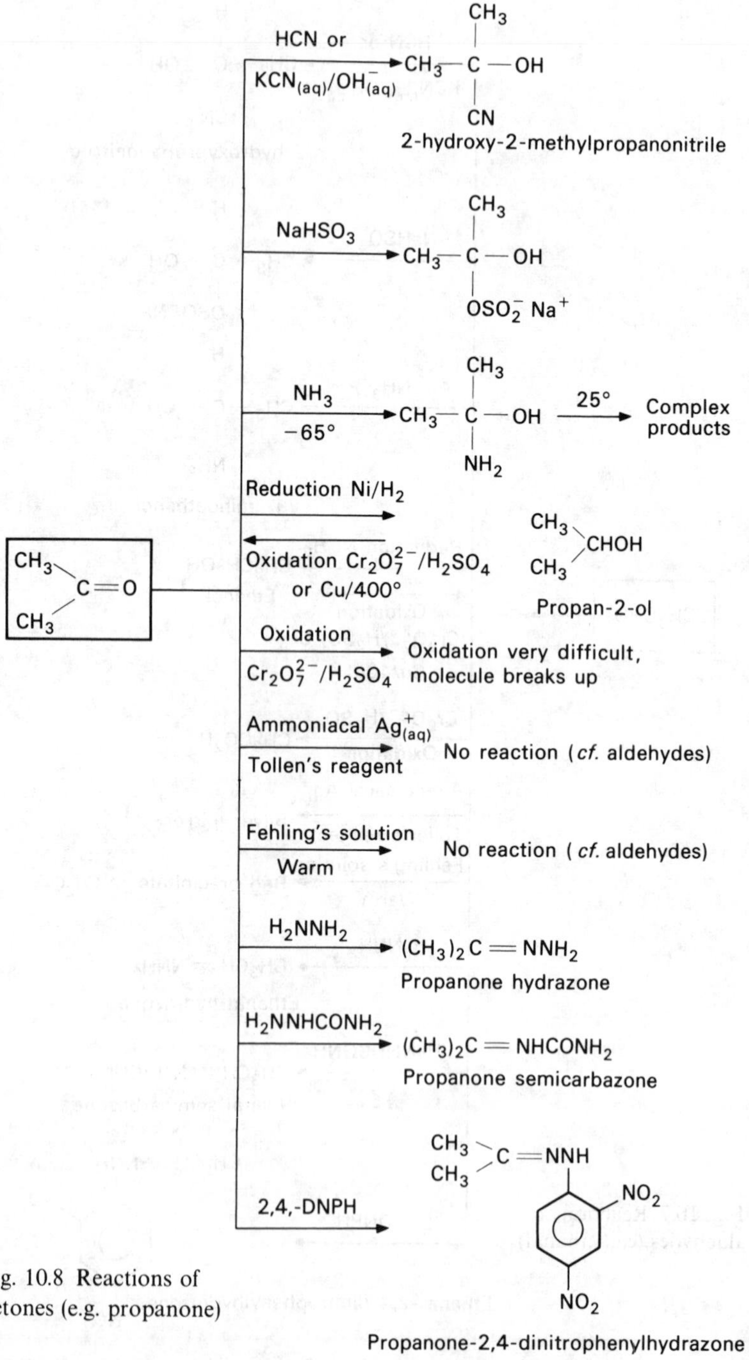

Fig. 10.8 Reactions of
ketones (e.g. propanone)

10.7
Calculation of empirical and molecular formulae of organic compounds

---

Specific objectives: *The expected learning outcome of this section is that the student is able to: (i) calculate percentage of carbon, hydrogen and halogen in an organic compound from analytical data; (ii) define empirical formula and molecular formula and state the relationship between them; (iii) calculate empirical and molecular formulae of organic compounds, given their percentage composition and relative molecular mass.*

(a) *Quantitative organic analysis*

Organic compounds are usually composed of only a few elements – such as hydrogen, oxygen, nitrogen, halogen and sulphur – in addition to carbon. The percentage of carbon and hydrogen in an organic substance is determined by oxidising a weighed sample to carbon dioxide and water respectively by oxygen in the presence of copper(II)oxide:

$$(-C, H_2) + CuO \xrightarrow{\quad O_2 \quad} CO_2 + H_2O + Cu$$
in organic
compound

The carbon dioxide is absorbed in weighed tubes containing potassium hydroxide and the water in tubes containing magnesium chlorate(VII) (magnesium perchlorate). As the relative atomic masses of carbon and hydrogen are 12.011 and 1.008 respectively and the relative molecular masses of carbon dioxide and water are 44.009 and 18.015, it is apparent that:

As 44.009 g CO_2 contains 12.011 g of carbon
Percentage of carbon in the compound =

$$\frac{12.011}{44.009} \times \frac{\text{mass of } CO_2 \text{ obtained}}{\text{mass of sample}} \times 100$$

and 18.015 g of H_2O contains $2 \times 1.008 = 2.016$ g of hydrogen
Percentage of hydrogen in the compound =

$$\frac{2.016}{18.015} \times \frac{\text{mass of } H_2O \text{ obtained}}{\text{mass of sample}} \times 100$$

Nitrogen is usually determined by measuring the volume of gaseous nitrogen (at a known temperature and pressure) obtained from a weighed sample of the compound after oxidising the material with heated copper(II) oxide in the absence of air:

1 mole of nitrogen ($= 28$ g of N_2 molecules) occupies $22\,414$ cm^3 at s.t.p.

Halogen (chlorine, bromine or iodine) and sulphur are precipitated and weighed as silver halide and barium sulphate(VI) by adding an excess of aqueous silver nitrate(V) or barium chloride respectively, after oxidising weighed samples of the substance by heating with fuming nitric(V)acid. This treatment converts any halogen in the organic compound to halide ions, e.g.

$$-\text{Cl} \xrightarrow{\text{fuming HNO}_3} \text{Cl}^-_{(aq)} \xrightarrow{\text{AgNO}_{3(aq)}} \text{AgCl}_{(s)}$$

in weighed   precipitate
sample of the   filtered off,
compound   washed, dried
                                                     and weighed

while sulphur is converted to sulphate(VI)ions:

$$-\text{S} \xrightarrow{\text{fuming HNO}_3} \text{SO}^{2-}_{4(aq)} \xrightarrow{\text{BaCl}_{2(aq)}} \text{BaSO}_{4(s)}$$

in weighed   precipitate
sample of the   filtered off,
compound   washed, dried
                                                     and weighed

Percentage of chloride in the compound =

$$\frac{\text{RAM of Cl}}{\text{RMM of AgCl}} \times \frac{\text{mass of AgCl obtained}}{\text{mass of sample}} \times 100$$

Percentage of sulphur in the compound =

$$\frac{\text{RAM of S}}{\text{RMM of BaSO}_4} \times \frac{\text{mass of BaSO}_4 \text{ obtained}}{\text{mass of sample}} \times 100$$

Oxygen is not determined directly but is found by difference, i.e. by subtracting the sum of the percentages of the other elements present in the compound from 100%.

(b) Calculation of empirical and molecular formulae

The *empirical formula* of a compound shows the *ratio* of the numbers of atoms of the different elements present in a molecule of the substance.

The *molecular formula* of a compound shows the *actual numbers* of the atoms of the elements present in a molecule of the substance.

Methanal, CH_2O, ethanoic acid, CH_3CO_2H or $C_2H_4O_2$, and glucose, $C_6H_{12}O_6$, for example, all have the same empirical formula (CH_2O), as the molecules of each of these compounds contain carbon, hydrogen and oxygen atoms in the ratio of $1:2:1$. The molecular formula of these compounds is $(CH_2O)_n$ where n is a whole number for any compound.

The molecular formula of a compound is readily obtained from its empirical formula if the relative molecular mass of the substance is known, thus:

Molecular formula = (Empirical formula)$_n$

and,

$$n = \frac{\text{RMM of the compound}}{\text{Empirical formula mass}}$$

For example, if the RMM of a compound of empirical formula (CH_2O) is 180 (RAM of $C = 12$, $H = 1$ and $O = 16$) the molecular formula $(CH_2O)_n$ of the compound is $(CH_2O)_6$ or $C_6H_{12}O_6$ as

$$n = \frac{\text{RMM of } (CH_2O)_n}{\text{Empirical formula mass}} = \frac{180}{30} = 6$$

The calculation of the empirical formula and molecular formula of an organic compound from analytical data is described in the following example.

Example 10.2
0.065 07 g of a colourless, organic liquid, A, yielded 0.1478 g of carbon dioxide and 0.060 49 of water on combustion. If the approximate RMM of A is 57, calculate (i) the percentage composition, (ii) the empirical formula and (iii) the molecular formula of A.

A gives an orange precipitate with Brady's reagent (2,4-DNPH), but it does not reduce Fehling's solution. What is the structure of A?

Solution
(i) *Percentage composition*

$$\% \, C = \frac{12.011}{44.009} \times \frac{0.1478}{0.065\,07} \times 100 = 62.0$$

$$\% \, H = \frac{2.016}{18.015} \times \frac{0.060\,49}{0.065\,07} \times 100 = 10.40$$

These percentages do not add up to 100% within the limits of experimental error, and the difference is equal to the oxygen content of the compound.

$\therefore \% \text{ oxygen in } A = 100 - (62.0 + 10.40) = 27.60$

(ii) *Calculation of empirical formula*

	C	H	O
Ratio of percentages	62.0 :	10.40 :	27.60
Divide by RAM	$\dfrac{62.0}{12}$:	$\dfrac{10.40}{1}$:	$\dfrac{27.60}{16}$
	5.167 :	10.40 :	1.725
Divide by smallest quotient	$\dfrac{5.167}{1.725}$:	$\dfrac{10.40}{1.725}$:	$\dfrac{1.725}{1.725}$
Ratio of numbers of atoms	2.995 :	6.03 :	1
To nearest whole numbers	3 :	6 :	1
i.e., Empirical formula of $A = (C_3H_6O)$			

(iii) *Calculation of molecular formula*
Molecular formula of $A = (C_3H_6O)_n$

$$n = \frac{RMM}{\text{E.F. mass}} = \frac{57}{58} = 1 \text{ (to the nearest whole number)}$$

The molecular formula of A is thus the same as its empirical formula, i.e. C_3H_6O.

Structure of A
The formation of an orange precipitate with 2,4-DNPH indicates the presence of a carbonyl group in A. Possible structural formulae for A are thus:

propanal   propanone

The fact that A is not oxidised by Fehling's solution indicates the absence of an aldehyde group, thus A is propanone, CH_3COCH_3.

Example 10.3
0.021 20 g of an organic compound B, yielded 6.54 cm³ of nitrogen at 21 °C and a pressure of 742.3 mm of mercury. What is the percentage of nitrogen by mass in B?

Solution
(i) *To convert the volume of nitrogen to s.t.p.*

$$\frac{P_1 V_1}{T_1} = \frac{P_2 V_2}{T_2}$$

$P_1 = 742.3$ mm Hg, $T_1 = 273 + 21 = 294$K, $V_1 = 6.54$ cm^3. At s.t.p. (see Section 3.5(b)) $T_2 = 273$K and $P_2 = 760$ mm Hg

$$\frac{742.3 \times 6.54}{294} = \frac{760 \times V_2}{273}$$

where V_2 = volume of nitrogen at s.t.p. = 5.93 cm^3.

(ii) *Calculation of percentage of nitrogen*

1 mole of nitrogen (N_2) = 22 414 cm^3 at s.t.p. weighs 28 g.

5.93 cm^3 of N_2 at s.t.p. weighs $\dfrac{28}{22\,414} \times 5.93 = 0.007\,408$ g

$$\% \text{ N in compound } B = \frac{\text{mass of nitrogen obtained}}{\text{mass of compound}}$$

$$= \frac{0.007\,408}{0.021\,20} \times 100$$

$$= 34.94\%$$

Summary

1. The general formula of the alcohols (alkanols) is ROH.

2. Alcohols are classified as primary, secondary or tertiary: 1° alcohols contain a —CH$_2$OH grouping, 2° alcohols a $\diagdown$CHOH and 3° alcohols a —COH group.

3. The general formula of the phenols is ArOH, where Ar is an aryl group. The hydroxyl group in phenols is linked directly to a carbon atom forming part of an aromatic ring.

4. The alcohols differ in their oxidation products:

$$\text{—CH}_2\text{OH} \xrightarrow{\text{oxidation}} \text{—CHO}$$
$$\text{1° alcohol} \qquad\qquad \text{aldehyde}$$

$$\diagdown\!\text{CHOH} \xrightarrow{\text{oxidation}} \diagdown\!\text{C}=\text{O}$$
$$\text{2° alcohol} \qquad\qquad \text{ketone}$$

5. The hydroxyl group in phenol is acidic: it yields salts with aqueous alkalis, but is too weak an acid to displace carbon dioxide from carbonates.

6. The chemical properties of ethanol and phenol are summarised in figs. 10.3 and 10.4 respectively.

7. The general formula of the carboxylic (alkanoic) acids is $C_nH_{2n+1}CO_2H$, where n = 0, 1, 2, 3 etc. Aromatic (aryl) carboxylic acids, e.g. $C_6H_5CO_2H$ (benzoic acid), have the general formula $ArCO_2H$.

8. The chemical properties of ethanoic acid are summarised in fig. 10.9.

9. The general formulae of primary, secondary and tertiary amines are

$$RNH_2\,(1°), \quad \overset{\displaystyle R}{\underset{\displaystyle R}{\diagdown\!\!\!\diagup}}NH\,(2°) \text{ and } R_3N\,(3°).$$ Phenylamine (aniline), $C_6H_5NH_2$, is an example of a primary aromatic amine.

10. Amines are weak bases and form salts with strong acids,

e.g. $CH_3NH_2 + HCl \longrightarrow \qquad CH_3NH_3^+Cl^-$
       methylamine   methylammonium chloride

11. The general reactions of the carbonyl group of aldehydes (General formula RCHO) and ketones (RCOR) are summarised in figs. 10.7 and 10.8 respectively.

12. Aldehydes and ketones may be distinguished by oxidation reactions. Aldehydes are readily oxidised:

$$RCHO \xrightarrow{\text{oxidation}} RCO_2H$$

whereas ketones are not. Aldehydes will reduce ammoniacal silver nitrate(V) (Tollen's reagent) to silver and Fehling's solution to copper(I)-oxide, but ketones have no effect on these reagents.

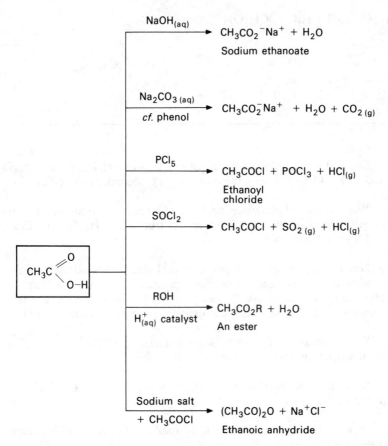

Fig. 10.9 Reactions of ethanoic (acetic) acid

Questions

1. What are the general formulae of (a) the alcohols (alkanols) and (b) the phenols? What is the essential structural difference between these two classes of hydroxy compounds?

2. What are the general formulae of primary, secondary and tertiary alcohols?

3. Name the following compounds: (a) $(CH_3)_2CHOH$, (b) $(CH_3)_3COH$,

(c) $CH_3CH_2CH(CH_3)CH_2OH$,

(d) 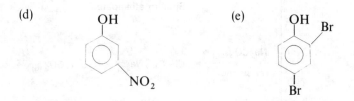 (e)

4. Draw the structural formulae of the alcohols of formulae C_3H_8O and $C_4H_{10}O$ and classify them as primary, secondary or tertiary.

5. Write chemical equations and give the reaction conditions for the preparation of ethanol from (a) glucose or fructose $(C_6H_{12}O_6)$, (b) ethene and (c) ethyl ethanoate.

6. Name the products and give chemical equations and the reaction conditions for the reaction between propan-2-ol and (a) sodium, (b) phosphorus pentachloride, (c) red phosphorus and iodine, (d) ethanoic acid, (e) acidified potassium dichromate(VI) solution, (f) heated alumina.

7. What is meant by the saponification of a fat or oil? Write an equation for the reaction and explain the action of soap.

8. Compare the action of oxidising agents on propan-1-ol and propan-2-ol.

9. How and under what conditions does ethanol react with concentrated sulphuric(VI)acid?

10. How do you account for the fact that an aqueous solution of phenol (carbolic acid) does not liberate carbon dioxide from sodium carbonate solution?

11. Describe *two* chemical tests which may be used to distinguish an aqueous solution of phenol from an aqueous solution of ethanoic acid.

12. Write equations where possible and give the conditions for the reaction of phenol with (a) aqueous sodium hydroxide, (b) iron(III)-chloride, (c) bromine water.

13. Suggest methods of preparing the following compounds starting from ethanol: (a) ethanal, (b) ethyl ethanoate, (c) ethylamine, (d) sodium ethanoate, (e) 1,2-dibromoethane, (f) ethane, (g) ethanoyl chloride.

14. Methyl ethanoate, $CH_3CO_2CH_3$, and propanoic acid, CH_3CH_2 CO_2H, are isomeric. Give two chemical tests which may be used to distinguish between these compounds.

15. Explain how the preparation of a solid ester may be used to identify a particular alcohol.

16. Write structural formulae and name the carboxylic acids and esters which are isomeric with butanoic acid, $C_3H_7CO_2H$.

17. Write chemical equations, giving the reaction conditions and name the products of the reaction of propanoic acid with (a) sulphur dichloride oxide (thionyl chloride), (b) sodium hydrogen carbonate (sodium bicarbonate), (c) methanol.

18. 4.7 g of ethanoic ethanoate was obtained by treating 5 cm³ of ethanol (d $= 0.8$ g cm^{-3}) with an excess of ethanoic acid. Calculate the percentage yield of the ester. (Relative atomic masses: C $= 12$, H $= 1$, O $= 16$).

19. 2.8 g of 2,4,6-tribromophenol was obtained by treating 1 g of phenol with an excess of bromine water. Calculate the percentage yield of the product. (RAM of bromine $= 80$.)

20. Describe how benzoic acid may be converted into benzoyl chloride. Write equations and give the conditions for the reaction of benzoyl chloride with (a) aqueous sodium carbonate and (b) phenol.

21. Give the structural formulae and the names of the amines of formula C_3H_9N and classify them as primary, secondary or tertiary.

22. Write equations for the reactions of ammonia with bromoethane.

23. Explain what is meant by the statement: phenylamine (aniline) is a much weaker base than methylamine.

24. Outline one method of preparing phenylamine from benzene. How does phenylamine react with aqueous hydrochloric acid?

25. The aldehydes and ketones are isomeric. Give the structural formulae and names of the carbonyl compounds of formula C_4H_8O.

26. Describe the reaction conditions and the precautions you would take to convert ethanol into (a) ethanal and (b) ethanoic acid.

27. What is (a) an addition reaction and (b) a condensation reaction? Illustrate your answer by reference to suitable reactions of aldehydes or ketones.

28. Write equations and describe the conditions for the reaction of ethanal with (a) ammonia, (b) sodium hydrogen sulphate(IV), (c) hydrogen cyanide, (d) ammoniacal silver nitrate(V) and (e) 2,4-DNPH.

29. Describe, by reference to suitable examples, how oxidation reactions may be used to distinguish between aldehydes and ketones.

30. Describe how Brady's reagent (a solution of 2,4-dinitrophenyl hydrazine) is used (a) to show that a compound contains an aldehyde or ketone group and (b) to identify a particular aldehyde or ketone.

31. Compare and contrast the reaction of aldehydes and ketones with (a) reducing agents and (b) oxidising agents.

32. Write equations, name the products and give the conditions for the reaction of methanal with (a) Fehling's solution, (b) semicarbazide, (c) phenyl hydrazine.

33. Why is ammoniacal silver nitrate(V) (Tollen's reagent) prepared in small quantities as required, rather than storing the reagent in a bottle?

The following data may be used for questions 34–39.
   Relative atomic masses: $C = 12$, $H = 1$, $O = 16$, $N = 14$, $Cl = 35.45$, $Ag = 108$.
   Molar volume of an ideal gas at s.t.p. (273 K and 760 mm of mercury or 101 325 Nm^{-2} pressure) = 22 414 cm^3.
   $TK = t°C + 273$.

34. 0.04972 g of an organic compound, C, yielded 0.09943 g of carbon dioxide and 0.04068 g of water on combustion. What is (a) the percentage composition and (b) the empirical formula of C?

35. 0.04707 g of an organic compound, D, yielded 0.07920 g of carbon dioxide and 0.0378 g of water on combustion. If 0.1743 g of D yielded 0.3187 g of silver chloride after treatment with fuming nitric(V)acid followed by an excess of silver nitrate(V), calculate (a) the percentage composition and (b) the empirical formula of D.

36. 0.03599 g of an organic liquid, E, yielded 0.02596 g of carbon dioxide and 0.01593 g of water on combustion. 0.0488 g of E yielded 9.83 cm^3 of nitrogen at 22° and 749.6 mm of mercury. Calculate (a)

the percentage composition and (b) the empirical formula of *E*.

37. An organic compound, *F*, of approx. RMM 133 contains C, 17.99%; H, 2.25% and Cl, 79.72%. What is the molecular formula of *F*?

38. An organic compound, *G*, of RMM 30, contains 40.0% C and 6.67% H. What is (a) the molecular formula and (b) the structural formula of *G*?

39. An organic liquid, *H*, contains C, 39.13%; H, 8.70% and O, 52.17%. If the RMM of *H* is 92, calculate the molecular formula of *H*.

Appendix I

SI units

The following SI base units are employed in this book:

Quantity	Name	Symbol
Length	metre	m
Mass	kilogram	kg
Time	second	s
Electric current	ampère	A
Thermodynamic temperature	kelvin	K
Amount of substance	mole	mol

The unit of thermodynamic temperature (the *kelvin*) is the fraction 1/273.16 of the thermodynamic temperature at the triple point of water

$$T K = t°C + 273.15$$

The unit of the amount of substance (the *mole*) is defined as the amount of the substance which contains as many particles (atoms, ions, molecules, electrons etc.) as there are atoms in exactly 12 grams of the pure carbon C–12 isotope.

1 mole of atoms = Relative molecular mass in grams
1 mole of molecules = Relative molecular mass or 'formula weight' in grams

The remaining SI units are formed by combinations of these base units. For example,

Area m^2
Volume m^3
Density $kg\ m^{-3}$
Concentration mol m^{-3} or, more practically, mol dm^{-3} (or mol $litre^{-1}$)

Other examples of such derived units are shown in Table I.

Multiples and submultiples of units are indicated by the addition of the appropriate prefix (see Table II).

For example,

1 mm = 1 millimetre = 0.001 or 10^{-3} m
1 cm = 1 centimetre = 0.01 or 10^{-2} m

Table I   Derived units

Quantity	Name	Symbol	Unit
Frequency	hertz	Hz	s^{-1}
Energy or work	joule	J	Nm
Force	newton	N	$kg\ m\ s^{-2}$
Pressure	pascal	Pa	Nm^{-2}
Resistance	ohm	Ω	VA^{-1}
Conductance	siemens	S	AV^{-1} or Ω^{-1}
Potential difference	volt	V	WA^{-1}
Power	watt	W	Js^{-1}

Table II   Prefixes to indicate multiples and submultiples of units

Prefix	Symbol	Factor by which the unit is multiplied	
giga	G	1 000 000 000	$= 10^9$
mega	M	1 000 000	$= 10^6$
kilo	k	1000	$= 10^3$
hecto	h	100	$= 10^2$
deca	da	10	$= 10^1$
		1	$= 10^0 = 1$
deci	d	0.1	$= 10^{-1}$
centi	c	0.01	$= 10^{-2}$
milli	m	0.001	$= 10^{-3}$
micro	μ	0.000 001	$= 10^{-6}$
nano	n	0.000 000 001	$= 10^{-9}$
pico	p	0.000 000 000 001	$= 10^{-12}$

$$1\ nm = 1\ nanometre = 10^{-9}\ m$$
$$1\ kg = 1\ kilogram = 10^3\ g$$
$$1\ \mu g = 1\ microgram = 10^{-6}\ g$$
$$1\ dm^3 = 1\ 000\ cm^3 = 1\ litre$$

Appendix II

Important physical constants

Molar volume of an ideal gas at s.t.p. = 22.414 litre mol^{-1}. Standard temperature and pressure (s.t.p.) = a temperature of 0°C (273.15 K) and a pressure of 101 325 Pa (1 atm = 760 mm of mercury).

General gas constant (R) = 8.314 JK^{-1} mol^{-1}

Avogadro's constant (L) = number of particles in 1 mole
= 6.022 × 10^{23} mol^{-1}

Faraday constant (F) = total charge of 1 mole of electrons
= 96 484.56 C (coulombs = amp–seconds)

Conversion factors

1 calorie = 4.184 J

1 atmosphere (atm) = 760 mm of mercury = 101 325 Pa (or Nm^{-2})

1 mm of mercury = 1 torr = 133.32 Pa

$T/K = t/°C + 273.15$

1 Angstrom unit (Å) = 10^{-8} cm = 10^{-10} m

Appendix III

Relative atomic masses and electronic configurations

Element	Symbol	Atomic Number	Relative atomic mass	Electronic configuration
Hydrogen	H	1	1.008	$1s^1$
Helium	He	2	4.003	$1s^2$
Lithium	Li	3	6.941	$(He)2s^1$
Beryllium	Be	4	9.012	$(He)2s^2$
Boron	B	5	10.81	$(He)2s^2 2p^1$
Carbon	C	6	12.011	$(He)2s^2 2p^2$
Nitrogen	N	7	14.007	$(He)2s^2 2p^3$
Oxygen	O	8	15.9994	$(He)2s^2 2p^4$
Fluorine	F	9	18.9984	$(He)2s^2 2p^5$
Neon	Ne	10	20.179	$(He)2s^2 2p^6$
Sodium	Na	11	22.9898	$(Ne)3s^1$
Magnesium	Mg	12	24.305	$(Ne)3s^2$
Aluminium	Al	13	26.9815	$(Ne)3s^2 3p^1$
Silicon	Si	14	28.086	$(Ne)3s^2 3p^2$
Phosphorus	P	15	30.9738	$(Ne)3s^2 3p^3$
Sulphur	S	16	32.06	$(Ne)3s^2 3p^4$
Chlorine	Cl	17	35.453	$(Ne)3s^2 3p^5$
Argon	Ar	18	39.984	$(Ne)3s^2 3p^6$
Potassium	K	19	39.102	$(Ar)4s^1$
Calcium	Ca	20	40.08	$(Ar)4s^2$
Scandium	Sc	21	44.956	$(Ar)3d^1 4s^2$
Titanium	Ti	22	47.90	$(Ar)3d^2 4s^2$
Vanadium	V	23	50.94	$(AR)3d^3 4s^2$

Element	Symbol	Atomic Number	Relative atomic mass	Electronic configuration
Chromium	Cr	24	51.996	$(Ar)3d^54s^1$
Manganese	Mn	25	54.938	$(Ar)3d^54s^2$
Iron	Fe	26	55.847	$(Ar)3d^64s^2$
Cobalt	Co	27	58.93	$(Ar)3d^74s^2$
Nickel	Ni	28	58.71	$(Ar)3d^84s^2$
Copper	Cu	29	63.546	$(Ar)3d^{10}4s^1$
Zinc	Zn	30	65.37	$(Ar)3d^{10}4s^2$
Gallium	Ga	31	69.72	$(Ar)3d^{10}4s^24p^1$
Germanium	Ge	32	72.59	$(Ar)3d^{10}4s^24p^2$
Arsenic	As	33	74.92	$(Ar)3d^{10}4s^24p^3$
Selenium	Se	34	78.96	$(Ar)3d^{10}4s^24p^4$
Bromine	Br	35	79.904	$(Ar)3d^{10}4s^24p^5$
Krypton	Kr	36	83.80	$(Ar)3d^{10}4s^24p^6$
Rubidium	Rb	37	85.47	$(Kr)5s^1$
Strontium	Sr	38	87.62	$(Kr)5s^2$
Yttrium	Y	39	88.91	$(Kr)4d^15s^2$
Zirconium	Zr	40	91.22	$(Kr)4d^25s^2$
Niobium	Nb	41	92.91	$(Kr)4d^45s^1$
Molybdenum	Mo	42	95.94	$(Kr)4d^55s^1$
Technetium	Tc	43	(99)	$(Kr)4d^65s^1$
Ruthenium	Ru	44	101.07	$(Kr)4d^75s^1$
Rhodium	Rh	45	102.91	$(Kr)4d^85s^1$
Palladium	Pd	46	106.4	$(Kr)4d^{10}5s^0$
Silver	Ag	47	107.87	$(Kr)4d^{10}5s^1$
Cadmium	Cd	48	112.40	$(Kr)4d^{10}5s^2$
Indium	In	49	114.82	$(Kr)4d^{10}5s^25p^1$

Element	Symbol	Atomic Number	Relative atomic mass	Electronic configuration
Tin	Sn	50	118.69	$(Kr)4d^{10}5s^25p^2$
Antimony	Sb	51	121.75	$(Kr)4d^{10}5s^25p^3$
Tellurium	Te	52	127.60	$(Kr)4d^{10}5s^25p^4$
Iodine	I	53	126.90	$(Kr)4d^{10}5s^25p^5$
Xenon	Xe	54	131.30	$(Kr)4d^{10}5s^25p^6$
Caesium	Cs	55	132.91	$(Xe)6s^1$
Barium	Ba	56	137.34	$(Xe)6s^2$
Tungsten	W	74	183.85	$(Xe)4f^{14}5d^46s^2$
Platinum	Pt	78	195.09	$(Xe)4f^{14}5d^96s^1$
Gold	Au	79	196.97	$(Xe)4f^{14}5d^{10}6s^1$
Mercury	Hg	80	200.59	$(Xe)4f^{14}5d^{10}6s^2$
Lead	Pb	82	207.2	$(Xe)4f^{14}5d^{10}6s^26p^2$

Appendix IV

I.U.P.A.C. nomenclature

The International Union of Pure and Applied Chemistry (I.U.P.A.C.) has recommended the adoption of a systematic nomenclature for all compounds. The I.U.P.A.C.-recommended names of organic compounds have been used throughout this book; however traditional (and frequently non-systematic) names are still in use for many common organic substances (see Table III).

Inorganic compounds are named according to the Stock system of nomenclature. The oxidation number of an atom or the central atom in a complex is indicated by a Roman numeral in brackets after the name of that element. For example, sulphur(VI)oxide and phosphoric(V)acid are SO_3 and H_3PO_4 respectively. The oxidation numbers of sodium, potassium, calcium and other elements of invariable oxidation state are omitted. The recommended names and the common current names of a number of inorganic compounds are listed in Table IV.

Table III Traditional and I.U.P.A.C.-recommended names of common organic compounds

Traditional (trivial or current) name	Formula	I.U.P.A.C.-recommended name
Acetaldehyde	CH_3CHO	Ethanal
Acetic acid	CH_3CO_2H	Ethanoic acid
Acetic anhydride	$(CH_3CO)_2O$	Ethanoic anhydride
Acetone	CH_3COCH_3	Propanone
Acetyl chloride	CH_3COCl	Ethanoyl chloride
Acetylene	C_2H_2	Ethyne
Aniline	$C_6H_5NH_2$	Phenylamine
Carbon tetrachloride	CCl_4	Tetrachloromethane
Chloroform	$CHCl_3$	Trichloromethane
Diethyl ether (or 'ether')	$(C_2H_5)_2O$	Ethoxyethane
Ethyl acetate	$CH_3CO_2C_2H_5$	Ethyl ethanoate
Ethyl alcohol	C_2H_5OH	Ethanol
Ethyl chloride	C_2H_5Cl	Chloroethane
Ethylene	C_2H_4	Ethene
Formaldehyde	CH_2O	Methanal
Formic acid	HCO_2H	Methanoic acid
Methyl alcohol	CH_3OH	Methanol
Methyl ethyl ketone (M.E.K.)	$CH_3CH_2COCH_3$	Butanone
iso-Propyl alcohol	$CH_3CHOHCH_3$	Propan-2-ol
n-Propyl alcohol	$CH_3CH_2CH_2OH$	Propan-1-ol
Propylene	$CH_3CH{=}CH_2$	Propene
Salicylic acid	$C_6H_4(OH)CO_2H$	2-Hydroxybenzoic acid
Tartaric acid	$(CHOHCO_2H)_2$	2,3-Dihydroxybutanedioic acid
Toluene	$C_6H_5CH_3$	Methylbenzene
Urea	NH_2CONH_2	Carbamide
Vinyl chloride	$CH_2{=}CHCl$	Chloroethene

Table IV Systematic nomenclature of inorganic compounds and ions

Traditional (trivial or current) name	Formula	I.U.P.A.C.-recommended name
chromate ion	CrO_4^{2-}	chromate(VI)ion
cuprous oxide	Cu_2O	copper(I)oxide
cupric oxide	CuO	copper(II)oxide
dichromate ion	$Cr_2O_7^{2-}$	dichromate(VI)ion
ferric chloride	$FeCl_3$	iron(III)chloride
ferricyanide ion	$[Fe(CN)_6]^{3-}$	hexacyanoferrate(III)ion
ferrocyanide ion	$[Fe(CN)_6]^{4-}$	hexacyanoferrate(II)ion
hypochlorite ion	ClO^-	chlorate(I)ion
chlorate ion	ClO_3^-	chlorate(V)ion
perchlorate ion	ClO_4^-	chlorate(VII)acid
manganese dioxide	MnO_2	manganese(IV)oxide
nitrate ion	NO_3^-	nitrate(V)ion
nitrite ion	NO_2^-	nitrate(III)ion
nitric acid	HNO_3	nitric(V)acid
permanganate ion	MnO_4^-	manganate(VII)ion
bisulphite ion	HSO_3^-	hydrogen sulphate(IV)ion
sulphite ion	SO_3^{2-}	sulphate(IV)ion
sulphate ion	SO_4^{2-}	sulphate(VI)ion
sulphur dioxide	SO_2	sulphur(IV)oxide
sulphur trioxide	SO_3	sulphur(VI)oxide
thionyl chloride	$SOCl_2$	sulphur dichloride oxide

Appendix V

Preparation of common laboratory reagents

The dilute acids and bases required for the experiments described in this book should be approximately 2 M. The concentrations of the commercially available materials and the volumes required for the preparation of 2 litres of 2 M solution are listed in Table V. Concentrated sulphuric(VI)acid should always be diluted by adding the acid slowly with stirring to water, and *not* vice versa. *Safety goggles must be worn.*

Other solutions may be prepared by diluting these solutions or by direct weighing. The water of crystallisation must be included in the relative molecular mass (or 'formula weight') when preparing solutions from hydrated salts. For example, a 0.1 M solution of copper(II)sulphate(VI) contains 24.97 g of the pentahydrate, $CuSO_4 5H_2O$, per litre (RMM of $CuSO_4 5H_2O = 249.7$) and not 15.96 g (RMM of anhydrous $CuSO_4 = 159.6$). Indicators and other laboratory reagents may be obtained directly from chemical suppliers.

Table V   Preparation of 2 M solutions of acids and bases

Reagent	Concentration (/M)	Density (/g cm^{-3})	Volume required to prepare 2 l of 2 M solution (/cm^3)
0.880 ammonia	15	0.88	215
Ethanoic acid (glacial)	17	1.05	225
Concentrated hydrochloric acid	12	1.19	400
Concentrated nitric(V)acid	16	1.42	250
Concentrated sulphuric(VI)acid	18	1.84	230

Appendix VI

Specialised reagents

Ammonium thiocyanate solution
Dissolve 43 g of ammonium thiocyanate (Analytical grade reagent) in distilled water and dilute the solution to 500 cm³.

Ammoniacal silver nitrate(V) (Tollen's reagent)
This solution should be prepared in *small* quantities as required as it may explode on storage owing to the instability of the dry reagent (see Section 10.6(*d*)(iii)).

Brady's reagent (2,4-DNPH)
Dissolve 1 g of 2,4-dinitrophenyl hydrazine in 30 cm³ of methanol and 10 cm³ of water. Add 2 cm³ of concentrated sulphuric(VI)acid slowly with shaking.

Bromine water
Shake 4–5 cm³ of bromine (*Care!*) with 100 cm³ of distilled water. Decant off the clear solution as required.

Chlorine water
Bubble gaseous chlorine through cold distilled water until it is saturated (approx. 0.7%).

Fehling's solution
Prepare by mixing equal volumes of Fehling's solution I and II. Fehling's solution I contains about 7 g of hydrated copper(II)sulphate(VI) ($CuSO_4 5H_2O$) in 100 cm³ of water. Fehling's solution II is prepared by dissolving 10 g of sodium hydroxide pellets (*Care: this substance is caustic*) and 5 g of potassium, sodium-2,3-dihydroxybutanedioate (tartrate), $C_6H_4O_6NaK4H_2O$ (Rochelle salt), in 100 cm³ of water.

Iron(III)chloride (ferric chloride) solution
Dissolve 7 g of $FeCl_3 6H_2O$ in 100 cm³ of water containing about 1 cm³ of concentrated hydrochloric acid. *Neutral iron(III)chloride solution* is prepared by adding dilute aqueous ammonia to the iron(III)-chloride stock solution until a precipitate appears. Some of the original iron(III)chloride solution is then added drop by drop until the precipitate just dissolves.

Methyl orange
Dissolve 0.3 g of methyl orange (sodium salt) in 500 cm³ of boiling water.

Screened methyl orange is prepared by dissolving 0.3 g of methyl orange-xylene cyanol in 500 cm^3 of distilled water.

Phenolphthalein
Dissolve 1 g of phenolphthalein in 100 cm^3 of industrial methylated spirit (IMS).

Potassium dichromate(VI) solution
A 1% aqueous solution may be employed.

Potassium hydrogen phthalate buffer (0.05 M (pH = 4.000 at 15°))
Dissolve 10.21 g of pure, dry potassium hydrogen phthalate (pH standard) in freshly distilled water and dilute to 1 litre. Potassium hydrogen phthalate may be dried by heating in an oven for 2 hours at 110°.

Potassium manganate(VII) (permanganate) solution (acidic)
Add 10 cm^3 of dilute sulphuric(VI)acid to 100 cm^3 of 1% aqueous potassium manganate(VII) solution.

Potassium manganate(VII) solution (alkaline)
Add about 4 g of potassium carbonate to 100 cm^3 of 1% aqueous potassium manganate(VII) solution.

Saturated sodium hydrogen sulphate(IV) (sodium bisulphite)
Sodium disulphate(IV) (sodium metabisulphite), $Na_2S_2O_5$, is generally used to prepare a saturated aqueous solution of this reagent, as it is less susceptible to atmospheric oxidation than sodium hydrogen sulphate(IV). It yields the hydrogen sulphate(IV) (bisulphite) ion by hydrolysis in aqueous solution:

$$S_2O_5^{2-} + H_2O \longrightarrow 2HSO_3^-$$

The supernatant liquid is decanted from the crystals in contact with the saturated solution.

Answers to numerical questions

Chapter Two

10. -76 kJ mol^{-1}; 11(a) Enthalpy of formation of ethane is -86 kJ mol^{-1}, the reaction is exothermic; (b) Enthalpy of formation of ethyne is $+49$ kJ mol^{-1}, the reaction is endothermic; 12. $+90$ kJ mol^{-1}. The formation of carbon disulphide from its elements is an endothermic process; 13. -265 kJ mol^{-1}; 14. -847 kJ mol^{-1}; 17. -55.4 kJ mol^{-1}; 18. -197.4 kJ mol^{-1}; 19. -726 kJ mol^{-1}; 20. -388 kJ mol^{-1}; 21. -2222 kJ mol^{-1}; 22. $+1.9$ kJ mol^{-1}. The energy diagram is:

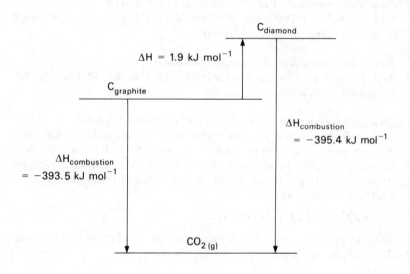

Chapter Three

10(a) None, (b) an increased yield of dinitrogen tetroxide, (c) none; 16. endothermic;
18(a) 36 cm^3. 1 mol of water (H_2O, density 1 g cm^{-3}) weighs 18 g and occupies 18 cm^3. $\therefore$ 2 mol $=$ 36 g, occupies 36 cm^3 as a liquid. (b) 77.6 l. 1 mol of any gas occupies 22.4 l at s.t.p. $\therefore$ 2 mol of water would occupy 2×22.4 l at s.t.p. (i.e. at 273K) as a gas. Volume occupied at 473K $= 2 \times 22.4 \times 473/273 = 77.6$ l.

20. Equilibrium concentrations

$$CH_3CO_2H + C_2H_5OH \rightarrow CH_3CO_2C_2H_5 + H_2O$$

$$0.5 - 0.086 \quad 0.09 - 0.086 \qquad 0.086 \qquad 0.086$$

$$\underbrace{0.414 \text{ mol}} \quad \underbrace{0.004 \text{ mol}} \qquad 0.086 \text{ mol} \qquad 0.086 \text{ mol}$$

Equilibrium constant, $K_c = \dfrac{(0.086)^2}{0.414 \times 0.004} = 4.47$

Chapter Four

14. (a)(i) 10^{-7} mol l^{-1}, (ii) 10^{-7} mol l^{-1}, (iii) 7, (iv) 7; (b)(i) 10^{-13} mol l^{-1}, (ii) 0.1 mol l^{-1}, (iii) 13, (iv) 1; (c)(i) 10^{-4} mol l^{-1}, (ii) 10^{-10} mol l^{-1}, (iii) 4, (iv) 10. 15(a) alkaline, (b) acidic, (c) alkaline, (d) acidic, (e) neutral, (f) acidic, (g) alkaline. 16(a) 11.11, (b) 1.58.

Chapter Five

16.	Spontaneous cell reaction	E.m.f. (/V) for cell as written in cell diagram
(a)	$Zn_{(s)} + 2H^+_{(aq)} \rightarrow Zn^{2+}_{(aq)} + H_{2(aq)}$	-0.76
(b)	$Fe_{(s)} + Pb^{2+}_{(aq)} \rightarrow Fe^{2+}_{(aq)} + Pb_{(s)}$	$+0.31$
(c)	$Pb_{(s)} + Cu^{2+}_{(aq)} \rightarrow Pb^{2+}_{(aq)} + Cu_{(s)}$	-0.47
(d)	$Fe_{(s)} + 2Ag^+_{(aq)} \rightarrow Fe^{2+}_{(aq)} + 2Ag$	-1.24
(e)	$Mg_{(s)} + Cu^{2+}_{(aq)} \rightarrow Mg^{2+}_{(aq)} + Cu_{(s)}$	$+2.71$

Chapter Seven

3.

Atom	protons	Number of neutrons	electrons
$^{19}_{9}F$	9	10	9
$^{40}_{20}Ca$	20	20	20
$^{39}_{19}K$	19	20	19
$^{238}_{92}U$	92	146	92
$^{208}_{82}Pb$	82	126	82

7. Elements are arranged in the Periodic Table in order of increasing atomic number, not of increasing atomic mass. The Atomic Numbers of argon and potassium are 18 and 19 respectively. Naturally occurring argon and potassium are both mixtures of isotopes. The relative proportions are: ^{36}Ar 0.34%, ^{38}Ar 0.063%, ^{40}Ar 99.6%; ^{39}K 93.1%, ^{40}K (radioactive) 0.012%, ^{41}K 6.9%. 9.(a) $\Delta H = 735 + 1450 = 2185 \, kJ \, mol^{-1}$, (b) $\Delta H = 519 + 7\,300 + 11\,800 = 19\,619 \, kJ \, mol^{-1}$, (c) $\Delta H = 577 + 1\,820 + 2\,740 = 5\,137 \, kJ \, mol^{-1}$. 10(a) 2,5 (nitrogen); (b) 2,2 (beryllium).

Chapter Nine

9(a) $C_{10}H_{22}$, (b) $C_{10}H_{20}$, (c) $C_{10}H_{18}$, (d) $C_{10}H_{21}OH$, (e) $C_9H_{19}CO_2H$. 10(a) butan-2-ol, (b) butanoic acid, (c) tri-iodomethane, (d) iodobenzene, (e) nitromethane. 11(a) Either a carbon–carbon triple bond or two carbon–carbon double bonds, C_3H_4 is either $H_2C{=}C{=}CH_2$ or $CH_3C{\equiv}CH$; (b) alkene double bond, (c) hydroxy group and carboxylic acid group, (d) an aldehyde group, (e) the carbonyl group, (f) chlorine atom and hydroxy group.

Chapter Ten

3(a) Propan-2-ol, (b) 2-methylpropan-2-ol, (c) 2-methylbutan-1-ol, (d) 3-nitrophenol, (e) 2,4-dibromophenol. 4. C_3H_8O: $CH_3CH_2CH_2OH$ ($1°$), $CH_3CHOHCH_3$ ($2°$); $C_4H_{10}O$: $CH_3CH_2CH_2CH_2OH$ and $(CH_3)_2CHCH_2OH$ ($1°$), $CH_3CH_2CHOHCH_3$ ($2°$); $(CH_3)_3COH$ ($3°$). 16. Acids: $CH_3CH_2CH_2CO_2H$ (butanoic acid), $(CH_3)_2CHCO_2H$ (2-methylpropanoic acid). Esters: $HCO_2CH_2CH_2CH_3$ (propyl methanoate), $HCO_2CH(CH_3)_2$ (1-methylethyl or *iso*-propyl methanoate), $CH_3CO_2C_2H_5$ (ethyl ethanoate), $C_2H_5CO_2CH_3$ (methyl propanoate). 18. 61%. Density of ethanol $= 0.8 \, g \, cm^{-3}$. 5 cm^3 of ethanol weighs $5 \times 0.8 = 4$ g.

$$C_2H_5OH + CH_3CO_2H \longrightarrow CH_3CO_2C_2H_5 + H_2O$$
1 mol = 46 g $\qquad\qquad$ 1 mol = 88 g

Theoretical yield of ethyl ethanoate from 4 g of ethanol $= 88/46 \times 4 = 7.65$ g.

$$\text{Percentage yield} = \frac{\text{Actual yield}}{\text{Theoretical yield}} \times 100 = \frac{4.7}{7.65} \times 100 = 61\%.$$

19. $C_6H_5OH + 3Br_2 \longrightarrow C_6H_3Br_2OH + 3HBr$
1 mol = 94 g $\qquad\qquad$ 1 mol = 331 g

Theoretical yield of 2,4,6-tribromophenol from 1 g of phenol $= 331/94 = 3.52$ g.
Percentage yield $= 2.8/3.52 \times 100 = 79.5\%$.
21. Primary amines: $CH_3CH_2CH_2NH_2$ (1-aminopropane or *n*-propyl-

amine), $(CH_3)_2CHNH_2$ (2-aminopropane or *iso*-propylamine). Secondary amine: $CH_3CH_2NHCH_3$ (ethylmethylamine). Tertiary amine: $(CH_3)_3N$ (trimethylamine). 25. $CH_3CH_2CH_2CHO$ (butanal), $(CH_3)_2CHCHO$ (2-methylpropanal), $CH_3CH_2COCH_3$ (butanone or ethylmethyl ketone). 34(a) C, 54.55%; H, 9.09%; O, 36.36%. (b) C_2H_4O. 35(a) C, 45.89%; H, 8.92%; Cl, 45.19%. (b) C_3H_7Cl. 36(a) C, 19.67%; H, 4.92%; N, 22.96%; O, 52.45%. (b) Empirical formula = CH_3NO_2. 37. Molecular formula

$$= C_2H_3Cl_3.\ 38(a)\ CH_2O\ (b)\quad \overset{\displaystyle H}{\underset{\displaystyle H}{\diagdown\!\!\diagup}}C{=}O\ (methanal)\ 39.\ C_3H_8O_3.\ H\ is$$

propane-1,2,3-triol (glycerol) $CH_2OHCHOHCH_2OH$.

Index